LAKE TAHOE
LAKE OF THE SKY

LAKE OF THE SKY

by

George Wharton James

A new edition of the famous 1915 Classic

Published by Stanley Paher
NEVADA PUBLICATIONS
Box 15444
Las Vegas, Nevada 89114

Books by George Wharton James

California, Romantic & Beautiful, 1914

Exposition Memories: Panama-California Exposition, San Diego, 1916

Francisco Palou's Life and Apostolic Labors of . . .Father Junipero Serra, 1913 (ed.)

Fremont in California, 1903

House Blessing Ceremony and Guest Book, 1917

In & Around the Grand Canyon: The Grand Canyon of the Colorado . . ., 1900

Indian Blankets and Their Makers, 1914

Indian Basketry, 1902

Indians of the Painted Desert Region, 1904

Old Franciscan Missions of California, 1915

Rose Hartwick Thorpe and the Story of "Curfew Shall Not Ring Tonight," 1916

Singing through Life with God, 1920

Utah: The Land of the Blossoming Valleys, 1922

Wonders of the Colorado Desert, 1906

The Lake of the Sky: Lake Tahoe, 1915

Photo Credits are as Follows:

A Peep at Washoe, 94-95.
Comstock Mining and Miners, 126.
Hubbard, Duke, 89-90.
Kaminski, Doc, 2–3, 14, 229.
National Archives, 30, 50.
Roughing It, 215.
Southern Pacific pamphlet, 19, 73, 78, 79, 100, 159.
Southwest Museum, 2 (inset), 9.

All other pictures are either from the publisher's collection or were originally included in the first edition of *The Lake of the Sky: Lake Tahoe.*

The splendid hand-tinted color views of Emerald Bay and the Truckee Canyon on the cover of this volume are from the portfolio *The Overland Trail: A Scenic Guidebook "Through the Heart of the Sierra" on the Line of the Southern Pacific*, published in 1923. Color separations by Imperial Color, Reno, Nevada.

Typesetting by Lynne Hughes Productions, Silver City, Nevada.
Camera-ready pagination produced at White Sage Studios, Virginia City, Nevada.

Proudly printed in the United States of America.

TABLE OF CONTENTS

APPENDICES

INTRODUCTION

BY PHILLIP I. EARL
Nevada Historical Society

Born in Gainsborough, Lincolnshire, England on September 27, 1858, George Wharton James (1858-1923) was to make his mark in the American Southwest as an ethnologist, archaeologist, historian, editor and travel writer. A precocious, but sickly child, he very early demonstrated a feel for people and seemed destined for the clergy. After coming to the United States in 1881, he was ordained a Methodist minister, his first pulpit being in Eureka, Nevada.. In 1882, he moved on to Battle Mountain where he taught school for five years in addition to pursuing his church duties.

During his Nevada years, James began to develop an interest in scholarly pursuits, becoming a member of the Royal Historical Society, London, the British Astronomical Society, the Microscopical Society, the Geological Society of London and the Victorian Institute. In later years, he was to acknowledge his literary debt to such writers as Carlyle, Ruskin, Darwin, Tyndall and Huxley. He also made the acquaintance of pioneering naturalist John Muir, geologist Joseph LeConte and John Wesley Powell in the course of his long life.

In 1891, James moved from the pulpit to the platform, lecturing on the Chautauqua circuit for the Brooks Humane Fund of Pasadena. He also spoke at universities and before scientific bodies, but writing was his true vocation. One critic has described James as "a man of hobbies, enthusiasms and sympathies rather than a scholar or an artist," classifying him as representing "the Ruskin-Browning tradition transplanted to the soil of Thoreau, and finding the sun not in Italy, but in the Painted Desert."

Four of his best-known volumes on California, Arizona, New Mexico and Utah were written for the *See America First* series published by Little, Brown & Co., Boston. In the same vein were *The Grand Canyon of Arizona* (1910), *Our American Wonderlands* (1915) and *The Lake of the Sky* (1915), a pioneering work on Lake Tahoe. James also took an interest in California's Hispano-Mexican heritage, in his *In and Out of the Old Missions of California* being perhaps the best of a half-dozen books on the subject.

James also studied the dialects, customs, beliefs and arts of the Indians of the Southwest — The Wallapi, Navajo, Apache, Havasupi, Zuni, Hopi, Acoma and other native peoples — and was adopted into several tribes. His writings on basketry, blankets and symbolism of Indian design are among the earliest works on the subjects. He was also among the first white men to

1919 photograph of author George Wharton James, (1858-1923)

witness the Hopi Snake Dance and appreciate its ritual significance, but his interest in the Indians went beyond culture. At the time of his death, he was a member of an advisory committee formed by the Secretary of the Interior to reconsider government policies toward the tribes.

In addition to his own writing, James served as the editor of the *Basket* (1903-04), associate editor of the *Craftsman* (1904-05), editor of *Out West* (1912-14) and literary editor of the Oakland Tribune (1919). As editor of *Out West*, he published the works of such budding and established authors as Joaquin Miller, Herbert Bashford, Jean Brooke Burt, L.T. Crittenden, Josephine Clifford McCracken, Berth Hirsh Baruch and a hundred or so others. He also began to focus attention on California's literary heritage, his "The Effect of California's Isolation Upon Literature" as part of the series "The Historical Elements of California's Literature" published in the magazine in 1913 and 1914 being among the most incisive critiques in the literary history of the Golden State.

Under his editorship, *Out West* also began to focus upon Nevada. James' "By the Walker River in Sunny Mason Valley," April, 1914, is perhaps the first literary treatment of that section of the state and his "Western Nevada — The Artist's Paradise," July, 1914, called the attention of the artistic world tot he scenic and thematic potential of the state. An article by Dr. James Edward Church, "The Romance of the University of Nevada," May-June, 1914, focused upon the state's sole institution of higher education and James' "What's the Matter with Nevada," April, 1914, a critique of the state's growing divorce trade, reflected an ethical and moral bent which characterized much of his literary work. A special issue devoted to the Woman Suffrage Movement in Nevada, August, 1914, was an indication of one aspect of James's interest in the reforms of the Progressive Era.

James' widow and step-daughter donated his collection of manuscripts, documents and rare books to the Southwest Museum in Los Angeles where they have been made available to researchers. In addition to general literature on California or by Californians, the collection includes extensive magazine files, legislative and scientific reports, accounts of explorations in English, French and Spanish and considerable rare material relating to the Franciscan missions and the Indians of the Southwest.

George Wharton James' classic book, *Lake of the Sky, Lake Tahoe,* has long been unavailable in popular book stores. Anyone wishing a copy had to search among the shelves of used and out-of-print book dealers. Often the only opportunity to read this book has been copies found in public libraries.

Librarians have long relied upon *Lake of the Sky* to secure information about Lake Tahoe's varied history —its Indians, towns, the first automobile routes, steamer travel, and early twentieth century recreational activity. More than this, George Wharton James also furnishes the reader information on the area's first explorers, the lake's various names, physical and geological characteristics, as well as Lake Tahoe Basin flowers, birds, animals, trees and plants.

The first edition of *Lake of the Sky* which appeared in 1915 was followed by a second edition in 1921. Other printings appeared during the 1930s. All of these were bound in a standard five-by-seven-and-a-half book format with special pictorial leaves inserted to accommodate approximately 125 views depicting lake Tahoe scenery and settlements as they appeared during the time of World War I.

Now in 1992 Nevada Publications has issued the best edition yet of this classic work. The text has been entirely reset to allow for an enlarged $8^{1}/_{2}$ inch wide and 11 inches high format, and the pictures have been appropriately relocated to appear throughout the text. About a quarter of the pictures in early editions of *Lake of the Sky* were simply too inferior to reproduce, in spite of modern camera techniques. Even the balance of James' historic photographs were reproduced with great difficulty.

Additionally, editor Stanley Paher has added several other historic Lake Tahoe photographs which he found unusually appealing. Paher was assisted in layout and design by Paul Cirac of White Sage Studios in Virginia City. Paher also edited the text, rearranging some material and modernizing some spellings and hyphenation. He differs with author James' characterization of the Indians of the Tahoe region.

This well-known book is worthy of being reprinted, and Nevada Publications is to be commended for making author James' early twentieth century book available once more to the reading pubic.

Phillip I. Earl,
Curator of History,
Nevada Historical Society,
Reno, Nevada

AUTHOR'S INTRODUCTION

California is proving itself more and more the wonderland of the United States. Its hosts of annual visitors are increasing with marvelous rapidity; its population is growing by accretions from the other states faster than any other section in the civilized world. The reasons are not far to seek. They may be summarized in five words — climate, topography, healthfulness, productiveness and all-around livableness. Its climate is already a catch word to the nations; its healthfulness is attested by the thousands who have come here sick and almost hopeless and who are now rugged, robust and happy; its productiveness is demonstrated by the millions of dollars its citizens annually receive for the thousands of car-loads (one might almost say train-loads) of oranges, lemons, grapefruit, walnuts, almonds, peaches, figs, apricots, onions, potatoes, asparagus and other fruits of its soil; and its all-around home qualities are best evidenced by the growth, in two or three decades, of scores of towns from a merely nominal population to five, ten, twenty, forty or fifty thousand, and of the cities of San Francisco, Los Angeles and Oakland to metropolises.

As far as its topography, its scenic qualities, are concerned, the world of tourists already has rendered any argument upon that line unnecessary. It is already beginning to rival Switzerland, though that Alpine land has crowded populations within a day's journey to draw from. One has but to name Monterey, the Mt. Shasta region, Los Angeles, San Diego and Coronado, the Yosemite, Lake Tahoe, the Big Trees, the King and Kern River Divide, Mono Lake and a score of other scenic regions in California to start tongues to wagging over interesting reminiscences, whether it be in London, Paris, Berlin or Madrid.

Books galore are being published to make California's charms better known, and it has long seemed strange to me that no book has been published on Lake Tahoe and its surrounding country of mountains, forests, glacial valleys, lakes and canyons, for I am confident that in one or two decades from now its circle of admirers and regular visitors will include people from all over the civilized world, all of whom will declare that it is incomparable as a lake resort, and that its infinite variety of charm, delight and healthful allurement can never adequately be told.

Discovered by the "Pathfinder" Frémont; described in the early days of California history and literature by

John Le Conte, Mark Twain, Thomas Starr King, Ben C. Truman, and later by John Vance Cheney and others; for countless centuries the fishing haunt of the peaceable Nevada *Washoes*, who first called it Tahoe — High or Clear Water — and of the California *Monos;* the home of many of their interesting legends and folk-lore tales; occasionally the scene of fierce conflicts between the defending Indians and those who would drive them away, it early became the object of the jealous and inconsequent squabbling of politicians.

Its discoverer had named it Mountain Lake, or Lake Bonpland, the latter name after the traveling and exploring companion of Baron von Humboldt, whose name is retained in the Humboldt River of Nevada, but when the first reasonably accurate survey of its shores was made, John Bigler was the occupant of the gubernatorial chair of the State of California and it was named after him. Then, later, for purely political reasons, it was changed to Tahoe, and finally back to Bigler, though of the thousands who visit it annually but a very small proportion have ever heard that such a name was applied to it.

In turn, soon after its discovery, Tahoe became the scene of a mining excitement that failed to "pan out," the home of vast logging and lumber operations and the objective point to which several famous "Knights of the Lash" drove world-noted men and women in swinging Concord coaches. In summer it is the haunt of Nature's most dainty, glorious and alluring picturesqueness; in winter the abode, during some days, of the Storm King with his cohorts of hosts of clouds, filled with rain, hail, sleet and snow, of fierce winds, of dread lightnings, or majestic displays of rudest power.

Suddenly, after having covered peak and slope, meadow and shore, with snow to a depth of six, eight, ten or more feet, the Storm King retires and Solus again reigns supreme. And then! ah, then is the time to see Lake Tahoe and its surrounding country.

The placid summer views are exquisite and soul-stirring, but what of Tahoe now? The days and nights are free from wind and frost, the sun tempers the cold and every hour is an exhilaration. The American people have not yet learned, as have the Europeans in the Alps, the marvelous delights and stimulations of the winter in such a place as Lake Tahoe.

But they will learn in time, and though a prophet is generally without honor in his own country, I will assume a role not altogether foreign, and venture the assertion that I shall live to see the day when winter visitors to Lake Tahoe will number more than those who will visit it throughout the whole of the year (1914) in which I write. One of the surprises often expressed by those I have met here who have wintered in the Alps is that no provision is made for hotel accommodation during the winter at Lake Tahoe.

To return, however, to the charms of Tahoe that are already known to many thousands. Within the last two or three decades it has become the increasingly popular Mecca of the hunter, sportsman, and fisherman; the natural haunt of the thoughtful and studious lover of God's great and varied out-of-doors, and, since fashionable hotels were built, the chosen resort of many thousands of the wealthy, pleasure-loving and luxurious.

What wonder that there should be a growing desire on the part of the citizens of the United States — and especially of California and Nevada — together with well-informed travelers from all parts of the world, for larger knowledge and fuller information about Lake Tahoe than has hitherto been available.

To meet this laudable desire has been my chief incitement in the preparation of the following pages, but I should be untrue to my own devotion to Lake Tahoe, which has extended over a period of more than thirty years, were I to ignore the influence the Lake's beauty has had over me, and the urge it has placed within me. Realizing and feeling these emotions I have constantly asked with Edward Rowland Sill:

> What can I for such a world give back again?

And my only answer has been, and is, this:

> Could I only hint the beauty —
> Some least shadow of the beauty,
> Unto men!

In looking over the files of more or less ephemeral literature, as well as the records of the explorations of early days, I have been astonished at the rich treasures of scientific and descriptive literature that have Lake Tahoe as their object. Not the least service this unpretentious volume will accomplish is the gathering together of these little-known jewels.

It will be noticed that I have used the word *Sierran* rather than *Alpine* throughout these pages. Why not?

Why should the writer, describing the majestic, the glorious, the sublime of the later-formed mountain ranges of earth, designate them by a term coined for another and far-away range?

I would have the reader, however, be careful to pronounce it accurately. It is not *Sy-eer-an*, but *See-ehr-ran*, almost as if one were advising another to "See Aaron," the brother of Moses.

Tahoe is not *Teh-o*, nor is it *Tah-ho*, nor *Tah-o*. The Washoe Indians, from whom we get the name, pronounce it as if it were one syllable *Tao*, like a Chinese name, the "a" having the broad sound *ah* of the Continent.

Likewise *Tallac* is not pronounced with the accent on the last syllable (as is generally heard), but *Tal´-ac.*

While these niceties of pronunciation are not of vast importance, they preserve to us the intonations of the original inhabitants, who, as far as we know, were the first human beings to gaze upon the face of this ever-glorious and beautiful Lake.

When Mark Twain and Thomas Starr King visited Tahoe it as largely in its primitive wildness, though logging operations for the securing of timber for the mines of Virginia City had been going on for some time and had led to the settlement at Glenbrook (where four great saw mills were in constant operation so long as weather permitted), and the stage-road from Placerville to Virginia City demanded stopping-stations, as Myers, Yanks, Rowlands and Lakeside.

But today, while the commercial operations have largely ceased, the scenic attractions of Lake Tahoe and its region have justified the erection of over twenty resorts and camps, at least two of them rivaling in extent and elaborateness of plant any of the gigantic resort hotels of either the Atlantic or Pacific coasts, the others varying in size and degree, according to the class of patronage they seek. That these provisions for the entertainment of travelers, yearly visitors, and health seekers will speedily increase with the years there can be no doubt, for there is but one Lake Tahoe, and its lovers will ultimately be legion.

Already, also, it has begun to assert itself as a place of summer residence. Fifteen years ago private residences on Lake Tahoe might have been enumerated on the fingers of the two hands; now they number as many hundreds, and the sound of the hammer and saw is constantly heard, and dainty villas, bungalows, cottages, and rustic homes are springing up as if by magic.

Then Lake Tahoe was comparatively hard to reach. *Now*, the trains of the *Southern Pacific* and the *Lake Tahoe Railway and Transportation Company* deposit one on the very edge of the Lake easier and with less personal exertion than is required to go to and from any large metropolitan hotel in one city to a similar hotel in another city.

It is almost inevitable that in such a book as this there should be some repetition. Just as one sees the same peaks and lakes, shore-line and trees from different portions of the Lake — though, of course, at slightly or widely differing angles — so in writing, the attention of the reader naturally is called again and again to the same scenes. But this book is written not so much with an eye to its literary quality, as to afford the visitor to Lake Tahoe — whether contemplative, actual, or retrospective — a truthful and comprehensive account and description of the Lake and its surroundings.

It will be observed that in many places I have capitalized the common noun Lake. Whenever this appears it signifies Lake Tahoe — the chief of all the lakes of the Sierra.

While it is very delightful to sit on the verandah or in the swinging seats of the Tavern lawn, or at the choice nooks of all the resorts from Tahoe City completely around the Lake, it is not possible to write a book on Lake Tahoe there. One must get out and feel the bigness of it all; climb its mountains, follow its trout streams; ride or walk or push one's way through its leafy coverts; dwell in the shade of its forests; row over its myriad of lakes study its geology, before he can know or write about Tahoe.

This is what I have done.

And this is what I desire to urge most earnestly upon my reader. Don't lounge around the hotels all the time. Get all you want of that kind of recreation; then "go in" for the more strenuous fun of wandering and climbing. Go alone or in company, afoot or horseback, only go! Thus will Tahoe increase the number of its devoted visitants and my object in writing these pages be accomplished.

George Wharton James

Tahoe Tavern, June 1914.

EMERALD BAY, THE CROWN JEWEL OF LAKE TAHOE.

CHAPTER I

WHY 'THE LAKE OF THE SKY'?

LAKE TAHOE is the largest lake at its altitude — 23 miles long by 13 broad, 6225 feet above the level of the sea — with but one exception in the world. Then, too, it closely resembles the sky in its pure and perfect color. One often experiences, on looking down upon it from one of its many surrounding mountains, a feeling of surprise, as if the sky and earth had somehow been reversed and he was looking down upon the sky instead of the earth.

And, further, Lake Tahoe so exquisitely mirrors the purity of the sky; its general atmosphere is so perfect, that one feels it is peculiarly akin to the sky.

Mark Twain walked to Lake Tahoe in the early sixties, from Carson City, carrying a couple of blankets and an ax. He suggests that his readers will find it advantageous to go on horseback. It was a hot summer day, not calculated to make one of his temperament susceptible to fine scenic impressions, yet this is what he says:

> We plodded on, two or three hours longer, and at last the Lake burst upon us — a noble sheet of blue water lifted six thousand three hundred feet above the level of the sea, and walled in by a rim of snow-clad mountain peaks that towered aloft full three thousand feet higher still. It was a vast oval, and one would have to use up eighty or a hundred good miles in traveling around it. As it lay there with the shadows of the mountains brilliantly photographed upon its still surface I thought it must surely be the fairest picture the whole earth affords!

And there you have it! Articulate or inarticulate, something like this is what everyone thinks when he first sees Tahoe, and the oftener he sees it, and the more he knows it, the more grand and glorious it becomes. It is immaterial that there are lakes perched upon higher mountain shelves, and that one or two of them, at equal or superior altitudes, are larger in size. Tahoe ranks in the forefront both for altitude and size, and in beauty and picturesqueness, majesty and sublimity, there is no mountain body of water on this earth that is its equal.

Why such superlatives in which world-travelers generally — in fact, invariably — agree? There must be some reason for it. Nay, there are many. To thousands, the chief charm of Lake Tahoe is in the exquisite, rare, and astonishing colors of its waters. They are an endless source of delight to all who see them, no matter how insensible they may be ordinarily, to the effect of color. There is no shade of blue or green that cannot here be found and the absolutely clear and pellucid quality of the water enhances the beauty and perfection of the tone.

One minister of San Francisco thus speaks of the coloring:

> When the day is calm there is a ring around the Lake extending from a hundred yards to a mile from the shore which is the most brilliant green; within this ring there is another zone of the deepest blue, and this gives place to royal purple in the distance; and the color of the Lake changes from day to day and from hour to hour. It is never twice the same — sometimes the blue is lapis lazuli, then it is jade, then it is purple, and when the breeze gently ruffles the surface it is silvery-gray. The Lake has as many moods as an April day or a lovely woman. But its normal appearance is that of a floor of lapis lazuli set with a ring of emerald.

The depth of the water, varying as it does from a few feet to nearly or over 2000 feet, together with the peculiarly variable bottom of the Lake, have much to do with these color effects. The lake bottom on a clear wind-quiet day can be clearly seen except in the lowest depths. Here and there are patches of fairly level area, covered either with rocky boulders, moss covered rocks, or varicolored sands. Then, suddenly, the eye falls upon a ledge, or the yonder side of which the water suddenly becomes deep blue. That ledge may denote a submarine precipice, a hundred, five hundred, a thousand or more feet deep, and the changes caused by such sudden and awful depths are beyond verbal description.

Many of the softer color effects are produced by the light-colored sands that are washed down into the shallower waters by the mountain streams. These vary considerably, from almost white and cream, to deep yellow, brown and red. Then the mosses that grow on the massive boulders, rounded, square and irregular, of every conceivable size, that are strewn over the lake bottom, together with the equally varied rocks of the shore line, some of them towering hundreds of feet above the water — these have their share in the general enchantment and revelry of color.

Emerald Bay and Meek's Bay are justly world-famed for their triumphs of color glories, for here there seem to be those peculiar combinations of varied objects, and depths, from the shallowest to the deepest, with the variations of colored sands and rocks on the bottom, as well as queer-shaped and colored boulders lying on the varicolored sands, that are not found elsewhere.

The waving of the water gives a mottled effect surpassing the most delicate and richly shaded marbles and onyxes. Watered-silks of the most perfect manufacture are but childish and puerile attempts at reproduction, and finest Turkish shawls, Bokhara rugs or Arab sheiks' dearest-prized Prayer Carpets are but glimmering suggestions of what the Master Artist himself has here produced.

There are not the glowing colors of sunrises and sunsets; but they are equally sublime, awe-inspiring and enchanting. There are Alpine-glows, and peach-blooms and opalescent fires, gleams and subtle suggestions that thrill moment by moment, and disappear as soon as seen, only to be followed by equally beautiful, enchanting and surprising effects, and with it all, is a mobility, a fluidity, a rippling, flowing, waving, tossing series of effects that belong only to enchanted water — water kissed into glory by the sun and moon, lured into softest beauty by the glamour of the stars, and etherealized by the quiet and subtle charms of the Milky Way, and of the Suns, comets and meteors that the eye of man has never gazed upon.

There is one especially color-blessed spot. It is in Grecian Bay, between Rubicon Point and Emerald Bay. Here the shore formation is wild and irregular, with deep holes, majestic, grand and rugged rocks and some trees and shrubbery. Near the center of this is a deep hole, into which one of the mountain streams runs over a light-colored sandy bottom where the water is quite shallow. Around are varicolored trees and shrubs, and these objects and conditions all combine to produce a mystic revelation of color gradations and harmonies, from emerald green and jade to the deepest amethystine or ultramarine. When the wind slightly stirs the surface and these dancing ripples catch the sunbeams, one by one, in changeful and irregular measure, the eyes are dazzled with iridescences and living color-changes covering hundreds of acres, thousands, of them, as exquisite, glorious and dazzling as revealed in the most perfect peacock's tail feathers, or hummingbird's throat.

Over such spots one sits in his boat spellbound, color entranced, and the ears of his soul listen to color music as thrilling, as enchanting as melodies by Foster and Balfe, minuets by Mozart and Haydn, arias by Handel, nocturnes and serenades by Chopin and Schumann, overtures by Rossini, massive choruses and chorals by Handel, Haydn and Mendelssohn, fugues by Bach, and concertos by Beethoven.

The blue alone is enough to impress it forever upon the observant mind. Its rich, deep, perfect splendor is a constant surprise. One steps from his hotel, not thinking of the Lake — the blue of its rises through the trees, over the rocks, *everywhere,* with startling vividness. Surely never before was so large and wonderful a lake of inky blue, sapphire blue, ultramarine, amethystine richness spread out for man's enjoyment. And while the summer months show this in all its smooth placidity and quietude, there seems to be a deeper blue, a richer shade take possession of the waves in the fall, or when its smoothness is rudely dispelled by the storms of winter and spring.

So much for the color!

Yet there are those who are devoted to Lake Tahoe who seldom speak of the coloring of its waters. Perhaps they are fascinated by its fishing. This has become as world-famed as its colors. Thousands, hundreds of thousands, of the most gamey and delicately flavored trout are caught here annually, both by experts and amateurs. The Federal and State governments, and private individuals yearly stock the main Lake and the hundred and one smaller lakes of the region with the finest species of trout obtainable, and the results fully justify the labor and expense.

To the mountain lover the Tahoe region is an earthly paradise. One summer I climbed over twenty peaks, each over nine thousand feet high, and all gave me glimpses of Tahoe. Some of them went up close to 11,000 feet.

Are you an admirer of Alpine, nay, *High Sierran,* trees? You will find all the well-known, and several rare and entirely new species in this region. This field alone could well occupy a student or a mere amateur tree-lover a whole summer in rambling, climbing, collecting and studying.

And as for geology — the Grand Canyon of Arizona has afforded me nature reading material for nearly three decades and I am delighted by reading it yet. Still I am free to confess the uplift of these high-sweeping Sierra, upon whose lofty summits

> The high-born, beautiful snow comes down,
> Silent and soft as the terrible feet
> Of Time on the mosses of ruins;

the great glacial *cirques,* with their stupendous precipices from which the vast ice-sheets started, which gouged, smoothed, planed and grooved millions of acres to solid granite into lake beds, polished domes and canyon walls and carried along millions of tons of rock debris to make scores of lateral and terminal moraines; together with the evidences of uplift, subsidence and volcanic outpouring of diorite and other molten rocks, afford one as vast and enjoyable a field for contemplation as any ordinary man can find in the Grand Canyon.

But why compare them? There is no need to do so. Each is supreme in its own right; different yet compelling, unlike yet equally engaging.

Then there are the ineffable climate of summer, the sunrises, the sunsets, the Indians, the flowers, the sweet-singing birds, the rowing, in winter the snowshoeing, the camping out, and, alas! I must say it — the hunting.

Why man will hunt save for food is beyond me. I deem it that every living thing has as much right to its life as I have to mine, but I find I am in a large minority among a certain class that finds at Lake Tahoe its hunting Mecca. Deer abound, and grouse and quail are quite common, and in the summer of 1913 I knew of four bears being shot.

Is it necessary to present further claims for Lake Tahoe? Every new hour finds a new charm, every new day calls for the louder praise, every added visit only fastens the chains of allurement deeper. For instance, this is the day of athletic maids, as well as men. We find them everywhere. Very well! Lake Tahoe is the physical culturist's heaven.

In any one of its score of camps he may sleep out of doors, on the porch, out under the pines, by the side of the Lake or in his tent or cottage with open doors and windows. At sunrise, or later, in his bathing suit, or when away from too close neighbors, clothed, as dear old Walt Whitman puts it, "in the natural and religious idea of nakedness," the cold waters of the Lake invite him to a healthful and invigorating plunge, with a stimulating and vivifying swim.

A swift rub down with a crash towel, a rapid donning of rude walking togs and off, instanter, for a mile climb up one of the trails, a scramble over a rocky way to some hidden Sierra lake, some sheltered tree nook, some elevated outlook point, and, after feasting the eyes on the glories of incomparable and soul-elevating scenes, he returns to camp, eats a hearty breakfast, with a clear conscience, a vigorous appetite aided by hunger sauce, guided by the normal instincts of taste, all of which have been toned up by the morning's exercise—what wonder that such a one radiates Life and Vim, Energy and Health, Joy and Content.

Do you know what the lure must be when a busy man, an active man, an alert man, a man saturated with the nervous spirit of American commercial life, sits down in one of the seat overlooking the Lake, or spreads out his full length upon the grass, or on the beds of Sierran moss, which make a deliciously restful cushion, and stays there! He does nothing; doesn't even look consciously at the blue waters of the Lake, on the ineffable blue of the sky, or the rich green of the trees or the glory of the flowers — he simply sits or sprawls or lies and, though the influence is different, the effect is the same as that expressed in the old hymn:

My soul would ever stay,
In such a frame as this,
And sit and sing itself away,
To everlasting bliss.

There's the idea! Calm, rest, peace, bliss. Those are what you get at Lake Tahoe. And with them come renewed health, increased vigor, strengthened courage, new power to go forth and seize the problems of life, with a surer grasp, a more certain touch, a more clearly and definitely assured end.

There are some peculiarities of Lake Tahoe that should be noted, although they are of a very different character from the foolish and sensational statements that used to be made in the early days of its history among white men. A serious advertising folder years ago sagely informed the traveling public as follows: "A strange phenomenon in connection with the Truckee River is the fact that the Lake from which it flows (Tahoe) has no inlet, so far as anyone knows, and the lake into which it flows (Pyramid Lake, Nevada) has no outlet."

How utterly absurd this is. Lake Tahoe has upward of a hundred feeders, among which may be named Glenbrook, the Upper Truckee, Fallen Leaf Creek, Eagle Creek, Meek's Creek, General Creek, McKinney Creek, Madden Creek, Blackwood Creek, and Ward Creek, all of these being constant streams, pouring many thousands of inches of water daily into the Lake even at the lowest flow, and in the snow-melting and rainy seasons sending down their floods in great abundance.

To many it is a singular fact that Lake Tahoe never freezes over in winter. This is owing to its great depth, possibly aided by the ruffling and consequent disturbance of its surface by the strong northeasterly winter winds. The vast body of water, with such tremendous depth, maintains too high a temperature to be affected by surface reductions in temperature. Experiments show that the temperature in summer on the surface is 68 degrees Fahrenheit. At 100 feet, 55 degrees; at 300 feet, 46 degrees; at 1506 feet, 39 degrees.

Twenty years ago the thermometer at Lake Tahoe registered 18° F. *below zero,* and in 1910 it was 10° F. below. Both these years Emerald Bay froze over. Perhaps the reason for this is found in the fact that the entrance to the bay is very shallow, and that this meager depth is subject to change in surface temperature, becoming warmer in summer and colder in winter.

This narrow ridge once solidly frozen, the warmth of the larger body of water would have no effect upon the now-confined smaller body of Emerald Bay. Once a firm hold is taken by the ice, it would slowly spread its fingers and aid in the reduction of the temperature beyond, first producing slush ice, and then the more solid crystal ice, until the whole surface would be frozen solid.

An explanation of the non-freezing of the main Lake has been offered by several local "authorities" as owing to the presence of a number of hot springs either in the bed of the Lake or near enough to its shores materially to affect its temperature. But I know of few or no "facts" to justify such an explanation.

When I first visited Lake Tahoe over thirty years ago, I was seriously and solemnly informed by several (who evidently believed their own assertions) that, owing to the great elevation of the Lake, the density of the water, etc., etc., it was impossible for anyone to swim in Lake Tahoe. I was assured that several who had tried had had narrow escapes from drowning.

While the utter absurdity of the statements was self-evident, I decided I would give myself a practical demonstration. To be perfectly safe I purchased a clothesline, then, hiring a row boat, went as far away from shore as was desirable, undressed, tied one end of

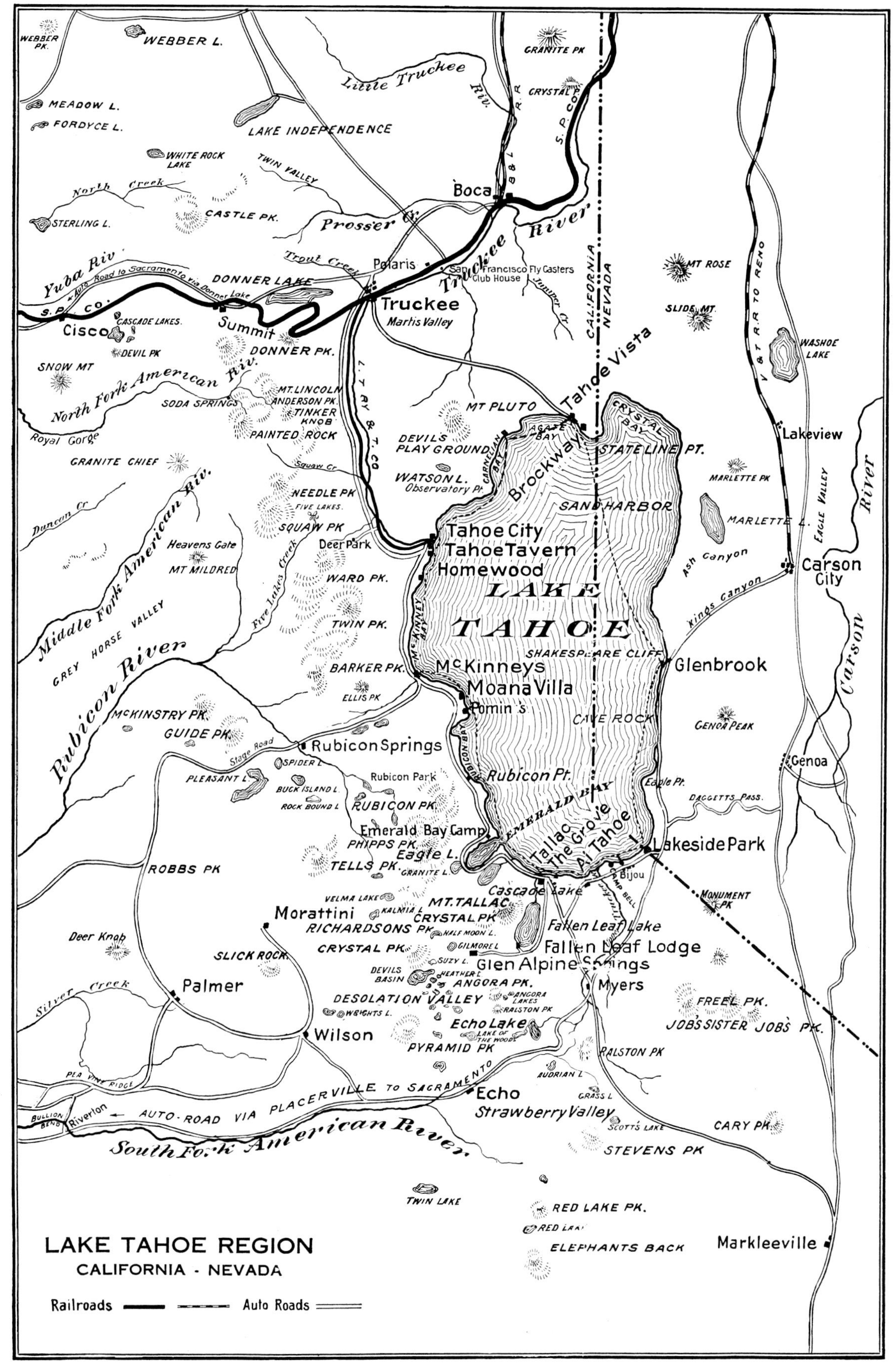
LAKE TAHOE REGION
CALIFORNIA - NEVADA
Railroads
Auto Roads
LAKE TAHOE
Truckee
Tahoe City
Tahoe Tavern
Homewood
McKinneys
Moana Villa
Rubicon Springs
Glenbrook
Lakeside Park
Carson City
Genoa
Lakeview
Tahoe Vista
Brockway
Boca
Polaris
Cisco
Summit
Myers
Palmer
Wilson
Echo
Riverton
Markleeville
Morattini
Fallen Leaf Lake
Fallen Leaf Lodge
Glen Alpine Springs
Emerald Bay Camp
Tallac
The Grove
Al Tahoe
Bijou
Strawberry Valley
DONNER LAKE
LAKE INDEPENDENCE
WEBBER L.
MT ROSE
WASHOE LAKE
MARLETTE L.
EMERALD BAY
Rubicon Pt.
SHAKESPEARE CLIFF
CAVE ROCK
STATE LINE PT.
SAND HARBOR
CRYSTAL BAY
AGATE BAY
MT. TALLAC
ECHO LAKE
DESOLATION VALLEY
Rubicon River
Truckee River
Carson River
South Fork American River
Middle Fork American Riv.
North Fork American Riv.
Little Truckee Riv.
Prosser Cr.
Yuba Riv.
AUTO-ROAD VIA PLACERVILLE TO SACRAMENTO
Auto Road to Sacramento via Donner Lake
San Francisco Fly Casters Club House
CALIFORNIA
NEVADA
L. T. RY & T. CO
S. P. CO.
V & T R.R. TO RENO
B & L R.R.
Kings Canyon
Ash Canyon
DAGGETTS PASS
FREEL PK.
JOBS SISTER
JOBS PK.
MONUMENT PK
RALSTON PK
STEVENS PK
CARY PK.
RED LAKE PK.
ELEPHANTS BACK
TWIN LAKE
PYRAMID PK
ANGORA PK.
CRYSTAL PK.
RICHARDSONS PK.
SLICK ROCK
ROBBS PK
Deer Knob
TELLS PK.
PHIPPS PK.
Eagle L.
Cascade Lake
RUBICON PK.
Rubicon Park
PLEASANT L.
GUIDE PK.
McKINSTRY PK.
ELLIS PK
BARKER PK.
TWIN PK.
WARD PK.
SQUAW PK
NEEDLE PK
WATSON L.
Observatory Pt.
DEVIL'S PLAY GROUND
MT PLUTO
GRANITE CHIEF
Heavens Gate
MT MILDRED
GREY HORSE VALLEY
Deer Park
PAINTED ROCK
SODA SPRINGS
Royal Gorge
SNOW MT
DEVIL PK
DONNER PK.
CASCADE LAKES
STERLING L.
CASTLE PK.
WHITE ROCK LAKE
TWIN VALLEY
MEADOW L.
FORDYCE L.
WEBBER PK.
GRANITE PK
CRYSTAL PK
SLIDE MT.
MARLETTE PK
GENOA PEAK
EAGLE VALLEY
Martis Valley

the rope around the seat, the other around my body, and—jumped in. I did not sink. Far from it. I was never more stimulated to swim in my life.

My ten or fifteen feet dive took me into colder water than I had ever experienced before and I felt as if suddenly, and at one fell swoop, I were flayed alive. Gasping for breath I made for the boat, climbed in, and in the delicious glow that came with the reaction decided that it was quite as important to feel of the temperature of lake water before you leaped, as it was to render yourself safe from sinking by anchoring yourself to a clothesline.

But I would not have my reader assume from the recital of this experience that Lake Tahoe is always too cold for swimming. Such is not the case. Indeed in June, July, August and September, the swimming is delightful to those who enjoy "the cool, silver shock of the plunge in a pool's living water," that Browning's *Saul* so vividly pictures for us. Hundreds of people — men, women and children — in these months indulge in the daily luxury, especially in the coves and beaches where the water is not too deep, and the sun's ardent rays woo them into comfortable warmth.

After a warm day's tramp or ride over the trails, too, there is nothing more delicious than a plunge into one of the lakes. A short, crisp swim, a vigorous rub down, and a resumption of the walk or ride and one feels *fit* enough to conquer a world.

It can be imagined, too, what a lively scene the Lake presents in the height of the season, when, from the scores of hotels, resorts, camps, private residence, fishermen's camps, etc.; fishing boats, row boats, launches, motor boats, and yachts ply to and fro in every direction, unconsciously vying with each other to attract the eye of the onlooker.

The pure blue of the Lake, with its emerald ring and varying shades of color, added to by the iridescent gleam that possesses the surface when it is slightly rippled by a gentle breeze, contrasting with the active, vivid, moving boats of differing sizes, splashed with every conceivable color by the hats and costumes of the occupants — all these conspire to demand the eye, to enchain the attention, to harmlessly hypnotize, as it were, those who sit on the shore and look.

And when is added to this the spontaneous shouts and shrieks of delight that the feminine "fishermen" give when they are successful and make a catch, the half-frenzied and altogether delighted announcements thereof, the whole-hearted or the half-jealous, half-envious return congratulations, while now and then the large steamer, *Tahoe*, or an elegant private yacht, as the Tevis's *Consuelo*, crosses the scene, one may partially but never fully conceive the joy and radiant happiness, the satisfaction and content that Lake Tahoe inspires and produces.

Lake Tahoe covers about 190 square miles, and its watershed is about 500 square miles. The boundary line between Nevada and California strikes the Lake on the northern border at the 120th meridian, and a point at that spot is called the State Line Point. The latitude parallel of this northern entrance is 39°15". The boundary line goes due south until about 38°28" and then strikes off at an oblique angle to the southeast, making the southern line close to Lakeside Park, a few miles east of the 120th meridian.

CHAPTER II

FREMONT AND THE DISCOVERY OF LAKE TAHOE

Like so many other great discoveries that were to have an important effect upon the lives of countless numbers of people, the discovery of Lake Tahoe was accidental. Nor did its finder comprehend the vast influence it was to possess, not only upon the residents of California and Nevada, but upon the travel-loving and sightseeing portion of the population of the whole world.

John C. Frémont, popularly acclaimed "the pathfinder," was its discoverer, on the 14th day of February, 1844. In the journal of his 1843-44 expedition he thus records the first sight of it:

> Accompanied by Mr. Preuss, I ascended today the highest peak to the right from which we had a beautiful view of a mountain lake at our feet, about fifteen miles in length, and so nearly surrounded by mountains that we could not discover an outlet.

It cannot be deemed out of place in these pages, owing to the significance of the discovery by Frémont, to give a brief account of the exploration and its purposes, in the carrying out of which Tahoe was revealed to the intrepid and distinguished explorer.

Fortunately for us, Frémont left a full story of his experiences in the Nevada country, complete in detail, and as fresh and vivid as if but written yesterday. This account, with illuminating introduction, and explanatory notes by James U. Smith, from whose pioneer father Smith Valley is named, was republished in the *Second Biennial Report of the Nevada Historical Society*, from which, with the kind permission of the secretary, Professor Jeanne Elizabeth Wier, the following extracts are made.

Frémont had already made his first exploration of the Rocky Mountains and South Pass in the summer of 1842. It was in this expedition that, standing on the highest peak of the Rockies, he looked down into the vast area beyond, known as the Great Basin, comprising with its mountain ranges the whole western portion of the continent of North America. This he determined to explore, and it was on this second expedition that Lakes Pyramid and Tahoe, the Truckee River, etc., were discovered.

Later, Frémont made his third western journey, that in which he came into conflict with the Mexican officials of California, became governor of California, and was finally placed under arrest by General Kearny, and

John C. Fremont, from 1856 campaign literature.

taken back to Washington to be tried for mutiny. The results of that unfortunate Kearny conflict are well known.

At the official close of the dispute he made his fourth expedition and finally his fifth, all of which are fully treated in Smucker's and Bigelow's *Life of Frémont.* To return now to the second expedition. In the words of Mr. Smith:

The object of the expedition was purely for the purpose of exploring and otherwise getting scientific information about the great territory between the Missouri frontier and the Pacific Ocean. Emigrants were making their way westward to the new Oregon Territory, and hunters and trappers had been visiting portions of that region. Farther north the fur companies had their posts and did a regular business with the trappers and Indians But little was known about the regions further south, and especially the great territory between the Rocky and Sierra Nevada Mountain chains, and that little was freely adulterated with fiction.

Great Salt Lake was supposed to be a very strange and wonderful lake, the islands of which were covered with woods and flowers, through which roamed all kinds of game, and whose waters were sucked down in a great awe-inspiring whirlpool into an underground passage under the mountains and valleys to the distant sea. Another myth, or rather pair of myths, in which geographers placed sufficient faith to give a place on the maps of the time, was the great Buenaventura River, and that semi-tropical Mary's Lake, the waters from which found their way through the Sierra Nevada to San Francisco Bay.

Mary's Lake was supposed to be a body of water such as a traveler dreams about, whose clear waters were bordered by meadows ever green, a place on whose shores he could pitch his tent and cast aside all thought or care of the morrow. Frémont counted on this lake as a place where he could recuperate and make ready for a final dash eastward across the unknown country to the Rocky Mountains and thence home to the Mississippi River. Contrast these anticipations with the hardships and fears he encountered while groping his way through the Black Rock Desert, north of Pyramid Lake.

But Frémont was a good leader followed by courageous men, and disappointments did not make weaklings of either him or his men. His party, on leaving Missouri, consisted of thirty-nine men — Creoles, Canadian-Frenchmen, Americans, a German or two, a free negro and two Indians. Charles Preuss was Frémont's assistant in topography, and it is likely that he made his sketches, several of which were published in the original report.

Another member of the party, and one who joined it in the Rocky Mountains and is of special interest to us, was Christopher Carson, commonly known as "Kit" Carson. Frémont speaks of him in very friendly and flattering terms. At the time of the meeting with Carson, he says: "I had here the satisfaction to meet our good buffalo hunter of 1842, Christopher Carson, whose services I considered myself fortunate to secure again." On another occasion, when Carson had successfully performed a responsible errand, he says: "Reaching St. Vrain's Fort ... we found ... my true and reliable friend, Kit Carson."

Frémont left Kansas City, Mo., May 29, 1843.

His general route was along the *old* "Oregon Trail," then the *new* "Oregon Trail," but at many places his route was different. He followed up the Kansas River instead of the Platte. But he crossed the Rocky Mountains over the South Pass, which is that of the Union

Pacific Railroad, and was common to the Oregon Trail and the emigrant road to California. During nearly the whole journey to Oregon Frémont divided his party. One part he placed in charge of Fitzpatrick. This consisted of the carts with the bulk of the supplies and about half of the men.

The other part consisted of a mounted party with packhorses and the howitzer. Frémont, of course, took charge of the latter party, for, traveling light as it did, he was able to make detours covering country he wished to explore, always,however, using the other train as a base of supplies. The course of the other party was generally along the emigrant road to Oregon.

After crossing the Rocky Mountains, Frémont went south with his party to explore Great Salt Lake. Thence he returned north again to the emigrant road, which then followed in a general way the Snake or Lewis River to the Columbia, with the exception of the great bend in northeastern Oregon which was traversed by a shorter route. Along the bank of the Columbia the road followed to the Mission Station at the Dalles, or great narrows of the river.

At this pint many of the emigrants transferred their baggage to barges and floated with the current to their destination on the Willamette River. Others continued by land down the river. Frémont's division reached the Dalles November 4th. Fitzpatrick's train did not come in until the 21st.

The latter left his carts at the mouth of the Walla Walla River according to Frémont's orders; and, after making pack saddles, transferred what was left of his baggage to the backs of his mules for the trip down to the Dalles. In the meantime Frémont, with Preuss and two of the other men, had gone down to Fort Vancouver in canoes. This was the headquarters of the Hudson Bay Company for the West. Here supplies for the return journey were obtained.

Having transported these supplies up to the Dalles in barges propelled by Indians, he was ready to take up the final preparation for the homeward journey. It is best to let him describe these preparations in his own words. He says:

"The camp was now occupied in making the necessary preparations for our homeward journey, which, though homeward, contemplated a new route, and a great circuit to the south and southeast, and the exploration of the Great Basin between the Rocky Mountains and the Sierra Nevada.

"Three principal objects were indicated, by report, or by maps, as being on this route, the character or existence of which I wished to ascertain, and which I assumed as landmarks, or leading points, on the projected line of return. The ;first of these points was the Tlamath Lake, on the tableland between the head of Fall River (this is now called by its French name, the Des Chutes River), which comes to the Columbia, and the Sacramento, which goes to the Bay of San Francisco, and from which lake a river of the same name makes its way westwardly direct to the ocean.

"This lake and river are often called Klamet, but I have chosen to write the name according to the Indian pronunciation. The position of this lake, on the line of inland communication between Oregon and California; its proximity to the demarcation boundary of latitude 42 deg.; its imputed double character of lake, or meadow, according to the season of the year; and the hostile and warlike character attributed to the Indians about it; — all make it a desirable object to visit and examine.

"From this lake our course was intended to be about southeast, to a reported lake called Mary's, at some days' journey in the Great Basin; and thence, still on southeast, to the reputed Buenaventura River, which has a place in so many maps, and countenanced the belief of the existence of a great river flowing from the Rocky Mountains to the Bay of San Francisco. From the Buenaventura the next point was intended to be in that section of the Rocky Mountains which includes the heads of Arkansas River, and of the opposite waters of the California Gulf; and thence down the Arkansas to Bent's Fort, and home.

"This was our projected line of return — a great part of it absolutely new to geographical, botanical, and geological science — and the subject of reports in relation to lakes, rivers, deserts, and savages, hardly above the condition of mere wild animals, which inflamed desire to know what this *terra incognita* really contained.

"It was a serious enterprise, at the commencement of winter, to undertake the traverse of such a region, and with a party consisting only of twenty-five persons, and they of many nations — American, French, German, Canadian, Indian, and colored — and most of them young, several being under twenty-one years of age.

"All knew that a strange country was to be explored, and dangers and hardships to be encountered; but no one blenched at the prospect. On the contrary, courage and confidence animated the whole party. Cheerfulness, readiness, subordination, prompt obedience, characterized all; nor did any extremity or peril and privation, to which we were afterward exposed, ever belie, or derogate from, the fine spirit of this brave and generous commencement.

"The course of the narrative will show at what pint, and for what reasons, we were prevented from the complete execution of this plan, after having made considerable progress upon it, and how we were forced by desert plains and mountain ranges, and deep snows, far to the south and near to the Pacific Ocean, and along the western base of the Sierra Nevada; where, indeed, a new and ample field of exploration opened itself before us."

From these quotations it is evident that Frémont had no idea of entering California at this time. He was simply driven to it by circumstances over which he had no control.

Leaving the Dalles, Frémont followed up the Des Chutes River to its headwaters in southeastern Oregon, thence he crossed over the divide to the waters of the Klamath, which he followed southward to what is known as Klamath Marsh. This he called "Klamath Lake."

Now started the hunt for Mary's Lake and the San Buenaventura River. The party came down through southeastern Oregon into Nevada, where they camped on the night of December 26, in Coleman Valley, on what is called Twelve-Mile Creek, and about 11 miles from the present California line. It may be noted here that at that time the parallel between Nevada and California on the south and Oregon on the north, was the southern boundary of the territory of the United States. Frémont was, therefore, about to cross into Mexican territory.

He then progressed southward through what are now Washoe, Humboldt, Churchill and Lyon counties, and over the California line into Mono County, back again into Douglas, and thence over the mountains south of Lake Tahoe, but did not find Mary's Lake, nor the places upon which he relied to recruit his animals and give rest to his party. He did, however, find Pyramid Lake.

this being the body of water into which the Truckee River flows, and the Truckee being the only outlet to Lake Tahoe, it is well that this portion of the account be given in full. Frémont and Carson were on ahead. The day was January 10, 1843. Frémont writes:

Leaving a signal for the party to encamp, we continued our way up the hollow, intending to see what lay beyond the mountain. The hollow was several miles long, forming a good pass (some maps designate this pass as Frémont Pass, others as San Emidio Canyon), the snow deepened to about a foot as we neared the summit. Beyond, a defile between the mountains descended rapidly about two thousand feet; and, filling up all the lower space, was a sheet of green water, some twenty miles broad (Pyramid Lake).

It broke upon our eyes like the ocean. The neighboring peaks rose high above us. One peak, on the eastern side of the lake, rises nearly forty-four hundred feet above the lake, and on the side (toward which Frémont was looking) one peak rises 4925 feet above the lake; and we ascended one of them to obtain a better view.

The waves were curling in the breeze, and their dark green color showed it to be a body of deep water. For a long time we sat enjoying the view, for we had become fatigued with mountains, and the free expanse of moving waves was very grateful. It was set like a gem in the mountains, which, from our position, seemed to inclose it almost entirely.

At the western end it communicated with the line of basins we had left a few days since; and on the opposite side it swept a ridge of snowy mountains, the foot of the great Sierra. Its position at first inclined us to believe it Mary's Lake, but the rugged mountains were so entirely discordant with descriptions of its low rushy shores and open country, that we concluded it some unknown body of water, which it afterwards proved to be.

On January 13th we followed again a broad Indian trail along the shore of the lake to the southward. For a short space we had room enough in the bottom; but, after traveling a short distance, the water swept the foot of the precipitous mountains, the peaks of which are about 3000 feet above the lake. The trail wound around the base of these precipices, against which the water dashed below, by a way nearly impracticable for the howitzer.

During a greater part of the morning the lake was nearly hid by a snowstorm, and the waves broke on the narrow beach in a long line of foaming surf, five or six feet high. The day was unpleasantly cold, the wind driving the snow sharp against our faces; and, having advanced only about twelve miles, we encamped in a bottom formed by

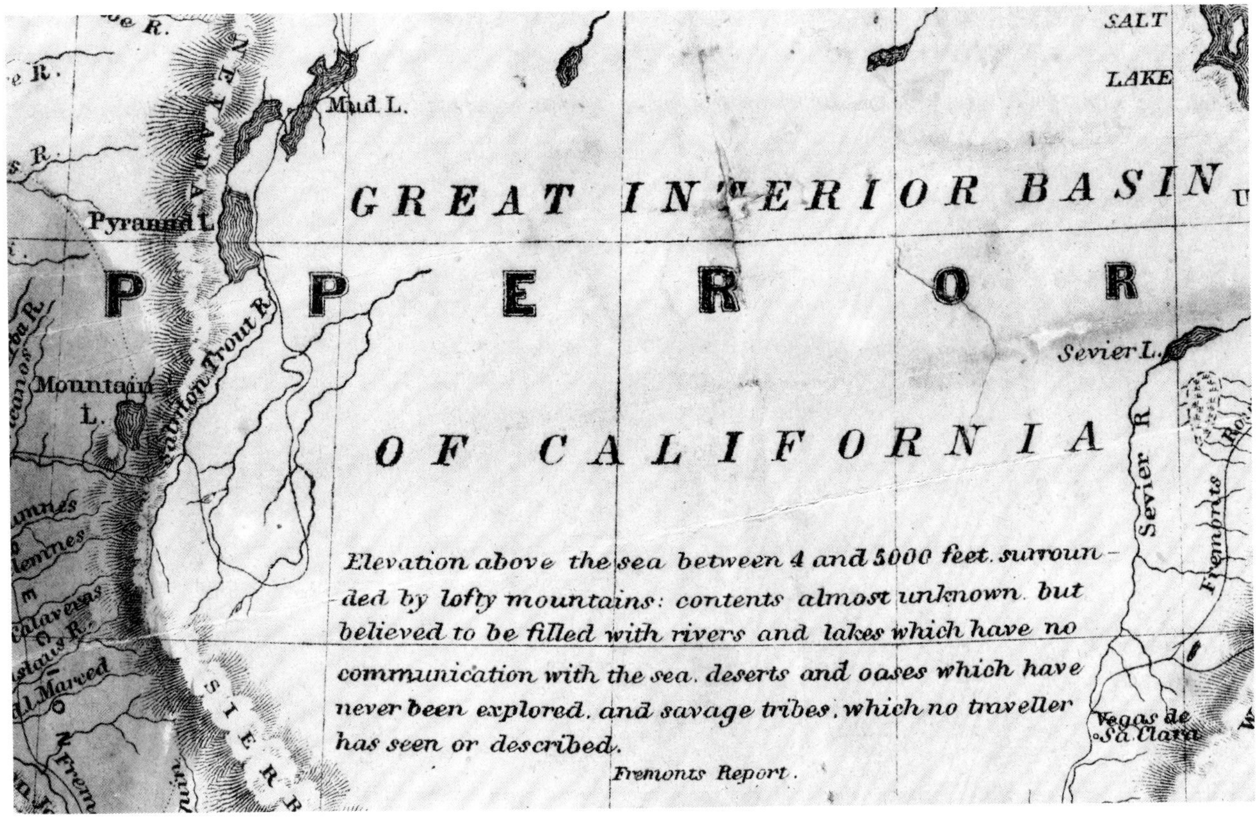

This 1848 map of the Tahoe-Great Basin region was issued four years after John Fremont's party spotted Mountain Lake, later called Bigler and finally Lake Tahoe. It became part of Utah Terr. in 1850 and Nevada Terr. in 1861.

a ravine, covered with good grass, which was fresh and green.

We did not get the howitzer into camp, but were obliged to leave it on the rocks until morning. The next morning the snow was rapidly melting under a warm sun. Part of the morning was occupied in bringing up the gun; and, making only nine miles, we encamped on the shore, opposite a very remarkable rock in the lake, which had attracted our attention for many miles. It rose, according to our estimate, 600 feet above the water, and, from the point we viewed it, presented a pretty exact outline of the great pyramid of Cheops.

Like other rocks, along the shore, it seemed to be incrusted with calcareous cement. This striking features suggested a name for the lake, and I called it Pyramid Lake; and though it may be deemed by some a fanciful resemblance, I can undertake to say that the future traveler will find much more striking resemblance between this rock and the pyramids of Egypt than there is between them and the object from which they take their name ....

The elevation of this lake above the sea is 4890 feet, being nearly 700 feet higher than the Great Salt Lake, from which it lies nearly west, and distant about eight degrees of longitude. The position and elevation of this lake make it an object of geographical interest.

It is the nearest lake to the western rim, as the Great Salt Lake is to the eastern rim of the Great Basin which lies between the base of the Rocky Mountains and the Sierra Nevada — and the extent and character of which, its whole circumference and contents, it is so desirable to know.

The Indians then directed him to a river of which he says:

Groves of large cottonwood, which we could see at the mouth, indicated that it was a stream of considerable size, and, at all events, we had the pleasure to know that now we were in a country where human beings could live. Reaching the groves, we found the inlet of a large fresh-water stream (the Truckee River), and all at once were satisfied that it was neither Mary's River nor the waters of the Sacramento, but that we had discovered a large interior lake, which the Indians informed us had no outlet. It is about 35 miles long, and, by the mark of the water-line along the shore, the spring level is about 12 feet above its present waters.

In the meantime, such a salmon-trout feast as is seldom seen was going on in our camp, and every variety of manner in which fish could be prepared — boiled, fried and roasted in the ashes — was put into requisition; and every few minutes an Indian would be seen running off to spear a fresh one. Whether these Indians had seen whites before, we could not be certain; but they were evidently in communication with others who had, as one of them had some brass buttons, and we noticed several other articles of civilized manufacture.

We could obtain from them but little information about the country. They made on the ground a drawing of the river, which they represented as issuing from another lake in the mountains three or four days distant, in a direction a little west of south; beyond which, they drew a mountain; and further still, two rivers; on one of which they told us that people like ourselves traveled.

They still wandered to the south, passing near where Dayton, Nevada, now is, and reaching Bridgeport and Mono and Twin Lakes. Here they struck north and west again and soon had to leave the howitzer. Passing through Antelope Valley they reached Markleeville in deep snow, passed Grover's Springs, entered Faith and Hope Valleys, and here it was Frémont gained his view of Lake Tahoe. It was February 14, 1844. He says:

The dividing ridge of the Sierra is in sight from this encampment. Accompanied by Mr. Preuss, I ascended to-day the highest peak to the right [probably Stevens Peak, 10,100 feet above sea-level], from which we had a beautiful view of a mountain lake at our feet, about fifteen miles in length, and so entirely surrounded by mountains that we could not discover an outlet [Lake Tahoe].

We had taken with us a glass, but though we enjoyed an extended view, the valley was half hidden in mist, as when we had seen it before. Snow could be distinguished on the higher parts of the coast mountains, eastward, as far as the eye could extend. It ranged over a terrible mass of broken snowy mountains, fading off blue in the distance. The rock composing the summit consists of very coarse, dark, volcanic conglomerate; the lower parts appeared to be of a slaty structure.

The highest trees were a few scattered cedars and aspens. From the immediate foot of the peak, we were two hours reaching the summit, and one hour and a quarter in descending. The day had been very bright, still, and clear, and spring seemed to be advancing rapidly. While the sun is in the sky the snow melts rapidly, and gushing springs cover the face of the mountain in all exposed places, but their surface freezes instantly with the disappearance of the sun.

I obtained to-night some observations, and the result from these, and others made during our stay, gives for the latitude 38 deg. 41′ 57″, longitude 120 deg. 25′ 57″ [the correct longitude for this place is 119 deg. 58′], and rate of the chronometer 25.82.

The next night they encamped on the headwaters of a little creek, where at last the water found its way to the Pacific. The following morning they started early.

The creek acquired a regular breadth of about 20 feet, and we soon began to hear the rushing of water below the icy surface, over which we traveled to avoid the snow; a few miles below we broke through, where the water was several feet deep, and halted to make a fire and dry our clothes. We continued a few miles further, walking being very laborious without snowshoes.

I was now perfectly satisfied that we had struck the stream on which Mr. Sutter lived; and, turning about, made a hard push, and reached the camp at dark. Here we had the pleasure to find all the remaining animals, 57 in number, safely arrived at the grassy hill near camp; and here, also, we were agreeably surprised with the sight of an abundance of salt.

Some of the horse-guard had gone to a neighboring hut for pine nuts, and discovered unexpectedly a large cake of very white, fine grained salt, which the Indians told them they had brought from the other side of the mountain; they used it to eat with their pine uts, and readily sold it for goods.

On the 19th, the people were occupied in making a road and bringing up the baggage; and, on the afternoon

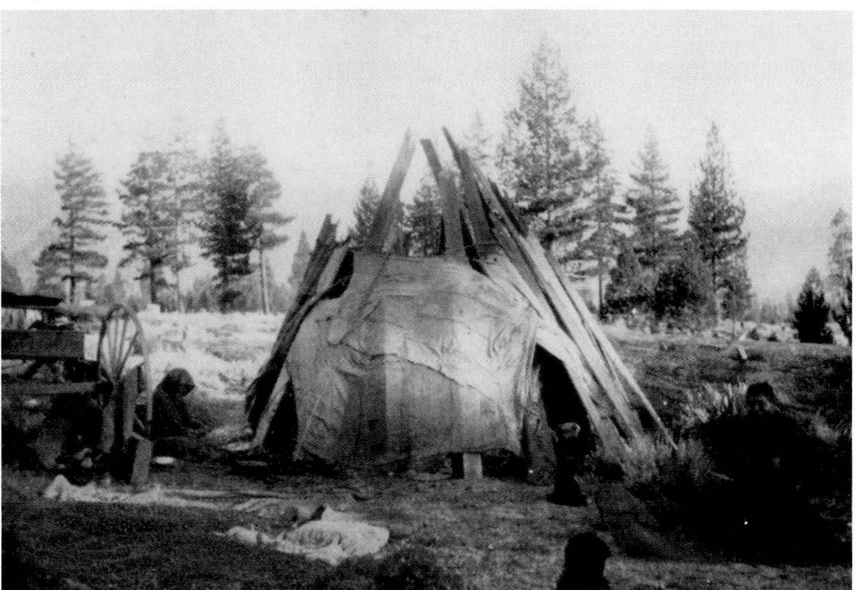

A Washoe Indian Campoodie, Near Lakeside Park, Lake Tahoe.

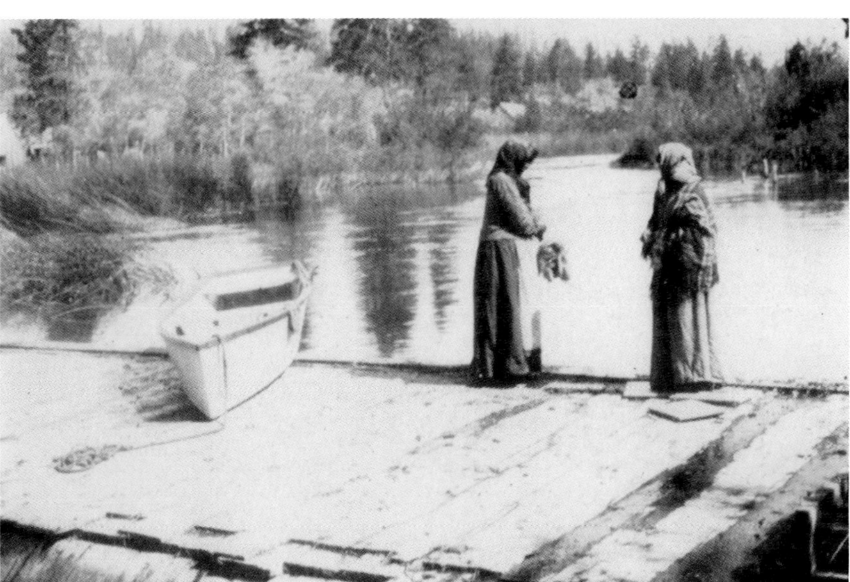

Washoe Indians at a private dock, at Lake Tahoe.

OPPOSITE: The Signal Code design of the Dat-So-La-Lee baskets.

of the next day, February 20, we encamped, with the animals and all the *materiel* of the camp, on the summit of the pass [Carson Pass, at the head of Hope Valley] in the dividing ridge, 1000 miles by our traveled road from the Dalles to the Columbia.

The people, who had not yet been to this point, climbed the neighboring peak to enjoy a look at the valley.

The temperature of boiling water gave for the elevation of the encampment, 9338 feet above the sea.

This was 2000 feet higher than the South Pass in the Rocky Mountains, and several peaks in view rose several thousand feet still higher. Thus, at the extremity of the continent, and near the coast, the phenomenon was seen of a range of mountains still higher than the great Rocky Mountains themselves.

This extraordinary fact accounts for the Great Basin, and shows that there must be a system of small lakes and rivers scattered over a flat country, and which the extended and lofty range of the Sierra Nevada prevents from escaping to the Pacific Ocean. Latitude 38 deg. 44', longitude 120 deg. 28'. [This latitude is that of Stevens Peak, the highest in that ridge, 10,100 feet, and of course he did not go over the top of that peak, when Carson Pass, 1600 feet lower, was in plain view; this pass is the lowest one visible from the route on which they had come; another pass much lower leads out from the other or northern end of Hope Valley, but was not visible from their trail. The summit of Carson Pass is approximately latitude 38 deg. 41' 50"; longitude 199 deg. 59'. Frémont longitude readings are unreliable, owing to error in his chronometer.]

From this point on, following the south fork of the American River, sixteen days from the summit landed Frémont and his party at Sutter's Fort, March 8. Of their arrival Frémont says:

A more forlorn and pitiable sight than they presented cannot well be imagined. They were all on foot, each man weak and emaciated, leading a horse or mule as weak and emaciated as themselves. They had experienced great difficulty in descending the mountains, made slippery by rains and melting snows, and many horses fell over precipices and were killed, and with some were lost the packs they carried.

Among these was a mule with the plants which we had collected since leaving Fort Hall, along a line of 2000 miles of travel. Out of 67 horses and mules, with which we commenced crossing the Sierra, only 33 reached the valley of the Sacramento, and they only in a condition to be led along.

In conclusion, it should not be overlooked that on his maps of the expedition of 1843-44 Frémont called the mountain lake he had discovered "Lake Bonpland." He says in a private letter: "I gave to the basin river its name of Humboldt and to the mountain lake the name of his companion traveler, Bonpland, and so put it in the map of that expedition."

Amadé Bonpland was born at Rochelle, France, in 1773. He was educated as a physician but became a noted botanist. He accompanied Humboldt to America, and subsequently became a joint author with the great traveler and scientist of several valuable works on the botany, natural history, etc., of the New World.

He was detained as a prisoner for nearly ten years by Dictator Francia of Paraguay to prevent him from, or to punish him for, attempting to cultivate the maté, or Paraguay tea, in that country. He died in 1858 at Montevideo, the Capital of Uruguay, in South America.

His name as applied to Lake Tahoe is practically unknown, save to the curious investigator or historian. Other names given by Frémont have "stick" to this day, amongst them being Humboldt, Walker, Owen, Kern and Carson rivers, Pyramid and Walker lakes, etc.

The vicissitudes of the naming of Lake Tahoe is of sufficient interest to occupy a whole chapter (see Chapter V).

CHAPTER III

THE INDIANS OF LAKE TAHOE

Since Lake Tahoe was the natural habitat of one of the most deliciously edible fishes found in the world, the Indians of the region were bound, very early in their history here, to settle upon its shores. These were the Paiutis and the Washoes. The former, however, ranging further east in Nevada, were always regarded as interlopers by the latter if they came too near to the Lake, and there are legends current of several great struggles in which many lives were lost, where the Washoes battled with the Paiutis to keep them from this favored locality.

Prior to the coming of the emigrant bands in the early 1840s, the only white men the Indians ever saw were occasional trappers who wandered into the new and strange land. Then, the beautiful Indian name, soft and limpid as an Indian maiden's eyes, was *Wasiu*—not the harsh, Anglicized, *Washoe*.

Their range seemed to be from Washoe and Carson valleys on the east in winter, up to Tahoe and over the Sierra for fishing and hunting in the summer. They never ventured far westward, as the Monos and other mountain tribes claimed the mountain regions for their acorns and the deer and other game which abounded there.

While in the early days of the settlements of whites upon their lands the Washoes now and again rose in protest, and a few lives were lost, in the main they have been a peaceable and inoffensive tribe. The Paiutis were far more independent and warlike, placing their yoke upon the weaker tribe. Indeed, when I first talked with the older Washoes and Paiutis they were full of stories of big wars between themselves.

They showed me rocks near to the present town of Verdi, on the line of the Southern Pacific, on which their ancestors had made certain inscriptions which they interpreted as warnings to the Paiutis not to dare trespass beyond that sign, and the Paiutis had similar notices inscribed upon boulders near to their boundary lines. As a result of one of their fights the Washoes were forbidden the use of horses, and it is only since the whites have exercised control that the weaker tribe has dared to disregard this prohibition.

Today they number in the region of six hundred men, women and children. On account of their nomadic habits it is impossible to secure a complete census.

In appearance they are heavy and fat, though now and again a man of fine, muscular form and good

height is found. The women have broad, shapeless figures and clumsy, deliberate movements. The older they get the more repulsive and filthy they become.

While young some of the women have pleasing, intelligent and alert faces, while children of both sexes are attractive and interesting. But with them as with all aboriginal people who have absorbed the vices and none of the virtues of the whites, the Washoes are fast losing power, vigor and strength by disease and dissipation. The smoke of the *campoodie* fire is also ruinous to their eyes and ophthalmia is prevalent among them. It is no uncommon thing to see a man or woman entirely blind.

The old-time methods of clothing have entirely disappeared. When I first knew them it was not unusual to find an old Indian wrapped in a blanket made of twisted rabbit skins, but I doubt if one could be found today. The white man's overalls, blouse and ordinary coat and vest for the men, with calico in variegated colors for the women, seem to have completely taken the place of their own primitive dress. A pair of moccasins, however, now and again may be found in use at a dance or on some special occasion.

They still paint and tattoo their faces, hands and wrists, in lines, triangles and circles. On their bodies also stripes of irregular design and varying colors are often used, all having a symbolic meaning originally, now lost, however, at least to all the younger members of the tribe. Painting the face has a definite and useful purpose. It softens the skin and prevents the frosts of winter from cracking it.

Their dwellings are of the rudest character, mere brush shacks in summer, and in winter, nondescript structures of brush, old boards, railroad ties, tin cans, barrel staves, old carpet, canvas, anything that will sustain a roof and keep out wind, rain and as much of the cold as possible. Their name for this structure is *campoodie.*

Of course there is no pretense of sanitation, cleanliness or domestic privacy. The whole family herds together around the smoking fire, thus early beginning the destruction of their eyesight by the never-ceasing and irritating smoke.

Their native food consists of fish, the products of the chase, which include deer, antelope, an occasional bear, rabbits, squirrels and even coyotes, mountain lions and wildcats, with acorns, manzanita berries, currants and the seeds of wild peaches and the various grasses, together with a large assortment of roots. While they gather and eat pine nuts, they generally save them for purposes of barter or sale. Their carrying baskets contain a good wheelbarrow load and are called *mo-ke-wit.*

They are great gamblers, their chief game being a guessing contest, where sides are chosen, the fortune of each side depending on its ability to guess who holds a certain decorated stick. Men and women alike play the game, though generally the sexes separate and play by themselves. Quiet chanting or singing often accompanies the game. All alike smoke the cigarette.

Of their religious beliefs little can be said. The fact is their simple nature worship and the superstitions connected with it have been abolished, practically, by their association with the whites, and we have given them nothing as substitutes. As Mrs. W.W. Price of Fallen Leaf Lodge says in a letter to me:

> In several talks with Susan and Jackson, after the death of Susan's sister, I endeavored to find out some of their religious beliefs. But these talks were not very satisfactory. Neither one knew what he did believe. Their old Indian religion — whatever it may have been — seemed to have passed, and the religion of the white man had not taken very deep hold.
>
> While Susan felt that she must cut her hair short and burn all her sister's things and do just so much wailing each day to drive off the evil spirits (on the occasion of her sister's death), she took most *comfort* in doing as "white woman" do — putting on a black dress.
>
> The most interesting result of my talks with Jackson was the following ghost story, which he told me to show that Indians sometimes did live again after death. His grandmother had told him the story and had heard it herself from the man to whom it had happened. It is as follows:
>
> "An Indian woman died, leaving a little child and her husband. The latter spent the accustomed four days and nights watching at her grave without food or drink. On the fourth night the grave suddenly opened and the woman stepped out before him. 'Give me my child,' said she. The man said not a word but went quickly and brought the little child. The woman did not speak but took the child and suckled it. Then holding it close in her arms, she began to walk slowly away. The man followed her, but he did not speak. On, on they went, through forest and meadow, up hill and down dale.
>
> "By and by the man made a movement as though he would take hold of her to stop her. But the woman warded him off with a wave of her hand. 'Touch me not,' she said. 'If you touch me, you must die too!' She stood and suckled the child once more, then laid him gently in her husband's arms. 'Go home,' she said, and faded from his sight.

> "Home he went with the child, full of awe and fear.
>
> "A few days afterwards the child died, though there was nothing the matter with it. The man, however, lived to be very old."
>
> Jackson was not sure whether he believed this story or not. But his manner of telling it indicated that it was very real to him.

Now and again near Tallac one may see the dances of the Washoes. Though war is past with them they still occasionally indulge in their War Dance and its consequent Scalp Dance. There are not more than ten or a dozen of the old warriors still living who actually engaged in warfare in the old days, and these are too old and feeble to dance.

But as the young men sing and throw their arms and limbs about in the growing frenzy of the arousing dance, and the tom-tom throbs its stimulating beat through the air, these old men's eyes flash, and their quavering voices become steady and strong in the excitement, and they live in the conflicts of the past.

Another of the dances that is still kept up is the Puberty Dance. Many white people have seen this, but not having any clue to its significance, it seemed absurd and frivolous. When a girl enters the door of young womanhood the Washoe idea is to make this an occasion for developing wiriness, strength, and vigor.

contrary to the method of the white race, she is made, for four consecutive days, to exert herself to the utmost. She must walk and climb mountains, ride and run, and when night comes on the fourth day, she and her mother, and as many of the tribe as are available, begin to dance at sunset and keep it up all night. The girl herself is designated by a long and slim pole which she carries in her hand, and which towers above her head. By her side stands her mother.

The leader of the dance begins a song, a simple, rhythmic, weird chant, the words of which are archaic and have no significance to the Indians of today, but merely give syllables to hang the tune upon. As the leader sings he slowly moves his legs in a kind of oblique walk. The young men take his hand and follow. The women unite, and a rude circle is made, generally, however, open, at the place where the dance leader stands.

After once or twice around, the leader moves first one foot, then the other, sideways, at the same time jogging his body up and down in fairly rapid movement, in perfect time to his song. In a few moments all are bobbing up and down, with the onward side-shuffling movement, and the real dance is on. This continues according to the will of the leader.

When his voice gives a sudden drawling drop that dance ends. There are a few minutes for relaxation and breath, and then he lines out a new song, with new syllables, and a new dance begins. This continues practically all night, the dance leader showing his memory power or his composing genius by the number of new songs he introduces. I have counted as many as thirty to forty different tunes on one occasion.

Just at sunrise the mother of the girl fetches one or two buckets of cold water, while the maiden undresses. The water is suddenly dashed over her "to make her vigorous and strong," and the dance comes to an end.

This rude and rough treatment, in the early days, was made to have all the potency and sanctity of a religious rite. The reason for it was clear. The Washoes were surrounded by people with whom they were often at war. Indian warfare takes no cognizance of sex or its special disabilities.

In order that their women should not be regarded as *hors de combat*, or enfeebled, at such times and thus hamper the movement of the tribe in case a sudden flight was needed, the shamans or medicine men taught that strength, activity and vigor were just as possible at that time as any other. "Those Above" commanded that it be so. Hence all the sanctity and seriousness of a religious rite was thrown around these dances, and though the Indians of today have lost many of their old customs, this is one that is still rigorously observed.

Another singular custom that still obtains is where, after the birth of a first child, the *husband* and *father* is required to fast and work arduously from the day of the birth until the child's navel shrivels off. This is to make him strong and vigorous, so that he may be able to give as much strength to his second and later children as he did to the first.

As soon as a girl matures she is marriageable. Several and simple are the ways in which a Washoe youth shows his preference and desire for marriage. Equally simple are the girl's signs of acceptance or rejection. There is no ceremony as the White Race understands that term, though to the Indian there is everything that is necessary to make the rite as binding as it is to his white brother and sister.

Though polygamy has always been practiced, the custom today limits the wives to two, and only a few men have more than one wife. Where plural wives are taken they are generally sisters. There is little intermarriage among other tribes. Though it occasionally occurs it is fiercely frowned upon and all parties are made to feel uncomfortable.

Prostitution with the whites and Chinese is not uncommon, and children born of such relationship have just as good a standing as those born in wedlock. The Indian sees no sense in punishing an innocent child for what it is in no way responsible for. He frankly argues that only a silly fool of a white man or woman would do so cruel and idiotic a thing.

Children are invariably welcomed and made much of at birth, though it is seldom a Washoe woman has more than four or five babies. They are always nursed by the mother, and not often weaned until they are four or five years old.

In the early days the labor of the sexes was clearly defined. The man was the hunter and the warrior, the guardian of the family. The woman was the gatherer of the seeds, the preparer of the food, the caretaker of the children.

Today there is not much difference in the division of labor. The breaking down of all the old customs by contact with the whites has made men and women alike indifferent to what work they do so that the family larder and purse are replenished thereby.

In the early days the Washoes were expert hunters of bear and deer. They used to cross over into the mountains of California for this purpose, and the women would accompany them. A camp would be established just below the snow line, and while the men and youths went out hunting the women gathered acorns.

My informant, an old Indian, was a lad of eighteen at the time of which he spoke. In effect he said: "One day while I was out I found the tracks of a bear which I followed to a cave. Then I went to camp. But we Indians are not like you white men. You would have rushed in and shouted to everybody, 'I've found a bear's track!'

"Instead I waited until night and when all the squaws had gone to bed I leisurely told the men who were chatting around the campfire. They wished to know if I knew where the cave was, and of course I assured them I could go directly to it. The next morning early my uncle quietly aroused me, saying, 'Let's go and get that bear.' I was scared but had to go. When we arrived he took some pieces of pitch-pine from his pocket, and lighting them, gave me one, and told me to stand at the mouth of the cave ready to shoot the bear, while he went in and drove it out.

"I didn't like the idea, but I daren't confess my cowardice, for he at once went in. In a few moments I heard terrific growlings and roarings and then the bear rushed out. I banged away and he fell, and I was proud to tell my uncle, when he came out, that I had killed the bear. 'No, you didn't,' said he; 'your shots all went wild. Here's the shot that killed him,' and sure enough it was a shot of a different size from that of my gun.

"Another time when I found a bear in a cave he said, 'You must go in this time and drive out the bear.' I was sure I couldn't do it, but he insisted, and thrusting the lighted sticks into my hands bade me crawl in, keeping my eyes fixed the while, as soon as I saw them, upon those of the bear. I was to keep my back to the wall, and when I got well in, was to dash the light behind the bear and give a yell.

I crawled in all right and soon got to where I could just about stand up, but when I saw the bear and he began to growl I was scared and backed out pretty quick and said I didn't have light enough. My uncle grabbed the sticks from me, called me a coward, rushed in, and as the bear dashed out shot and killed it."

It is generally thought that Indians are good shots, but the testimony of the hunters of the Tahoe region is that the Washoes are very poor shots. One hunter tells me he has seen an Indian take as fine a standing shot as one need desire, again and again, and miss every time. On one occasion he was hunting deer with an Indian. The latter had gone up a steep slope, when, suddenly, he began to fire, and kept it up until fourteen shots were fired.

Said he: "I was sure he must have a bunch of deer and was making a big killing, and hurried up to his side. When I got there I found he had sent all those shot after one buck, and had succeeded only in breaking its leg. With one shot I killed the wounded animal, went up to it and was about to cut its throat, when he begged me not to do so, asserting that if I cut the deer's throat that way I should never get a standing shot again, the deer would always be able to smell me."

This is a quaint superstition. The Indians believe that though the particular deer be slain it had the power of communicating with living deer and informing them of the peculiar "smell" of the hunter. Hence, as in the olden days they had no guns, only bows and arrows, and were compelled to creep up much nearer to their prey than is needful with a gun, anything that seemed to add to the deer's power of scenting the hunter must studiously be avoided.

And, although the gun had rendered the old methods of hunting unnecessary, this particular precaution still persisted and had all the force of established custom.

My friend then continued: "Another superstition I found out as I cleaned this deer. I cut out the paunch, the heart and the liver and offered them to the Indian. He refused them, saying it was food fit only for women, children and old men. If he were to eat them he would never have luck in hunting again."

This superstition is common with many Indian tribes. It is based upon the idea that one becomes like that which he eats. If one eats the heart of a mountain lion or bear he becomes daring and courageous. But to eat the heart of the timid deer is to make oneself timorous and cowardly.

As soon after puberty as possible a boy is taken out by his father or uncle on a hunt. Prior to that time he is not allowed to go. But before he can eat of the product of the chase he must himself kill a deer with large enough horns to allow him to crawl through them.

A friend of mine was out with a Washoe Indian whose boy was along on his first hunting expedition.

They hunted a deer for nearly three days, but as soon as they found tracks the father, after studying them awhile, said:"This is a little fellow. No good. He not big enough" — thus signifying to his son that his horns were not large enough to allow him to crawl through, hence it was no use following the animal further.

The Indian is quite sure that deer can smell him and know when he is on the hunt. He becomes skillful in detecting and following their tracks, and knows just how to circle around their hiding place and suddenly walk in upon them. My friend, referred to above, who is a great hunter, was once out with a Washoe. They had had three "bad" days, when suddenly they found a deer's track.

It was fresh, but when they came to the hole where he had lain down to rest, though the place was quite warm, the deer had gone. The Indian at once exclaimed: "That deer smell me. I must get rid of the Indian smell."

Accordingly he scooped out a hole in the ground, heated a number of rocks in it, then, spreading fir boughs over them, lay down over the rocks and took a "fir sweat" for fully ten to fifteen minutes. As he arose, he exclaimed: "Deer no smell me tomorrow," and my friend said he did no longer smell like an Indian, but like burnt fir wood.

Turning to the Indian, however, he said: "You're all right, but how about me?" to which the reply instantly came: "You all right. Deer only smell Indian. He not smell white man."

Chief among the women's work is the making of baskets. The best Washoe basket makers are not surpassed by any weavers in the world. At Tallac, Fallen Leaf, Glen Alpine and several other resorts, basket makers may be found, preparing their splints, weaving or trying to sell their baskets.

Not far from Tahoe Tavern, about a quarter of a mile away in the direction of Tahoe City, it the little curio store of A. Cohn, whose headquarters are in Carson City, the capitol of the State of Nevada. Mr. and Mrs. Cohn hold a unique position in their particular field. Some 25 years ago they purchased a beautiful basket from a Washoe Indian woman, named *Dat-so-la-le* in Washoe, or Luisa Keyser in American, for she was the wife of Charley Keyser, a general roustabout Indian, well known to the citizens of Carson.

Luisa was a large, heavy, more than buxom — literally fat — ungainly squaw. But her fingers were under the perfect control of a remarkably artistic brain. She was not merely an artist but a genius. She saw exquisite baskets in her dreams, and had the patience, persistence and determination to keep on weaving until she was able to reproduce them in actuality. She also was possessed by an indomitable resolution to be the maker of the finest baskets of the Washoe tribe.

While she was still a young woman she gained the goal of her ambition, and it was just about this time that she offered one of her baskets to Mr. Cohn. He saw it was an excellent basket, that the shape was perfect, the color harmony superior to any he had seen before, the stitch small, fine, and even, the weave generally perfect, the design original and worked out with artistic ability.

He saw all this, yet, because it was Indian work, and the woman was a rude, coarse mountain of flesh, a feminine Falstaff, of a lower order of beings and without Falstaff's geniality and wit, he passed the basket by as merely worth a dollar or two extra, and placed it side by side with the work of other Washoe and Paiuti squaws. A Salt Lake dealer came into the store soon thereafter and saw this basket. "How much?" he asked. The price was given — rather high thought Mr. Cohn, "Twenty five dollars!" "I'll take it!" came the speedy response.

A month or two later Cohn received a photograph from the purchaser, accompanied by a letter. "You know the basket, herewith photographed, which I purchased from you. Have you any more by the same weaver, or of as good a weave? If so, how many, and at what price? Wire reply at my expense."

Then Mr. Cohn awoke, and he's been awake ever since. He wired his list of Dat-so-la-le's baskets, but he had had no reply, and that was 25 years ago. He then made arrangements with Dat-so-la-le and her husband. He provides them house, food, clothing and a certain amount of cash yearly, and he takes all the work Luisa makes.

Every basket as soon as begun is noted as carefully as every breeding of a thoroughbred horse or dog. Also the date the basket is finished. It is then numbered and photographed and either offered for sale at a certain price, which is never changed, or is put in the safety-deposit vault of the bank, to await the time when such aboriginal masterpieces will be eagerly sought after by the growingly intelligent and appreciative of our citizens, for their museums or collections, as specimens of work of a people — the first American families — who will then, possibly, have passed away. The photographs, here reproduced, are of some of Dat-so-la-le's finest work.

Our Ancestral Hunters design

Washoe Happy Homes design (far right)

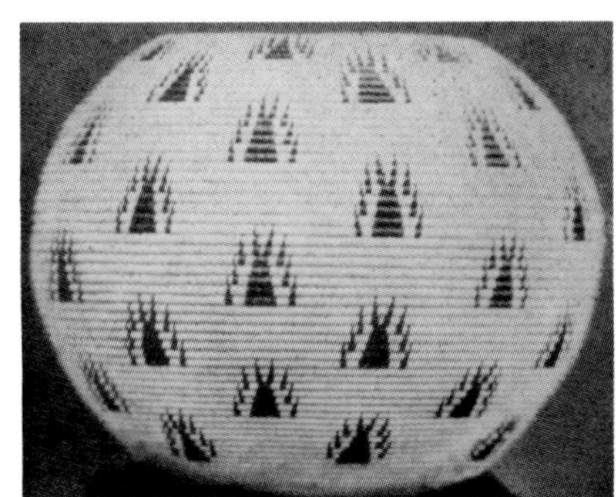

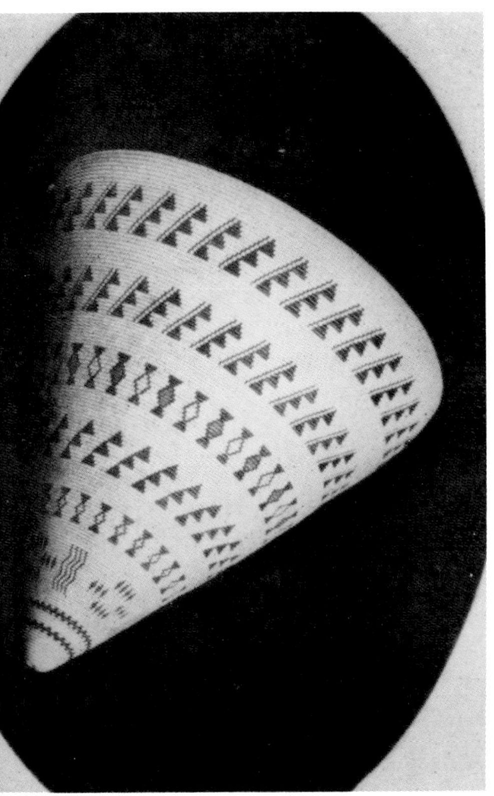

One of Dat-So-La-Lee's masterpieces — Our Hunters design.

Dat-So-La-Lee, the artistic Washoe basket maker.

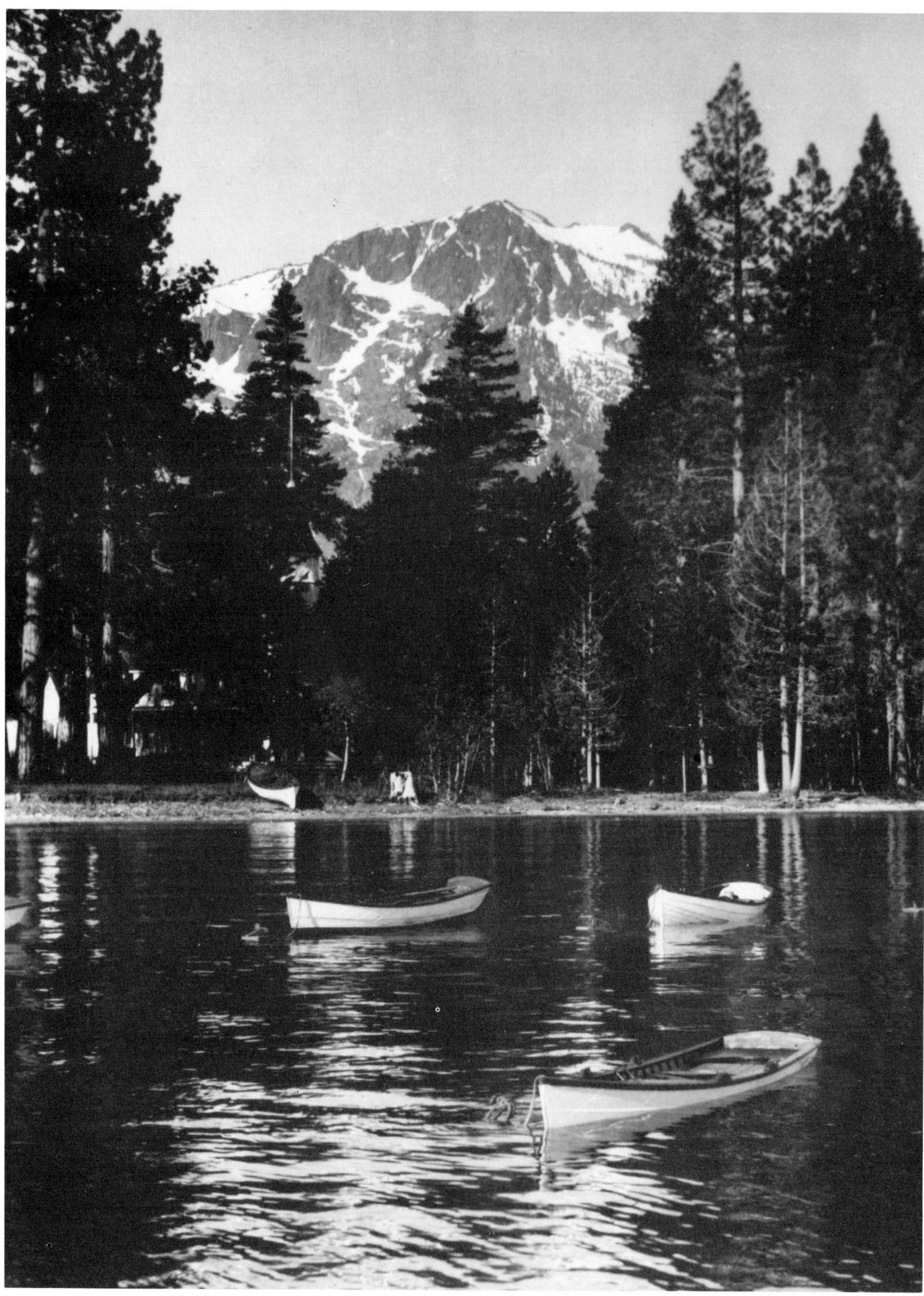

CHAPTER IV

INDIAN LEGENDS OF THE TAHOE REGION

AS all students of the Indian are well aware, these aboriginal and out-of-door dwellers in the forests, canyons, mountains, valleys and on lake and seashores are great observers of Nature, and her many and varied phenomena. He who deems the Indian dull, stolid and unimpressionable, simply because in the presence of the White Race he is reserved and taciturn, little knows the observing and reflecting power hidden behind so self-restrained a demeanor.

Wherever natural objects, therefore, are of a peculiar, striking, unusual, unique, or superior character, it is reasonable to assume that the Indians, living within sight of them, should possess myths, legends, folklore, creation stories or the like in connection with their creation, preservation, or present-day existence. This is found exemplified in the legends of Havasupais, Hopis, Navajos and Wallapais as to the origin of the Grand Canyon of Arizona, of the Yohamities, Monos, Chuc-Chances, and others, of the distinctive features of the Yosemite Valley, the Hetch-Hetchy, etc.

While the present day, half educated, half civilized Washoes are by no means representatives of the highest elements of natural enlightenment among the Indian race, they do possess legends about Tahoe, the following being the most interesting.

All these stories, except the last, were gathered by Mrs. W.W. Price from Indians with whom she has been very familiar for several years, named Jackson and his wife Susan. There has been no attempt to dress them up in literary fashion. They are given as near to the Indians' mode of telling as possible. They are wonderfully different from certain stories recently published in current magazines, professing to be Legends of Lake Tahoe.

These latter are pure fiction, and to those familiar with Indian thought, reveal their origin in the imaginative brain of white writers who have but faint conceptions of Indian mentality. Mrs. Price is a graduate of Stanford University, and took great pains to preserve the Indians' exact mode of expression. As she herself writes:

> Long before the white man saw and wondered over the beauty of Tahoe, theorizing over its origin and concocting curious tales about its "unfathomable" depths, the Indians knew and loved it. And as among all other peoples, legends have grown up to account for every phenomenon of Nature, so among the Washoe Indians stories about Tahoe have been handed down from generation to generation.

I do not vouch for these legends. The modern Indian too often tells what he thinks you want to know — if only you will cross his hand with silver. But there are touches here and there that make me feel that for the most part they are remnants of very old legends.

THE ORIGIN OF TAHOE, FALLEN LEAF, AND OTHER LAKES

Long, long ago, before the white man came to Nevada, there lived in the meadow over beyond Glenbrook a good Indian. But though he was good, he was much annoyed by the Evil Spirit, who constantly interfered with all that he tried to do. Finally, he determined that he must move away and get over into the valleys of California. But when he tried to escape, the Evil One was always there ready to trip him in some way or other.

In his trouble the Good Spirit came to his aid, giving him a leafy branch which had certain magic qualities. He was to start on his journey. If he saw the Evil One coming he was to drop a bit of the branch and water would immediately spring up. The Evil One could not cross water, and thus, being delayed by going around, would give the Indian time to escape.

The Indian made his way well along to where Tallac Hotel now is, when, looking back, he saw the Evil One off in the distance approaching with such strides that his heart was filled with great fear. In his terror he tried to pluck a leaf but it snapped off and he dropped almost his whole branch. To his delight and relief the waters began to rise and soon "Tahoe" — *Big Water* — lay between him and his enemy.

Free-heartedly he hurried on his way up the canyon, but when he reached the spot where the head of Fallen Leaf Lake lies, he turned to reassure himself. Away off the Evil One was advancing. A new terror filled his soul. In his hand there remained of his magic branch only one little twig with a single leaf on it.

Plucking the leaf, he threw it down and watched it fall waveringly through the air. As it touched earth the waters again began to rise and "Doolagoga" — *Fallen Leaf* — sprang into being and on its surface floated the little leaf, as many leaves now float in the fall of the year.

Turning, he sped up the ravine, dropping bits of his twig as fear directed him, and in his path, Lily, Grass, and Heather lakes came up to guard his way.

At last he was over the crest of the mountains and found himself safe in the long-wished-for Valley of California.

THE LEGEND OF THE TWO BROTHERS

Once long ago in Paiuti-land, Nevada, there lived two brothers. The older was a hunter and brought home much game. His wife, whose name was Duck, used to cook this for him, but she was very stingy to the younger brothers, and often times he was hungry. When he begged her for food, she scolded him and drove him out of the *campoodie*, saying "Got none for you."

One day when the older brother was off hunting, Duck was cleaning some fish. She had been very cross to Little Brother, refusing to give him any good, and he was terribly hungry. Presently he came creeping up behind her and when he saw all the fish he became very angry. He took up a big club and before Duck could turn around he hit her on the head and killed her. Paying no attention to her dead body he cooked and ate all the fish he wanted and then lay down in the sunshine on a big rock and went fast asleep.

By and by his Hunter Brother came home. Of course when he found his wife dead, he was filled with great anger at his young brother, though his anger was lessened when he thought of his wife's cruelty. He shook him very roughly and said, "I no like you any more! I go away. Leave you alone!" But Little Brother begged, "Don't be angry! don't be angry! Let's go far away! I help you all the time! Don't be angry!"

Gradually he persuaded the Hunter Brother to forgive him and they started off together toward the "Big Water" — *Lake Tahoe.* On the way the Hunter Brother taught the Little Brother how to shoot with a bow and arrow. By the time they reached the spot now known as Lakeside both their belts were filled with squirrels that they had shot.

At dusk they built a good fire and when there were plenty of glowing coals, Hunter Brother dug a long hole, and filling it with embers, laid the squirrels in a row on the coals covering them all up with earth.

He was tired and lay down by the fire to rest till the squirrels should be cooked. With his head resting on his arms, the warmth of the fire soothing him, he soon fell fast, fast asleep.

Little Brother sat by the fire and as the night grew darker, he grew hungrier and hungrier. He tried to waken his brother, but the latter seemed almost like one dead and he could not rouse him. At last he made up his mind he would eat by himself. Going to the improvised oven, he began to dig up the squirrels, counting them as they came to light. One was missing. Little Brother was troubled.

"How that? My brother had so many, I had so many!" — counting on his fingers — "One gone!" And he forgot how hungry he was as he dug for the missing squirrel.

All at once he came upon a bigger hole adjoining the cooking hole. While he stood wondering what to do, out popped a great big spider.

"I'll catch you!" cried the spider.

"No, you won't!" said the boy, and up he jumped and away he ran, followed by the spider. They raced over stock and stone, dodging about trees and stumbling over fallen logs for a long time. At last Little Brother could run no more. The spider grabbed him and carried him back to his hole, where he killed him.

It was almost daybreak when Hunter Brother awoke. He called his brother to bring more wood, for the fire was almost out. Getting no answer he went to look at the cooking squirrels.

Greatly surprised to see them lying there all uncovered, he, too counted them. Discovering one gone, he thought his brother must have eaten it and was about to eat one himself when he saw the old spider stick his head out of the hole. Each made a spring, but the Hunter Brother was the quicker and killed the wicked spider with his knife.

Carefully he now went into the spider's hole. There, stretched out on the ground, lay Little Brother *dead!* Taking him up in his arms, he carried him outside. Now this hunter Brother was a medicine man of great power, so he lay down with Little Brother and breathed into his mouth and in a few minutes he came back to life and was all right. (Susan, who was telling this story, offered no reason why he had not restored Duck, his own wife, to life.)

The Hunter Brother was very happy to have his Little Brother alive again. He built up the fire and while they sat eating their long delayed meal, Little Brother told all that had happened to him.

The sun was quite above the horizon before the meal was finished, and soon Hunter Brother was anxious to be moving on, so they took their way along the lake shore. On their way they talked and laughed one with another and seemed to agree very well, until they had gone around the lake and reached where Tahoe City now is. Here they quarreled and the Hunter Brother left Little Brother to return and go up the Big Mountain — *Tallac* — where he had heard there were many squirrels. After his departure, Little Brother decided to follow him and get him to make friends again. So he trudged along the lake shore until he came to Emerald Bay.

There, lying on a log at the edge of the lake, lay a water baby. It was asleep with its head resting on its arms and its beautiful, sunshine-golden hair was spread over it.

"Oh," said Little Brother, "I'll get that beautiful sunshine hair as a present for my brother!" So he crept very softly down on the log, thinking to kill the water baby before it awoke. But he was not successful in this, for the creature opened its eyes as he laid his hand on its hair, and a furious fight ensued.

Sometimes it seemed as though Little Brother would be killed, but finally he was able to scalp the poor water baby and get possession of the beautiful sunshine-golden hair. Everyone can see where this fight occurred. The red hill near Emerald Bay stands as a memorial of the struggle, for its color is caused by the blood of the slain water baby.

Tucking his prize in his hunting shirt and hugging it close, Little Brother now went on, murmuring to himself, "Oh, my brother like this, my brother like this beautiful golden-sunshine hair!"

But suddenly, as he was climbing upward, he noticed the water lapping at his heels, and when he turned to see whence it came, he found that the big lake behind him was rapidly rising, and even as he stood wondering, it arose above his ankles.

Then he remembered what he had heard of revengeful water babies, but frightened though he was, he could not bear to throw away his prize. However, he knew he must do something, so he plucked out a few hairs from the scalp and threw them into the ascending waves. For a minute the water ceased to rise and he sped onward, but before long he felt the water at his heels again, and knew that once more he must gain a short respite by throwing out a few of the golden-sunshine hairs.

And ever and again he had to do this until at last he spied his brother ahead of him. "Ah, brother," he cried, drawing the scalp from his blouse, "see what a beautiful present I have for you!"

But when his brother turned toward him he saw only the angry, rising waters, and rushing forward he snatched the beautiful, sunshine-golden hair and cast it back into the waters, crying, "How dare you meddle with water babies? Don't you know water surely come up and get you?"

And poor Little Brother felt very sad; but the danger he had been in seemed to have endeared him once more to Hunter Brother and they stood arm in arm and watched the waters recede.

But there were hollows in the land and when the waters went back they held the water and so were formed that chain of lakes on the other side of Tallac and Emerald Bay, the Velmas, Kalmia, Cascade, and others.

The rest of the story is confused and full of repetitions. The gist of it is that

Little Brother was ever getting into trouble from which Hunter Brother had to rescue him, for which Little Brother was most grateful and would go off seeking for a present to give to the Big Brother who was so kind to him.

Once he got a young bear cub. He thought it was a dog. He petted it and brought it to his brother as a hunting dog.

Finally, after Hunter Brother had made a first-class hunter of Little Brother so that he could use his bow and arrows with great success, they went down toward the Sacramento Valley hunting deer.

They followed a fine buck over hill and dale but could not get a good shot at him. At last, worn out by running and suffering greatly, the Little Brother lay down and died. When his brother found him, he did not attempt to bring him to life again but buried him under a pile of rocks and leaves.

THE "WILD GRUB" HOLE AT GARDNERVILLE

Once upon a time there was an old Indian who lived over in Hope Valley with his two granddaughters. He was a mean old man. He made the girls work very hard all day long. They had to gather wild grass seeds and acorns and grind them into flour all the time. The old man caught plenty of fish and frogs which he took off for his own eating, but he gave the girls none.

One day he came in with a woodchuck skin and told the girls to fill it with wild wheat flour. He did not tell them what he canted it for. When the skin was full he left the *campoodie* without a word as to where he was going.

But the bag leaked and a little stream of flour trickled out and marked his path. He went away off to a lake where he caught plenty of fish and frogs on which he feasted until he could eat no more. Then he lay down by his fire and was soon fast asleep.

Meanwhile in the *campoodie* the two girls were talking about the old man's meanness. "He makes us work so hard and we never had any fish to eat. He keeps it all himself," said the older girl.

"I wonder where he's gone now?" said the younger one, going to the doorway and looking out. Suddenly she noticed the little line of flour trailing off through the woods. "Ah, now I'll find him!" And just calling to her sister that she would be back soon, she darted off.

It was dark when she came back weeping. She threw herself on the ground outside the *campoodie* and poured out her story. She had found the old man lying there fast asleep, gorged with fish. The remnants of his feast lay all about him. She had not dared to waken him or speak to him, but coming home, had made up her mind to run away and not work for the mean old man any more.

To this the sister agreed, and at daybreak they were scurrying off through the forest.

All day they traveled and when night came they were still in the wilds far from any Indian camp.

Worn out, they lay down under a great pine and looked up at the stars.

"Oh," said the older girl, "see that fine Star man up there! I'd like to marry him!"

"Oh, no!" said the younger, "he belongs to me. I'd like to marry him!"

They lay there telling what each would do could she only marry the Star man, until they fell asleep.

When they awoke in the morning, lo, they found themselves up in the sky, and the elder girl had a baby already — a star baby! At first the girls were very good to the star baby but it cried a great deal. One day the younger girl was very cross and put it outside of the *campoodie*.

The poor baby cried all the more until the elder sister took pity on it, but when he had fed it and it still cried, the younger sister became very angry and told her sister to put that "brat" outside. The sister was tired, too, so she put the poor baby outside.

When the baby could not make them come to him, he got up and went to find his grandfather, the Moon. He told him how mean his mother and aunt were to him. The old Moon was very angry. He took the star baby by the hand and went tramping back through the sky to find the cruel mother and her sister.

Now, the girls had been getting rather tired of their

sky-*campoodie* and they longed for their home on the earth. They used to go to a hole in the sky and look down on the earth, wishing they were there again. Indeed, at the time the star baby went off to find his grandfather, the Moon, they were at the hole in the sky, amusing themselves by looking through and indulging in vain regrets that they were no longer there.

"Oh, sister," suddenly said the elder, "there goes our old grandfather! Pool old man! I wish we were with him! See, he's carrying big bags of wild wheat flour and acorns!"

Just then the old Moon came tramping up, and the whole sky trembled. The people on earth said it was thundering. He grabbed the two girls by their hair and shaking them till they were almost dead, he hurled them down through the hole.

Down, down they went, straight down to where their old grandfather was walking along, little suspecting what was coming. They both hit him and, coming as they did with such force, they made a deep hole in the earth in which they were almost buried.

That hole is over by Gardnerville. In that hole Indians can always find plenty of wild grub — wild wheat, wild potato, wild acorn — plenty there. Snow very deep. No difference. Always plenty wild grub there. I see that hole. I believe that story!

THE ORIGIN OF THE DIFFERENT INDIAN TRIBES

Long, long ago, away over in Paiuti land, there were some young boys and girls playing. They played all sorts of games, but they liked hand ball best. And as they played, they sang songs of gladness.

There was one old woman, their grandmother, who would not play with them. She had a little baby, her youngest grandchild, whom she was trying to quiet, but the little one cried and cried continuously.

By and by the old woman heard a noise outside. She was frightened and called to the young folks. "Some one's coming! You better stop! Better hide! Maybe Evil One, devil, coming!"

But the young folks paid no attention to her warning. They kept on playing harder than ever. The old woman covered the baby with a big basket and hid her own face in her shawl.

Then the Evil One came in. All the young folks turned to see who was coming in and as soon as they looked upon his face, they fell dead. Only the old woman and the baby were left; for the Evil One did not see them.

When he was gone, the old woman snatched up the baby and hurried off down to the river. As she was hurrying along, she met an old man.

"Where are you going?" said he. Then the old woman saw that it was the Evil One himself. She was afraid but she did not want him to know it. she kept the baby covered in the basket and answered, "I'm going to the river to get wild potatoes!"

"Where are all the girls?" asked the Evil One.

"Oh, they are all over behind the big mountain, playing ball!"

The Evil One went off to find them, because he thought there were still some left, and the old woman quickly dug a big hole and hid herself and the baby away in it.

when the Evil One found that the old woman had told him a lie, he was very angry. He came back and hunted all day long till sundown for her that he might kill her. But he could not find any trace of her. He finally went home and then the old woman took the baby and hid on the top of a big rock, over near where Sheridan now is.

In the morning the Evil One came back to hunt further, but without success.

"I guess that the old woman is dead," said he, "or maybe she's gone across the river." But the Evil One loses his power if he touches water, so he dare not cross the river to follow her.

The old woman watched him from the top of the rock. Many times she feared lest he should find her, and she covered the baby more closely.

At last when he had given up the hunt, she saw him take a great basket and set it down in the road. Into this basket he put great bunches of elderberry roots, and as he put each bunch in, he gave it a name — Washoe, Digger, Paiuti, and so on. Then he put the lid on tightly and went off through the forest.

the old woman watched till the Evil One had gone. Creeping quietly down, she came with the child — she was a little girl now, not a wee baby any more — and sat down near the basket.

Presently there was a murmuring in the basket. "Oh, grandmother, what's that noise?" said the little girl.

"Never mind," said the grandmother, "don't you touch the basket!"

But the little girl kept teasing, "Oh, grandmother, what's in there?"

And the old woman would say, "Don't you touch it!"

The old woman turned her back just one minute and the little girl slipped up and raised the lid ever so little. There was a great whirring noise; the lid flew off and out came all the Indians. Off through the air they flew — Washoes to Washoe land; Diggers to Digger land; Paiutis to Nevada — each Indian to his own home.

The story given above is the one told by Jackson, but his wife, Susan tells the same story with these essential differences. In her narrative there is no Evil One. The old woman scolded the young people for playing, but they are not all killed. It is the old woman herself who took a Paiuti water bottle and after filling it with water, good wild seeds and placed them in the bottle, naming them the different Indian tribes.

The seeds swelled in the water until they were as big as eggs and out of these the Indians hatched like chickens, and began to fight. It is the noise of the fighting that the baby hears.

As in Jackson's story the baby lets them out, but it is the wind that carries them off to their various homes.

HOW THE INDIANS FIRST GOT FIRE

The Indians were having a "big time" in a great log cabin. All the birds were there, too, for in those days the Indians, birds and animals could talk to each other.

They were dancing all around the room and all were merry as could be. They had a huge wooden drum and, as they passed this, the dancers kicked it to make music.

Now, among the birds who were there was a big bluejay. He was a very saucy fellow, just full of mean tricks. When he came to the drum, he kicked it so hard that he broke it all to pieces. Of course, this caused a great commotion. Everyone was so provoked by his rudeness that they threw him out of the door.

It was raining hard and the impudence was soon washed out of Mr. Bluejay. He begged at the door in vain, and at last he huddled up on the branch of a tree, thinking himself greatly abused.

As he sat there, suddenly, far off, he saw a strange light. Now the Bluejay has an infinite amount of curiosity, so away he flew to investigate, quite forgetting his troubles.

It was fire which the Indian god had brought down to earth. The Jay got a piece and soon came flying back to the great cabin where the dance was still going on.

When he called now at the door, saying that he had something wonderful to show them, they knew that he was telling the truth. They let him come in, crowding about him to see this wonderful thing.

They did not know what to make of this strange new thing. Lest anything should happen to it, they dug a hole and buried the fire most carefully.

Tired out with the night's dancing, the Indians all went off to rest, leaving the birds to watch the previous fire. But the birds were tired, too, and it was not long before they were fast asleep. All except the owl. He was wide awake and he, being very wise, knew that the fire must be put in a safer place. He went out and, calling the yellow snake, the rat and the little "hummer" bird, he explained what he wanted them to do.

The snake was to worm his way in under the logs and wait there till the hummer-bird brought him the fire. The rat was to go in and chew all the birds' wings so that they should not be able to catch the little hummer. They were all so fast asleep that the rat was able to do this very easily.

All went just as they planned. The snake took the fire and hid a little spark of it in every buckeye tree. And there the Indians found it when they needed it. For rubbing a piece of cedar and buckeye together, they very quickly make the spark, and produce fire.

A LEGEND OF LAKE TAHOE

The following legend was published some years ago in *Sunset Magazine.* It was written by Miss Nonette V. McGlashan, who heard it from a Washoe squaw. The story was told with strange gestures and weird pathos:

The ong was a big bird, bigger than the houses of the white man. Its body was like the eagle's, and its wings were longer than the tallest pines. Its face was that of an Indian, but covered with hard scales, and its feet were webbed. Its nest was deep down in the bottom of the Lake, out in the center, and out of the nest rushed all the waters which fill the Lake.

There are no rivers to feed the Lake, only the waters from the ong's nest. All the waters flow back near the bottom, in great undercurrents, and after passing through the meshes of the nest are sent forth again. Every plant and bird and animal that gets into these undercurrents, and sometimes the great trout that are swept into the net-like nest, are there held fast to furnish food for the ong.

He ate everything, he liked everything, but best of all he liked the taste of human flesh. No one every heard or saw anything of such poor mortals as were drowned in these waters, for their bodies were carried to the ong's nest and no morsel ever escaped him.

Sometimes he would fly about the shores in quest of some child or woman or hunter, yet he was a great coward and was never known to attack anyone in camp, or when two or more were together. No arrow could pierce his feathers, nor could the strongest spear do more than glance from the scales on his face and legs; yet his coward's heart made him afraid, for his toes had no claws, and his mouth no beak.

Late one fall, the Washoes were making their final hunt before going to the valleys and leaving the Lake locked in its winter snows. The chief's daughter was sixteen years old, and before leaving the Lake he must select the greatest hero in the tribe for her husband, for such had been the custom of the Washoe chiefs ever since the tribe came out of the Northland. Fairer than ever maiden had been was this daughter, and every unmarried brave and warrior in the tribe wished that he had performed deeds of greater prowess, that he might be certain of winning the prize.

That last night at the Lake, around the big council fire, each was to recount to the chief the noblest achievement of his life, and when all were heard the chief would choose, and the women join the circle and the wedding take place. For many years the warriors had looked forward to this event, and the tribe had become famed because of acts of reckless daring performed by those who hoped to wed the chief's daughter.

It was the morning of the final day and much game and great stores of dried trout were packed ready for the journey. All were preparing for the wedding festivities, and the fact that no one knew who would be the bridegroom, among all that band of warriors, lent intensest excitement to the event. All were joyous and happy except the maiden and the handsome young brave to whom she had given her heart.

In spite of custom or tradition, her love had long since gone out to one whose feet had been too young to press the warpath when last the tribe gave battle to their hereditary foes, the Paiutis. He never had done deeds of valor, nor could he even claim the right to sit with the warriors around the council fire.

All day long he had been sitting alone on the jutting cliffs which overhang the water, far away from the laughter and shouts of the camp, eagerly, prayerfully watching the great Lake. Surely the Great Spirit would hear his prayer, yet he had been here for days and weeks in unavailing prayer and waiting.

The afternoon was well nigh spent and the heart of the young brave had grown cold as stone. In his bitter despair he sprang to his feet to defy the Great Spirit in whom he had trusted, but ere he could utter the words his very soul stood still for joy. Slowly rising from the center of the Lake, he saw the ong.

Circling high in the heavens, the monster swept now here, now there, in search of prey. The young brave stood erect and waited. When the ong was nearest he moved about slightly to attract its notice. He had not long to wait. With a mighty swoop, the bird dashed to earth, and as it arose, the young brave was seen to be clasped fast in its talons.

A great cry of horror arose from the camp, but it was the sweetest note the young brave had ever heard. The bird flew straight up into the sky until Lake and forest and mountains seemed small and dim. When it reached a great height, it would drop its prey into the Lake and let the current draw it to its nest. Such was its custom, and for this the brave had prepared by unwinding from his waist a long buckskin cord and tying himself firmly to the ong's leg. The clumsy feet could not grasp him to tightly as to prevent his movements.

At last the great feet opened wide, but the Indian did not fall. In a mighty rage, the ong tried in vain to grasp him in his teeth, but the strong web between the bird's toes sheltered him. Again and again the bird tried to use his horrid teeth, and each time his huge body would fall through the air in such twistings and contortions that those who watched below stared in bewilderment.

But what the watchers could not see was that every time the huge mouth opened to snap him, the young brave hurled a handful of poisoned arrowheads into the mouth and down the big throat, their sharp points cutting deep into the unprotected flesh. The bird tried to dislodge him by rubbing his feet together, but the thong held firm.

Now it plunged headlong into the Lake, but its feet were so tied that it could not swim, and though it lashed the waters into foam with its great wings, and though the man was nearly drowned and wholly exhausted, the poison caused the frightened bird such agony that it suddenly arose and tried to escape by flying toward the center of the Lake. The contest had lasted long and the darkness crept over the Lake, and into the darkness the bird vanished.

The women had been long in their huts ere the council fire was kindled and the warriors gravely seated themselves in its circle. No such trifling event as the loss of a young brave could be allowed to interfere with so important an event, and from most of their minds he had vanished. It was not so very unusual for the ong to claim a victim, and, besides, the youth had been warned by his elders that he should not go hunting alone as had been his habit of late.

But while the warriors were working themselves up into a fine frenzy of eloquence in trying to remind the old chief of their bygone deeds of daring, an Indian maiden was paddling a canoe swiftly and silently toward the middle of the Lake. Nona, the chief's daughter, understood no more than the rest why her lover had not been dropped into the Lake, nor why the ong had acted so queerly, but she knew that she could die with her lover.

She took her own frail canoe because it was so light and easy to row, though it was made for her when a girl, and would scarcely support her weight now. It mattered nothing to her if the water splashed over the sides; it mattered nothing how she reached her lover. She kept saying his name over softly to herself, "Tahoe! My darling Tahoe!"

When the council was finished, the women went to her hut to bid her come and hear the decision her father was about to render. The consternation caused by her disappearance lasted until the rosy dawn tinged the Washoe peaks and disclosed to the astounded tribe the body of the ong floating on the waters above its nest, and beside it an empty canoe. In the foreground, and gently approaching the shore was the strangest craft that every floated on water! It was one of the great ong's wings, and the sail was the tip of the other wing! Standing upon it, clasped in each other's arms, were the young brave, Tahoe, and the daughter of the chief. In the shouts of the tribe, shouts in which warriors and women and children mingled their voices with that of the chief, Tahoe was proclaimed the hero of heroes! The decision was rendered, but the ong's nest remains, and the drowned never rise in Lake Tahoe.

CHAPTER V

THE VARIOUS NAMES OF LAKE TAHOE

WE have already seen that Frémont, the discoverer of Lake Tahoe, first called it Lake Bonpland, after Humboldt's scientific co-traveler. That name, however, never came in general use. When the great westward emigration began it seemed naturally to be called by its Indian name, Tahoe

In *Innocents Abroad* Mark Twain thus petulantly and humorously expresses his dislike of the name, Tahoe, and sarcastically defines its meaning.

"Sorry and misfortune overtake the legislature that still from year to year permits Tahoe to retain its unmusical cognomen! Tahoe! It suggests no crystal waters, no picturesque shores, no sublimity. Tahoe for a sea in the clouds; a sea that has character, and asserts it in solemn calms, at times, at times in savage storms; a sea, whose royal seclusion is guarded by a cordon of sentinel peaks that lift their frosty fronts nine thousand feet above the level world; a sea whose every aspect is impressive, whose belongings are all beautiful, whose lonely majesty types the Deity!

"Tahoe means grasshoppers. It means grasshopper soup. It is Indian, and suggestive of Indians. They say it is Piute — possibly it is Digger. I am satisfied it was named by the Diggers — those degraded savages who roast their dead relatives, then mix the human grease and ashes of bones with tar, and 'gaum' it thick all over their heads and foreheads and ears, and go caterwauling about the hills and call it *mourning*. *These* are the gentry that named the Lake.

"People say that Tahoe means 'Silver Lake' — 'Limpid Water' — 'Falling Leaf.' Bosh! It means grasshopper soup, the favorite dish of the Digger tribe — and of the Piutes as well. It isn't worthwhile, in these practical times, for people to talk about Indian poetry — there never was any in them — except in the Fenimore Cooper Indians.

"But *they* are an extinct tribe that never existed. I know the Noble Red Man. I have camped with the Indians; I have been on the warpath with them, taken part in the chase with them — for grasshoppers; helped them steal cattle; I have roamed with them, scalped them, had them for breakfast. I would gladly eat the whole race if I had a chance.

"But I am growing unreliable."

With all due deference to the wisdom — as well as the humor — of Mark Twain as applied to Lake Tahoe, I emphatically disagree with him as to the Indians of the

FROM A PHOTOGRAPH TAKEN IN 18[illegible]
By H. W. Barnett, London

Tahoe region, and also as to the name of the Lake. Tahoe is quite as good-sounding a name as Como, Lucerne, Katrine or Lomond. A name, so long as its is euphonious, is pleasing or not, more because of its associations than anything else.

The genuine Indian, as he was prior to the coming of the white man, was uncorrupted, uncivilized, unvitiated, undemoralized, undiseased in body, mind and soul, a nature observer, nature lover and nature worshipper. He was full of poetic conceptions and fired with a vivid imagination that created stories to account for the existence of unusual, peculiar or exceptional natural objects, that, in brilliancy of conception, daring invention, striking ingenuity and vigor of detail *surpass,* or at least equal the best imaginative work of Kipling or *Mark Twain himself.*

It seems to me that his — the Indian's — name for this Lake — Tahoe — is both euphonious and full of poetic and scientific suggestion. It is poetic in that it expresses in a word the unequaled height and purity of so large a body of water, and scientific in that it is truthful and accurate.

But Frémont, the discoverer, evidently did not ask or seek to know its Indian name. As stated elsewhere he erroneously conceived it to be the headquarters of one of the forks of the American river, flowing into the Sacramento, and he so depicts it on his map, giving to it the two names "Mountain Lake" or "Lane Bonpland." But neither of these names was acceptable and they practically dropped out of sight.

When the first actual determination of Tahoe's outlet through the Truckee River was made is not definitely known, but its approximate location was well enough established in 1853 to enable the official map maker of the new State of California to depict it with reasonable accuracy, and, for some reason, to name it Lake Bigler, after John Bigler, the third Governor of California.

It was still known as Lake Bigler in 1862, for in the Nevada *Statutes* there is recorded an Act approved December 19, 1862, authorizing certain parties to construct a railroad "to be known as the *Lake Bigler and Virginia Railroad Co.,* to commence at a point on the Kingsbury-McDonald road known as the Kingsbury and McDonald Toll House, thence along the southern and eastern shores of *Lake Bigler,* and in most direct practical route, to the divide between Virginia City and Washoe Valley on east side Washoe Lake, over and through the most practical pass to Virginia City." and a further right to construct a branch road from Virginia to Carson City, Nevada.

In 1861, however, while Downey was Governor of California (he having been elected Lieut. Governor, and taking the office on the resignation of Governor Latham in January 1860), an attempt was made to change the name from Bigler to the fanciful one of Tula Tulia, but fortunately it failed and the old name remained in general use.

But in 1862 another effort was made in an entirely different direction and this time with success. It was brought about through the work of William Henry Knight, who has kindly furnished the following account:

In the year 1859 I was the youngest member of an overland company which crossed the plains and mountains from St. Joseph, Mo., to California. Our train was in three divisions and consisted of about twenty persons, and forty horses and mules.

One morning in the middle of August we left our camp

at the eastern base of the double summit of the Sierra Nevada and began our ascent. Mounted on my faithful steed, Old Pete, I pushed on in advance of the caravan, in order to get the first view of the already famous mountain lake, then known as Lake Bigler. The road wound through the defile and around the southern border of the Lake on the margin of which we camped for two days.

As I approached the summit I turned from the main road and followed a trail to the right which led to the top of a bare rock overlooking the valley beyond and furnishing an unobstructed view.

Thus my first view of that beautiful sheet of water was from a projecting cliff 1000 feet above its surface, and it embraced not only the entire outline of the Lake with its charming bays and rocky headlands but also the magnificent forests of giant pines and firs in which it was embosomed, and the dozen or more lofty mountain peaks thrusting their white summits into the sky at altitudes varying from 8000 to 11,000 feet above sea level.

The view was, indeed, the most wonderful combination of towering mountains, widespreading valley, gleaming lakes, umbrageous forests, rugged buttresses of granite, flashing streams, tumbling waterfalls, and overarching sky of deepest cerulean hue — all blended into one perfect mosaic of the beautiful, the picturesque, and the majestic, that mortal eye ever rested upon.

No imagination can conceive the beauty, sublimity and inspiration of that scene, especially to one who had for weary months been traversing dusty, treeless and barren plains. The contrast was overwhelming. Tears filled my eyes as I gazed upon the fairy scene. I recall the entrancing picture today, in all its splendid detail, so vividly was it photographed upon my brain.

Since that hour I have crossed the continent ten times, over various railway routes, visited most of the States of the Union, and seven foreign countries, heard the testimony of others whose travels have been worldwide, and I doubt if another scene of equal enchantment exists on the face of the globe.

In 1861, two years after my visit to Tahoe, I gathered the data for compiling the first general map of the Pacific States, which embraced the region from British Columbia to Mexico, and from the Rocky Mountains to the coast. It was ready for the engraver in February, 1862. I had instructed the draughtsman, V. Wackenreuder, afterward connected with the State Geological Survey, to omit the name of Lake Bigler, which was on contemporary maps.

Jackson, the Washoe Indian, telling traditions of his people about Lake Tahoe and Fallen Leaf Lake.

I invited John S. Hittell, editor of the *Alta California*, a leading San Francisco daily, and Dr. Henry DeGroot, writer on the *Evening Bulletin* and correspondent of the able *Sacramento Union*, to come round to Bancroft's publishing house and inspect the map.

Dr. DeGroot had just returned from a visit to the Comstock silver mines in the Washoe district of Western Nevada. He suddenly turned to me and said: "Why, Knight, you have left off the name of Lake Bigler." I remarked that many people had expressed dissatisfaction with that name, bestowed in honor of a Governor of California who had not distinguished himself by any signal achievement, and I thought that now would be a good time to select an appropriate name and fix it forever on that beautiful sheet of water.

The suggestion met with favor, and several names were proposed — Washington, Lincoln, then war President, Frémont, an early explorer, and other historic names. I asked Dr. DeGroot if he knew what the native Indians called the Lake.

He drew a memorandum from his pocket and read over a list of Indian names local to that region, and exclaimed: "Here it is; they call it 'Tahoe,' meaning 'big water,' or 'high water,' or 'water in a high place.' The word rhymes with Washoe.

I did not quite like the name at first mention, but its significance was so striking that I asked if they — Hittell and DeGroot — would favor its adoption and back it up with the support of their newspapers, and they agreed to do so.

They advocated the adoption of the new name in their respective journals, the country papers almost unanimously fell into line, I inserted it on the map which bore my name — William Henry Knight — as compiler, and which was published by the Bancroft house in 1862.

I immediately wrote to the Land Office at Washington, reported what I had done, and the sentiment that prevailed in California, and requested the Federal official to substitute the name of Tahoe for Bigler on the next annual map to be issued by his office, and in all the printed matter of the Department of the Interior thereafter. This was done.

A curious thing then happened. Nevada was under a territorial government appointed by the Democratic administration of President Buchanan. The Territorial Legislature was in session when the subject was agitated by the California newspapers. A young statesman of that body, thirsting for fame, rose to his feet and in vociferous tones and with frenzied gestures, denounced this high-handed action of California in changing the name of that Lake without consulting the sister commonwealth of Nevada, as, according to the map, half of that noble sheet of water was in Nevada, and such action would require joint jurisdiction.

But his impassioned words were wasted on the desert air of the Sagebrush State. He could not muster enough votes to enact his indignation into a law, and the calm surface of Lake Tahoe was unruffled by the tempestuous commotion raging in legislative halls at Carson City.

It was thus that the beautiful, euphonious, and significant name of "Tahoe" was first placed on my own map, and subsequently appeared on all other maps of the State, because it was universally accepted as a fitting substitute for the former name of "Bigler." A traveled writer refers to the Lake and the name selected in these terms:

"Thus it was that we went to Lake Tahoe, the beautiful 'Big Water' of the Washoe Indians — Tahoe with the indigo shade of its waters emphasized by its snow-capped setting. The very first glance lifts one's soul above the petty cares of the lower valleys, and one feels the significance of the Indian title — 'Big Water' — not referring to size alone, but to the greatness of influence, just as the all-pervading Power is the 'Big Spirit'."

One would naturally think that there had been changes enough. But no! In spite of the fact that the Federal government had accepted the change to Tahoe, and that the popular usage had signified the general approval of the name, the Hon. W.A. King, of Nevada County, during the Governorship of Haight, in California, introduced into the assembly a gill declaring that Lake Bigler should be "the official name of the said lake and the only name to be regarded as legal in official documents, deeds, conveyances, leases and other instruments of writing to be placed on state or county records, or used in reports made by state, county or municipal officers."

Historian Hittell thus comments on this: "The bill, which appears to have been well modulated to the taste and feelings of the legislature, went through with great success. It passed the Assembly on February 1, the Senate on February 7; and on February 10 it was approved by the Governor. It remains a monument, if not to Bigler, at least to the legislature that passed it; while the name of the Lake will doubtless continue to be *Tahoe* and its sometime former designation of *Bigler* be forgotten."

Now if Mark Twain really objected to the name Tahoe why did he not join the Biglerites and insist upon the preservation of that name?

On the Centennial Map of 1876 it was named "Lake Bigler or Lake Tahoe," showing that someone evidently was aware that, officially, it was still *Lake Bigler*.

And so, in fact, it is to this date, as far as *official* action can make it so, and it is interesting to conjecture what the results might be were some malicious person, or some "legal-minded stickler for rigid adherence to the law," to bring suit against those whose deeds, titles, leases, or other documents declare it to be Lake Tahoe.

CHAPTER VI

JOHN LE CONTE'S PHYSICAL STUDIES OF LAKE TAHOE

IN certain numbers, November and December 1883 and January 1884, of the *Overland Monthly,* Professor John Le Conte, of the State University, Berkeley, California, presented the results of his physical studies of Lake Tahoe in three elaborate chapters. From these the following quotations of general interest are taken:

Hundreds of Alpine lakes of various sizes, with their clear, deep, cold, emerald or azure waters, are embosomed among the crags of the Sierra Nevada Mountains. The most extensive, as well as the most celebrated, of these bodies of fresh water if Lake Tahoe.

This lake ... occupies an elevated valley at a point where the Sierra Nevada divides into two ranges. It is, as it were, engulfed between two lofty and nearly parallel ridges, one lying to the east and the other to the west. As the crest of the principal range of the Sierra runs near the western margin of this Lake, this valley is thrown on the eastern slope of this great mountain system.

The boundary line between the States of California and Nevada makes an angle of about 131 degrees in this Lake, near its southern extremity, precisely at the intersection of the 39th parallel of north latitude with the 120th meridian west from Greenwich.

Inasmuch as, north of this angle, this boundary line follows the 120th meridian, which traverses the Lake longitudinally from two to four miles from its eastern shore line, it follows that more than two-thirds of its area falls within the jurisdiction of California, the remaining third being within the boundary of Nevada. It is only within a comparatively recent period that the geographical coordinates of this Lake have been accurately determined.

Its greatest dimension deviates but slightly from a medium line. Its maximum length is about 21.6 miles, and its greatest width is about 12 miles. In consequence of the irregularity of its outline, it is difficult to estimate its exact area; but it cannot deviate much from 192 to 195 square miles.

The railroad surveys indicate that the elevation of the surface of its waters above the level of the ocean is about 6247 feet.

Its drainage basin, including in this its own area, is estimated to be about five hundred square miles. Probably more than a hundred affluents of various capacities, deriving their waters from the amphitheater

In 1859 Captain James H. Simpson traversed Central Nevada to determine the feasibility of a wagon route across Nevada's Great Basin. After leaving nearby Genoa, the Simpson party entered Lake Tahoe Basin, where a member of the party drew this sketch.

of snow-clad mountains which rise on all sides from 3000 to 4000 feet above its surface, contribute their quota to supply this Lake. The largest of these affluents is the Upper Truckee River, which falls into its southern extremity.

The only outlet to the Lake is the Truckee River, which carries the surplus waters from a point on its northwestern shore out through a magnificent mountain gorge, thence northeast, through the arid plains of Nevada, into Pyramid Lake. This river in its tortuous course runs a distance of over one hundred miles, and for about seventy miles (from Truckee to Wadsworth) the Central Pacific Railroad follows its windings. According to the railroad surveys, this river makes the following descent:

FALL	DISTANCE (MILES)	FALL (FEET)	PER MILE (FEET)
Lake Tahoe to Truckee	15	401	28.64
Truckee To Boca	8	313	39.12
Boca to State Line	11	395	35.91
State Line to Verdi	5	211	42.21
Verdi to Reno	11	420	38.18
Reno to Vista	8	103	12.87
Vista to Clark's	12	141	11.75
Clark's to Wadsworth	15	186	12.40
Wadsworth to Pyramid Lake	18	187	10.39
Lake Tahoe to Pyramid Lake	103	2357	23.11

During the summer of 1873, the writer embraced the opportunity afforded by a six weeks' sojourn on the shores of the Lake to undertake some physical studies in relation to this largest of the "gems of the Sierra." Furnished with a good sounding-line and a self-registering thermometer, he was enabled to secure some interesting and trustworthy physical results.

1. Depth.

It is well known that considerable diversity of opinion has prevailed in relation to the actual depth of Lake Tahoe. Sensational newsmongers have unhesitatingly asserted that, in some portions, it is absolutely fathomless. It is needless to say that actual soundings served to dispel or to rectify this popular impression.

The soundings indicated that there is a deep sub-aqueous channel traversing the whole Lake in its

greatest dimension, or south and north. Beginning at the southern end, near the Lake House, and advancing along the long axis of the Lake directly north towards the Hot Springs at the northern end — a distance of about eighteen miles — we have the following depths:

STATION	DEPTH IN FEET	DEPTH IN METERS
1	900	274.32
2	1385	422.14
3	1495	455.67
4	1500	457.19
5	1506	459.02
6	1540	469.38
7	1504	458.41
8	1600	487.67
9	1640	499.86
10	1645	501.39

These figures show that this lake exceeds in depth the deepest of the Swiss lakes (the Lake of Geneva), which has a maximum depth of 334 meters. On the Italian side of the Alps, however, Lakes Maggiore and Como are said to have depths respectively of 796.43 and 586.73 meters. These two lakes are so little elevated above the sea that their bottoms are depressed 587 and 374 meters below the level of the Mediterranean.

2. Relation of Temperature to Depth.

By means of a self-registering thermometer (Six's) secured to the sounding line, a great number of observations were made on the temperature of the water of the Lake at various depths and in different portions of the same. These experiments were executed between the 11th and 18th of August, 1873. The same general results were obtained in all parts of the Lake. The following table contains the abstract of the average results, after correcting the thermometric indications by comparison with a standard thermometer:

OBS.	DEPTH IN FEET	DEPTH IN METERS	TEMP. F. DEG.	TEMP. IN C.
1	0-Surface	0-Surface	67	19.44
2	50	15.24	63	17.22
3	100	30.48	55	12.78
4	150	45.72	50	10.00
5	200	60.96	48	8.89
6	250	76.20	47	8.33

7	300	91.44	46	7.78
8	330 (Bottom)	100.58	45.5	7.50
9	400	121.92	45	7.22
10	480 (Bottom)	146.30	44.5	6.94
11	500	152.40	44	6.67
12	600	182.88	43	6.11
13	772 (Bottom)	235.30	41	5.00
14	1506 (Bottom)	459.02	39.2	4.00

It will be seen from the foregoing numbers that the temperature of the water decreases with increasing depth to about 700 or 800 feet (213 or 244 meters), and below this depth it remains sensibly the same down to 1506 feet (459 meters). This constant temperature which prevails at all depths below say 250 meters is about 4 degrees Cent. (39.2 Fah.). This is precisely what might have been expected; for it is a well established physical property of fresh water, that it attains its maximum density at the above-indicated temperature.

In other words, a mass of fresh water at the temperature of 4 deg. Cent. has a greater weight under a given volume (that is, a cubic unit of it is heavier at this temperature) than it is at any temperature either higher or lower. Hence, when the ice-cold water of the snow-fed streams of spring and summer reaches the Lake, it naturally tends to sink as soon as its temperature rises to 4 deg. Cent.; and, conversely, when winter sets in, as soon as the summer-heated surface water is cooled to 4 deg., it tends to sink.

Any further rise of temperature of the surface water during the warm season, or fall of temperature during the cold season, alike produces expansion, and thus causes it to float on the heavier water below; so that water at 4 deg. Cent. perpetually remains at the bottom, while the varying temperature of the seasons and the penetration of the solar heat only influence a surface stratum of about 250 meters in thickness.

It is evident that the continual outflow of water from its shallow outlet cannot disturb the mass of liquid occupying the deeper portions of the Lake. It thus results that the temperature of the surface stratum of such bodies of fresh water for a certain depth fluctuates with the climate and with the seasons; but at the bottom of deep lakes it undergoes little or no change throughout the year, and approaches to that which corresponds to the maximum density of fresh water.

3. Why the Water Does Not Freeze in Winter.

Residents on the shore of Lake Tahoe testify that, with the exception of shallow and detached portions, the water of the Lake never freezes in the coldest winters. During the winter months, the temperature of atmosphere about this Lake must fall as low, probably, as 0 degrees Fah. (-17.78 deg. Cent.).

According to the observations of Dr. George M. Bourne, the minimum temperature recorded during the winter of 1873-74 was 6 deg. Fah. (-14.44 deg. Cent.). As it is evident that during the winter season the temperature of the air must frequently remain for days, and perhaps weeks, far below the freezing point of water, the fact that the water of the Lake does not congeal has been regarded as an anomalous phenomenon.

Some persons imagine that this may be due to the existence of subaqueous hot springs in the bed of the Lake — an opinion which may seem to be fortified by the fact that hot springs do occur at the northern extremity of the Lake. But there is no evidence that the temperature of any considerable body of water in the Lake is sensibly increased by such springs. Even in the immediate vicinity of the hot springs (which have in summer a maximum temperature of 55 deg. C. or 131 F.), the supply of warm water is so limited that it exercises no appreciable influence on the temperature of that portion of the Lake.

This is further corroborated by the fact that no local fogs hang over this or any other portion of the Lake during the winter which would most certainly be the case if any considerably body of hot water found its way into the Lake.

The true explanation of the phenomenon may, doubtless, be found in the high specific heat of water, the great depth of the Lake, and in the agitation of its waters by the strong winds of winter. In relation to the influence of depth, it is sufficient to remark that, before the conditions preceding congelation can obtain, the whole mass of water — embracing a stratum of 250 meters in thickness — must be cooled down to 4 deg. Cent.; for this must occur before the vertical circulation is arrested and the colder water floats on the surface.

In consequence of the great specific heat of water, to cool such a mass of the liquid through an average temperature of 8 deg. Cent. requires a long time, and the cold weather is over before it is accomplished. In the shallower portions, the surface of the water may reach the temperature of congelation, but the agitations due to the action of strong winds soon breaks up the thin pellicle of ice, which is quickly melted by the heat generated by the mechanical action of the waves.

Nevertheless, in shallow and detached portions of the Lake, which are sheltered from the action of winds and waves — as in Emerald Bay — ice several inches in thickness is sometimes formed.

4. Why Bodies of the Drowned Do Not Rise.

A number of persons have been drowned in Lake Tahoe — some fourteen between 1860 and 1874 — and it is the uniform testimony of the residents, that in no case, where the accident occurred in deep water, were the bodies ever recovered. This striking fact has caused wonder-seekers to propound the most extraordinary theories to account for it.

Thus one of them says, "The water of the Lake is purity itself, but on account of the highly rarified state of the air it is not very buoyant, and swimmers find some little fatigue; or, in other words, they are compelled to keep swimming all the time they are in the water; and objects which float easily in other water sink here like lead." Again he says, "Not a thing ever floats on the surface of this Lake, except for the boats which ply upon it."

It is scarcely necessary to remark that it is impossible that the diminution of atmospheric pressure, due to an elevation of 6250 feet (1905 meters) above the sea level, could sensibly affect the density of the water. In fact, the coefficient of compressibility of this liquid is so small that the withdrawal of the above indicated amount of pressure (about one-fifth of an atmosphere) would not lower its density more than one hundred-thousandth part!

The truth is, that the specific gravity is not lower than that of any other fresh water of equal purity and corresponding temperature. It is not less buoyant nor more difficult to swim in than any other fresh water; and consequently the fact that the bodies of the drowned do not rise to the surface cannot be accounted for by ascribing marvelous properties to its waters.

The distribution of temperature with depth affords a natural and satisfactory explanation of the phenomenon, and renders entirely superfluous any assumption of extraordinary lightness in the water. The true reason why the bodies of the drowned do not rise to the surface is evidently owing to the fact that when they sink into water which is only 4 deg. Cent. (7.2 deg. Fah.) above the freezing temperature, the gases usually generated by decomposition are not produced in the intestines. In other words, at this low temperature the bodies do not become inflated, and therefore do not rise to the surface. The same phenomenon would doubtless occur in any other body of fresh water under similar physical conditions.

5. Transparency of the Water.

All visitors to this beautiful Lake are struck with the extraordinary transparency of the water. At a depth of 15 to 20 meters (49.21 to 65.62 feet), every object on the bottom — on a calm sunny day — is seen with the greatest distinctness. On the 6th of September, 1873, the writer executed a series of experiments with the view of testing the transparency of the water. A number of other experiments were made August 28 and 29, under less favorable conditions.

By securing a white object of considerable size — a horizontally adjusted dinner plate about 9.5 inches in diameter — to the sounding line, it was ascertained that (at noon) it was plainly visible at a vertical depth of 33 meters, or 108.27 English feet. It must be recollected that the light reaching the eye from such submerged objects must have traversed a thickness of water equal to at least twice the measured depth; in the above case, it must have been at least 66 meters, or 216.54 feet.

Furthermore, when it is considered that the amount of light regularly reflected from such a surface as that of a dinner plate, under large angles of incidence in relation to the surface, is known to be a very small fraction of the incident beam (probably not exceeding three or four percent), it is evident that solar light must penetrate to vastly greater depths in these pellucid waters.

Moreover, it is quite certain that if the experiments in relation to the depths corresponding to the limit of visibility of the submerged white disk had been executed in winter instead of summer, much larger numbers would have been obtained. For it is now well ascertained, by means of the researches of Dr. F.A. Forel of Lausanne, that the waters of Alpine lakes are decidedly more transparent in winter than in summer. Indeed, it is reasonable that when the affluents of such lakes are locked in the icy fetters of winter, much less suspended matter is carried into them than in summer, when all the sub-glacial streams are in active operation.

Professor Le Conte goes into this subject (as he later does into the subject of the color of Lake Tahoe) somewhat exhaustively in a purely scientific manner and in too great length for the purposes of this chapter, hence the scientific or curious reader is referred to the original articles for further information and discussion.

Color of the Waters of Lake Tahoe.

One of the most striking features of this charming mountain Lake is the beautiful hues presented by its pellucid waters. On a calm, clear, sunny day, wherever the depth is not less than from fifty to sixty meters, to an observer floating above its surface, the water assumes various shades of blue; from a brilliant Cyan blue (greenish-blue) to the most magnificent ultramarine blue or deep indigo blue.

The shades of blue increasing in darkness in the order of the colors of the solar spectrum, are as follows: Cyan-blue (greenish blue), Prussian blue, Cobalt blue, genuine ultramarine blue, and artificial ultramarine blue (violet blue). While traversing one portion of the Lake in a steamer, a lady endowed with a remarkable natural appreciation and discrimination of shades of color declared that the exact tint of the water at this point was "Marie-Louise blue."

The waters of this Lake exhibit the most brilliant blueness in the deep portions, which are remote from the fouling influences of the sediment-bearing affluents, and the washings of the shores. On a bright and calm day, when viewed in the distance, it had the ultramarine hue; but when looked fair down upon, it was of almost inky blackness — a solid dark blue qualified by a trace of purple or violet. Under these favorable conditions, the appearance presented was not unlike that of the liquid in a vast natural dyeing vat.

A clouded state of the sky, as was to be expected, produced the well-known effects due to the diminished intensity of light; the shades of blue became darker, and, in extreme cases, almost black blue. According to our observations, the obscurations of the sky by the interposition of clouds produced no other modifications of tints than those due to a diminution of luminosity.

In places where the depth is comparatively small and the bottom is visibly white, the water assumes various shades of green; from a delicate apple green to the most exquisite emerald green. Near the southern and western shores of the Lake, the white, sandy bottom brings out the green tints very strikingly. In the charming *cul-de-sac* called "Emerald Bay," it is remarkably conspicuous and exquisitely beautiful.

In places where the stratum of water covering white portions of the bottom is only a few meters in thickness, the green hue is not perceptible, unless viewed from such a distance that the rays of light emitted obliquely from the white surface have traversed a considerable thickness of the liquid before reaching the eye of the observer.

The experiments with the submerged white dinner plate, in testing the transparency of the water, incidentally manifested, to some extent, the influence of depth on the color of the water. The white disk presented a blueish green tint at the depth of from nine to twelve meters; at about fifteen meters it assumed a greenish blue hue, and the blue element increased in distinctness with augmenting depth, until the disk became invisible or undistinguishable in the surrounding mass of blue waters.

The water intervening between the white disk and the observer did not present the brilliant and vivid green tint which characterized that which is seen in the shallow portions of the Lake, where the bottom is white. But this is not surprising, when we consider the small amount of diffused light which can reach the eye from so limited a surface of diffusion.

In studying the chromatic tints of these waters, a hollow pasteboard cylinder, five or six centimeters in diameter, and sixty or seventy centimeters in length, was sometimes employed for the purpose of excluding the surface reflection and the disturbances due to the small ripples on the water.

When quietly floating in a small rowboat, one end of this exploring tube was plunged under the water, and the eye of the observer at the other extremity received the rays of light emanating from the keeper portions of the liquid. The light thus reaching the eye presented essentially the same variety of tints in the various portions of the Lake as those which have been previously indicated.

Hence it appears that under various conditions — such as depth, purity, state of sky and color of bottom — the waters of this Lake manifest nearly all the chromatic tints presented in the solar spectrum between greenish yellow and the darkest ultramarine blue, bordering upon black blue.

It is well known that the waters of oceans and seas exhibit similar gradations of chromatic hues in certain regions. Navigators have been struck with the variety and richness of tints presented, in certain portions, by the waters of the Mediterranean Sea, the Atlantic and Pacific Oceans, and especially those of the Caribbean Sea.

In some regions of the oceans and seas, the green hues, and particularly those tinged with yellow, are observed in comparatively deep waters, or, at least, where the depths are sufficiently great to prevent the bottom from being visible. But this phenomenon seems to require the presence of a considerable amount of suspended matter in the water. In no portion of Lake Tahoe did I observe any of the green tints, except where the light-colored bottom was visible. This was, probably, owing to the circumstance that no considerable quantity of suspended matter existed in any of the waters observed.

Rhythmical Variations of Level in Lakes: or "Seiches."

As might be expected, the waters of Lake Tahoe are subject to fluctuations of level, depending upon the variable supplies furnished by its numerous affluents. In mid-winter, when these streams are bound in icy fetters, the level falls; while in the months of May and June, when the snows of the amphitheater of mountain slopes are melting most rapidly, the level of the Lake rises, and a maximum amount of water escapes through its outlet.

According to the observations of Capt. John McKinney, made at his residence on the western shore of this Lake, the average seasonal fluctuation of level is about 0.61 of a meter; but in extreme seasons it sometimes amounts to 1.37 meters. The Lake of Geneva, in like manner, is liable to fluctuations of level amounting to from 1.95 to 2.60 meters, from the melting of the Alpine snows.

But besides these variations of level due to the variable quantities of water discharged into them by their affluents, many lakes of moderate dimensions are liable to rhythmical oscillations of level of short duration, which are, obviously, but produced by fluctuations in the supply of water. It is to this kind of species of variation of level that our attention will be directed in the sequel.

This interesting phenomenon was first recognized in the Lake of Geneva; but was subsequently found to be common to all the Swiss lakes, as well as to those of Scotland. It is, therefore, a general phenomenon, which may be observed in all lakes of moderate dimensions. The inhabitants of the shores of the Lake of Geneva have long designated this rhythmical oscillation of the level of the water by the term of *Seiche;* and this designation has been adopted by scientific writers.

The disturbances of hydrostatic equilibrium which generate *Seiches* may be produced by a variety of causes. Among these, the following may be cited: (a) Sudden local variations of atmospheric pressure on different parts of the lake. (b) A descending wind, striking the surface of the lake over a limited area. (c) Thunder storms, hail storms, and water spouts; and especially when the accompanying winds act vertically. (d) The fall of a large avalanche, or of a land slide into the lake. (e) And lastly, earthquakes.

Observations show that the most frequent and evident of these causes are variations of atmospheric pressure and local storms. With regard to earthquake shocks as a cause of such fluctuations of level, it is a singular and significant fact that since Forel has established the delicate self-registering apparatus on the shores of the Lake of Geneva, no less than twelve earthquake shocks have been experienced in this portion of Switzerland, and they have had no sensible influence on these sensitive instruments.

In fact, a little consideration in relation to the character of such shocks renders it highly improbable that such brief tremors of the earth's crust could have been any agency in the generation of rhythmical oscillations of the whole mass of water in the lake. Indeed, it is very questionable whether any earthquake waves are ever produced in the ocean, except when the sea bottom undergoes a permanent vertical displacement.

From inquiries made of the inhabitants of the shores of Lake Tahoe, I was not able to discover that any rhythmical oscillations of the level of its waters have ever been noticed. some residents declared that they had observed sudden fluctuations of level, which, from their suddenness, they were disposed to ascribe to disturbances of the bottom of the Lake due to volcanic agencies, although they were unable to coordinate such oscillations with any earthquake manifestations on the adjacent shores.

It is evident, however, that until arrangements are consummated for recording systematic observations on the variations of the level of this Lake, we cannot expect that its *Seiches* will be detected. Of course, self-registering gauges would give the most satisfactory results; but any graduated gauge, systematically observed, would soon furnish evidence of the phenomenon.

As far as I am aware, true *Seiches* have never been

observed in any of the American lakes. This fact is the more remarkable from the circumstance that long-continued and careful observations have been made on the fluctuations of level of several of the large Canadian lakes, with the view of testing the possible existence of lunar tides. Perhaps these lakes may be too large to manifest the uninodal rhythmical oscillations which have been so successfully studies by Forel in the smaller lakes of Switzerland.

Be this as it may, there can be no doubt that Lake Tahoe is a body of water in all respects adapted for the manifestation of this species of oscillation; and that, like the Swiss lakes, it is subject to *Seiches*. Indeed, the far greater simplicity in the configuration of the basin of Lake Tahoe than that of the Lake of Geneva must render the phenomena much less complicated in the former than in the latter.

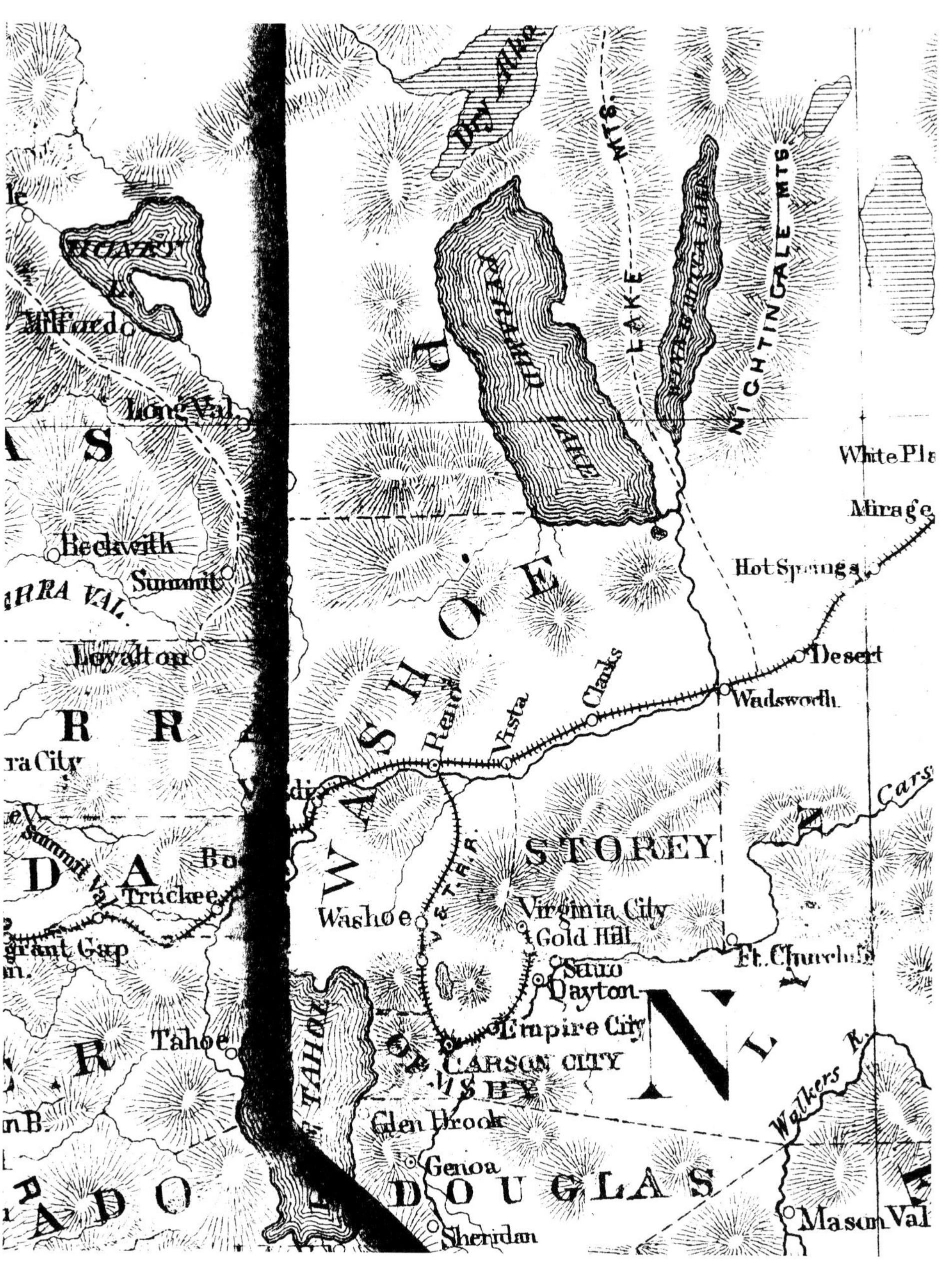

In this 1878 map, the full drainage system of Lake Tahoe to Pyramid Lake is plainly shown. Overflow from Tahoe created the Truckee River, which flowed north-northwest from Tahoe Basin to Truckee, thence eastward past Reno and Wadsworth, where the river turned northward to empty into Pyramid Lake.

CHAPTER VII

HOW LAKE TAHOE WAS FORMED

Lindgren, the geologist, affirms that after the Sierra Nevada range was thrust up, high into the heavens, vast and long continued erosion "planed down this range to a surface of comparatively gently topography." He claims that it must originally have been of great height. Traces of this eroded range (Cretaceous) "still remain in a number of flat-topped hills and ridges that rise above the later tertiary surface.

There is reason to believe that this planed-down mountain range had a symmetrical structure, for somewhat to the east of the present divide is a well-marked old crest line extending from the Grizzly Peak Mountains on the north, in Plumas County, at least as far south as Pyramid Peak, in Eldorado County. At some time in the later part of the Cretaceous period the first breaks took place, changing the structure of the range from symmetrical to monoclinal and outlining the present form of the Sierra Nevada."

This great disturbance, he thinks, "was of a twofold character, consisting of the lifting up of a large area including at least a part of the present Great Basin of Nevada and Utah and a simultaneous breaking and settling of the higher portions of the arch. Along the eastern margin a system of fractures was thus outlined which toward the close of the Tertiary was to be still further emphasized. The main break probably extended from a point south of Mono Lake to Antelope Valley and from Markleeville northward toward Sierra Valley.

A large part of the crust block to the west of this dislocation also sank down. This sunken area is now indicated by Lake Tahoe and by its northward continuation, Sierra Valley, separated from each other only by masses of Tertiary lavas ... It is worthy of note that within the area of the range no volcanic eruptions accompanied this subsidence."

He continues: "As a consequence of this uplift the erosive power of the streams was rejuvenated, the Cretaceous surface of gentle outline was dissected, and the rivers began to cut back behind the old divide, carrying their heads nearly to the present crest line that separated the slope of the Sierra from the depression of Lake Tahoe."

These rivers are the great gold bearing streams that caused the mining excitement of 1849. They all head near the Tahoe region, and include the Yuba, Feather, American, Mokelumne, Calaveras, Cataract, and Tuolumne.

Here, then, were two crest lines — the old Cretaceous line (with) the Crystal Range immediately overlooking Desolation Valley on the west, with Pyramid and Agassiz Peaks as its salient points — and the new Tertiary crest line, reaching somewhat irregularly from Honey Lake in the north to Mono Lake in the south.

At the north of Lake Tahoe, "southwest of Reno, a large andesitic volcano poured forth lavas which extend between the Truckee River Canyon and the Washoe Valley. In the region extending northward from Lake Tahoe to Sierra Valley enormous andesitic eruptions took place, and the products of these volcanoes are now piled up as high mountains, among which Mount Pluto nearly attains 9000 feet."

These are the volcanic lavas which united the two crests forming the eastern and western borders of the Tahoe basin or depression, and through which the Truckee River had in some way to find passage ere it could discharge its waters into Pyramid Lake, resting in the bosom of the Great Basin.

Here, then, we have the crude Tahoe basin ready for the reception of water. This came from the snow and rainfall on its large and mountainous drainage area, a hundred greater and lesser streams directly and indirectly discharging their flow into its tremendous gulf.

Its later topography has been materially modified by glacial action, and this is fully discussed by Professor Joseph Le Conte in the following chapter.

It should not be forgotten, however, that while Mt. Pluto was being formed, other vast volcanic outpourings were taking place. Well back to the west of the Tahoe region great volcanoes poured out rhyolite, a massive rock of light gray to pink color and of fine grain, which shows small crystals of quartz and sanidine in a streaky and glossy ground mass.

On the summits nearer to Tahoe the volcanic outflows were of andesite, a rough and porous rock of dark gray to dark brown color. Lindgren says: "By far the greater part of the andesite occurs in the form of a tuffaceous breccia in numerous superimposed flows. These breccias must have issued from fissures near the summit of the range and were, either before their eruption or at the time of issue, mixed with enormous quantities of water, forming mud flows sufficiently fluid to spread down the slope for distances of fifty or sixty miles.

The derivation of the water and the exact mode of eruption are difficult to determine .... Toward the summits the breccias gradually lose their stratified character and become more firmly cemented. Over large areas in the Truckee quadrangle the andesite masses consist of breccias containing numerous dykes and necks of massive andesite ...

"The andesite volcanoes were mainly located along the crest of the Sierra, in fact, almost continuously from Thompson Peak, west of Honey Lake, down to latitude 38° 10′. Farther south the eruptions diminished greatly in intensity.... Along the first summit of the range west of Tahoe the greatest number of vents are found. Beginning at Webber Lake on the north, they include Mount Lola, Castle Peak, Mount Lincoln, Tinker Knob, Mount Mildred and Twin Peak. The andesite masses here in places attain a thickness of 2000 feet.

"An interval followed in the northern part of the Pyramid Peak quadrangle where no important volcanoes were located, but they appear again in full force in Alpine County. Round Top, attaining an elevation of 10,430 feet, and the adjacent peaks, were the sources of the enormous flows which covered a large part of Eldorado County.

"Still another volcanic complex with many eruptive vents is that situated in the western part of Alpine County, near Markleeville, which culminates in Highland Peak and Raymond Peak, the former almost reaching 11,000 feet. The total thickness of the volcanic flows in this locality is as much as 4000 feet."

It is to these breccias we owe the volcanic appearances in the Truckee River Canyon, a few miles before reaching the Lake. There are several layers of the andesites breccias at the head of Bear Creek Canyon, above Deer Park Springs.

"None of the craters," says Lindgren, "of these volcanoes are preserved, and at the time of their greatest activity they may have reached a height of several thousand feet above the present summits."

CHAPTER VIII

THE GLACIAL HISTORY OF LAKE TAHOE

WE have already seen in the preceding chapter how the great basin, in which Lake Tahoe rests, was turned out in the rough from Nature's workshop. It must now be smoothed down, its angularities removed, its sharpest features eliminated, and soft and fertile banks prepared upon which trees, shrubs, plants and flowers might spring forth to give beauty to an otherwise naked and barren scene.

It is almost impossible for one to picture the Tahoe basin at this time. There may have been water in it, or there may not. All the great mountain peaks, most of them, perhaps, much higher by several thousands of feet than at present, were rude, rough, jagged masses, fresh from the factory of God.

There was not a tree, not a shrub, not a flower, not a blade of grass. No bird sang its cheering song, or delighted the eye with its gorgeous plumage; not even a frog croaked, a cicada rattled, or a serpent hissed. All was barren desolation, fearful silence and ghastly newness.

What were the forces that produced so marvelous a change?

Snowflakes — "flowers of the air" — as John Muir so poetically calls them. They accomplished the work. Falling alone they could have done nothing, but coming down in vast numbers, day after day, they piled up and became a power. Snow forms glaciers, and glaciers are mighty forces that create things.

Let us, if possible, stand and watch the Master Workman doing the work that is to make this region our source of present day joy. We will make the ascent and stand on the summit of Pyramid Peak. This is now 10,020 feet above sea level, rising almost sheer above Desolation Valley immediately at our feet.

The first thing that arrests the visitor's attention is the peculiar shape of the peak upon which he stands, and of the whole of the Crystal Range. Both east and west it is a great precipice, with a razor-like edge, which seems to have been especially designed for the purpose of arresting the clouds and snow blown over the mountain ranges of the High Sierra, and preventing their contents falling upon the waste and thirsty, almost desert-areas of western Nevada, which lie a few miles further east.

Whence do the rains and snowstorms come?

One hundred and fifty miles, a trifle more or less, to the westward is the vast bosom of the Pacific Ocean. Its warm current is constantly kissed by the fervid sun and its water allured, in the shape of mist and fog, to ascend into the heavens above. Here it is gently wafted by the steady ocean breezes over the land to the east.

In the summer the wind currents now and again swing the clouds thus formed northward, and Oregon and Washington receive rain from the operation of the sun upon the Pacific Ocean of the south. In June and July, however, the Tahoe region sees occasional rains which clear the atmosphere, freshen the flowers and trees, and give an added charm to everything.

But in the fall and winter the winds send the clouds more directly eastward, and in crossing the Sierra summits the mist and fog become colder and colder, until, when the clouds are arrested by the stern barriers of the Crystal Range, and necessity compels them to discharge their burden, they scatter snow so profusely that one who sees this region only in the summer has no conception of its winter appearance. The snow does not fall as in ordinary storms, but, in these altitudes, the very heavens seem to press down, laden with snow, and it falls in sheets to a depth of five, ten, twenty, thirty and even more feet, *on the level.*

Look now, however, at the western edge of the Crystal Range. It has no "slopes." It is composed of a series of absolute precipices, on the edge of one of which we stand. These precipices, and the razor edge, are fortified and buttressed by arms which reach out westward and form rude crescents, called by the French geologists *cirques,* for here the snow lodges, and is packed to great density and solidity with all the force, fervor and fury of the mountain winds.

But the snow does not fall alone on the western *cirques.* It discharges with such prodigality, and the wind demands its release with such precipitancy, that it lodges in equally vast masses on the eastern slopes of the Crystal Range. For, while the eastern side of this range is steep enough to be terms in general parlance "precipitous," it has a decided slope when compared with the sheer drop of the western side.

Here the configuration and arrangement of the rock masses also have created a number of *cirques,* where remnants of the winter's snow masses are yet to be seen. These snow masses are baby glaciers, or snow being slowly manufactured into glaciers, or, as some authorities, think, *the remnants of the vast glaciers that once covered this whole region* with their heavy and slowly moving ice cap.

On the Tallac Range the snow fell heavily toward Desolation Valley, but also on the steep and precipitous slopes that faced the north. So also with the Angora Range. Its western exposure, however, is of a fairly gentle slope, so that the snow was blown over to the eastern side, where there are several precipitous *cirques* of stupendous size for the preservation of the accumulated and accumulating snow.

Now let us in imagination ascend in a balloon over this region and hover there, seeking to reconstruct, by mental images, the appearance it must have assumed and the action that took place in the ages long ago.

Snow, thirty, fifty, one hundred or more feet deep lay, on the level, and on the mountain slopes or in precipitous *cirques* twice, thrice, or ten times those depths. Snow thus packed together soon changes its character. From the light, airy flake it becomes, in masses, what the geologists term *névé.* This is a granular snow, intermediate between snow and ice. A little lower down this *névé* is converted into true glacial ice beds, which grow longer, broader, deeper and thicker as the *névé* presses down from above.

Lay minds conceive of these great ice beds of transformed snow as inert, immovable bodies. They think the snow lies upon the surface of the rocks or earth. The scientific observer knows better. By the very inertia of its own vast and almost inconceivable weight the glacier is compelled to move. Imagine the millions of millions of tons of ice of these sloping masses, pressing down upon the hundreds of thousands of tons of ice that lie below. Slowly the mass begins to move.

But all parts of it do not move with equal velocity. The center travels quicker than the margins, and the velocity of the surface is greater than that of the bottom. Naturally the velocity increases with the slope, and when the ice begins to soften in the summertime its rate of motion is increased.

But not only does the ice move. There have been other forces set in motion as well as that of the ice. The fierce attacks of the storms, the insidious forces of frost, of expansion and contraction, of lightning, etc., have shattered and loosened vast masses of the mountain summits. Some of these have weathered into toppling masses, which required only a heavy wind or slight contractions to send them from their uncertain bases onto the snow or ice beneath. And the other causes mentioned all had their influences in breaking up the peaks and ridges and depositing great jagged boulders of rock in the slowly moving glaciers.

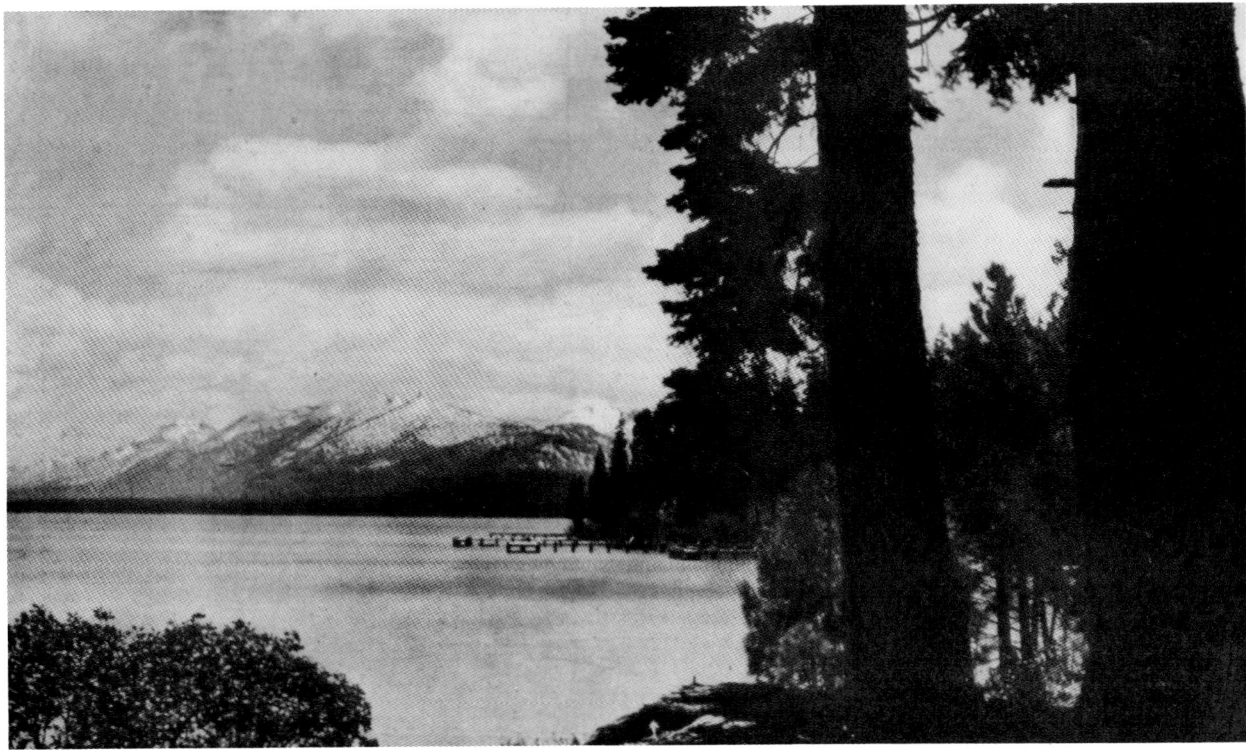

Lake Tahoe, looking south from a point near the old Tahoe Tavern (modern Tahoe City)

Little by little these masses or rock worked their way down lower into the ice bed. Sometime they must reach the bottom, yet, though they rest upon granite, and granite would cleave to granite, the irresistible pressure from above forces the ice and rock masses forward. Thus the sharp-edged blocks of granite become the *blades* in the tools that are to help cut out the contours of a world's surface.

In other words, the mass of glacial ice is the grooving or smoothing *plane*, and the granite blocks, aided by the ice, become the many and diverse blades in this vast and irresistible tool. Some cut deep and square, others with flutings and bevelings, or curves, but each helps in the great work of planing off, in some way, the rocky masses over which they move. Hence it will be seen that the grooving and marking, the fluting and beveling, the planing and smoothing processes of the ice are materially aided and abetted by the very hardness and weight of the granite and other rocks it carries with it.

Now let Joseph Le Conte take up the theme and give us of the rich treasure-store of his knowledge and observation. In the *American Journal of Science and Arts*, Third Series, for 1875, he discussed the very field we are now interested in, and his fascinating and illuminating explanations render the subject perfectly clear. Said he:

Last summer I had again an opportunity of examining the pathways of some of the ancient glaciers of the Sierra. One of the grandest of these is what I call the *Lake Valley Glacier*. Taking its rise in snow fountains among the high peaks in the neighborhood of Silver Mountain, this great glacier flowed northward down Lake Valley, and, gathering tributaries from the summit ridges on either side of the valley, but especially from the higher western summits, it filled the basin of Lake Tahoe, forming a great "mer de glace," 50 miles long, 15 miles wide, and at least 2000 feet deep, and finally escaped northeastward to the plains.

The outlets of this great "mer de glace" are yet imperfectly known. A part of the ice certainly escaped by Truckee Canyon (the present outlet of the Lake); a part probably went over the northeastern margin of the basin. My studies during the summer were confined to some of the larger tributaries of this great glacier.

TRUCKEE CANYON AND DONNER LAKE GLACIERS.

I have said that one of the outlets of the great "mer de glace" was by the Truckee River Canyon. The stage road to Lake Tahoe runs in this canyon for fifteen miles. In most parts of the canyon the rocks are volcanic and crumbling, and therefore ill adapted to retain glacial marks; yet in some places where the rock is harder these marks are unmistakable.

On my way to and from Lake Tahoe, I observed that the Truckee Canyon glacier was joined at the town of Truckee by a short but powerful tributary, which, taking its rise in an immense rocky amphitheater surrounding the head of Donner Lake, flowed eastward. Donner Lake, which occupies the lower portion of this amphitheater, was evidently formed by the down-flowing of the ice from the steep slopes of the upper portion near the *summit.*

The stage road from Truckee to the summit runs along the base of a *moraine* close by the margin of the lake on one side, while on the other side, along the apparently almost perpendicular rocky face of the amphitheater, 1000 feet above the surface of the lake, the Central Pacific Railroad winds its fearful way to the same place. In the upper portion of this amphitheater large patches of snow still remain unmelted during the summer.

My examination of these two glaciers, however, was very cursory. I hasten on, therefore, to others which I traced more carefully.

Lake Tahoe lies countersunk on the very top of the Sierra. This great range is here divided into two summit ridges, between which lies a trough 50 miles long, 20 miles wide, and 3000 to 3500 feet deep. This trough is Lake Valley. Its lower half is filled with the waters of Lake Tahoe. The area of this Lake is about 250 square miles, its depth 1640 feet, and its altitude 6200 feet. It is certain that during the fullness of glacial times this trough was a great "mer de glace," receiving tributaries from all directions except the north.

But as the Glacial Period waned — as the great "mer de glace" dwindled and melted away, and the lake basin became occupied by water instead, the tributaries still remained as separate glaciers flowing into the Lake. The tracks of these lingering small glaciers are far more easily traced and their records more easily read, than those of the greater but more ancient glacier of which they were once but the tributaries.

Of the two summit ridges mentioned above, the western is the higher. It bears the most snow *now,* and in glacial times gave origin to the grandest glaciers. Again: the peaks on both these summits rise higher and higher as we go toward the upper or southern end of the Lake. Hence the largest glaciers ran into the Lake at its *southwestern end.*

And, since the mountain slopes here are toward the northeast and therefore the shadiest and coolest, here also the glaciers have had the greatest vitality and lived the longest, and have, therefore, left the plainest records. Doubtless, careful examination would discover the pathways of glaciers running into the Lake form the eastern summit also; but I failed to detect any very clear traces of such, either on the eastern or on the northern portion of the western side of the Lake; while between the southwestern end and Sugar Pine Point, a distance of only eight or ten miles, I saw distinctly the pathways of five or six.

North of Sugar Pine Point there are also several. *They are all marked by moraine ridges running down from the summits and projecting as points into the Lake.* The pathways of three of these glaciers I studied somewhat carefully, and after a few preliminary remarks, will describe in some detail.

Mountains are the culminating points of the scenic grandeur and beauty of the earth. They are so, because they are also the culminating points of all geological agencies — igneous agencies in mountain *formation,* aqueous agencies in mountain *sculpture.* Now, I have already said that the mountain peaks which stand above the Lake on every side are highest at the southwestern end, where they rise to the altitude of 3000 feet above the lake surface, or between 9000 and 10,000 feet above the sea. Here, therefore, ran in the greatest glaciers; here we find the profoundest glacial sculpturings; and here also are clustered all the finest beauties of this, the most beautiful of mountain lakes.

I need only name Mount Tallac, Fallen Leaf Lake, Cascade Lake, and Emerald Bay, all within three or four miles of each other and of the Tallac House. These three exquisite little lakes (for Emerald Lake is also almost a lake), nestled closely against the loftiest peaks of the western summit ridge, are all perfect examples of glacial lakes.

South of Lake Tahoe, Lake Valley extends for fifteen miles as a plain, gently rising southward. At its lower end it is but a few feet above the lake surface, covered with glacial drift modified by water, and diversified, especially on its western side, by débris ridges, the moraines of glaciers which continued to flow into the valley or into the Lake long after the main glacier, of which they were once tributaries, had dried up.

On approaching the south end of the Lake by steamer, I had observed these long ridges, divined their meaning, and determined on a closer acquaintance. While staying at the Tallac House I repeatedly visited them and explored the canyons down which their materials were brought. I proceed to describe them.

FALLEN LEAF LAKE GLACIER.

Fallen Leaf Lake lies on the plain of Lake Valley, about one and a half miles from Lake Tahoe, its surface but 80 feet above the level of the later Lake; but its bottom far, probably several hundred feet, below that level. It is about three to three and one-half miles long and one and one-fourth miles wide. From its upper end runs a canyon bordered on either side by the highest peaks in this region. The rocky walls of this canyon terminate on the east side at the head of the lake, but on the west side, a little farther down.

The lake is bordered on each side by an admirably marked débris ridge (moraine) three hundred feet high, four miles long, and one and one-half to two miles apart. These moraines may be traced back to the termination of the rocky ridges which bound the canyon.

On one side the moraine lies wholly on the plain; on the other side its upper part lies against the slope of Mount Tallac. Near the lower end of the lake a somewhat obscure branch ridge comes off from each main ridge, and curving around it forms an imperfect terminal moraine through which the outlet of the lake breaks its way.

On ascending the canyon the glaciation is very conspicuous, and becomes more and more beautiful at every step. From Glen Alpine Springs upward it is the most perfect I have ever seen. In some places the white rocky bottom of the canyon, for many miles in extent, is smooth and polished and gently undulating, like the surface of a glassy but billowy sea. The glaciation is distinct also up the sides of the canyon 1000 feet above its floor.

There can be no doubt, therefore, that a glacier once came down this canyon filling it 1000 feet deep, scooped out Fallen Leaf Lake just where it struck the plain and changed its angle of slope, and pushed its snout four miles out on the level plain, nearly to the present shores of Lake Tahoe, dropping its débris on either side and thus forming a bed for itself. In its subsequent retreat it seems to have rested its snout some time at the lower end of Fallen Leaf Lake, and accumulated there an imperfect terminal moraine.

CASCADE LAKE GLACIER.

Cascade Lake, like Fallen Leaf Lake, is about one and one-half miles from Lake Tahoe, but, unlike Fallen Leaf Lake, its discharge creek has considerable fall, and the lake surface is, therefore, probably 100 feet above the level of the greater lake. On either side of this creek, from the very border of Lake Tahoe, runs a moraine ridge up to the lake, and thence along each side of the lake up to the rocky points which terminate the true mountain canyon above the head of the lake.

I have never anywhere seen more perfectly defined moraines. I climbed over the larger western moraine and found that it is partly merged into the eastern moraine of Emerald Bay to form a medial at least 300 feet high, and of great breadth. From the surface of the little lake the curving branches of the main moraine, meeting below the lake to form a terminal moraine, are very distinct.

At the head of the lake there is a perpendicular cliff over which the river precipitates itself, forming a very pretty cascade of 100 feet or more. On ascending the canyon above the head of the lake, for several miles, I found, everywhere, over the lip of the precipice, over the whole floor of the canyon, and up the sides 1000 feet or more, the most perfect glaciation.

There cannot, therefore, be the slightest doubt that this also is the pathway of a glacier which once ran into Lake Tahoe. After coming down its steep rocky bed, this glacier precipitated itself over the cliff, scooped out the lake at its foot, and then ran on until it bathed its snout in the waters of Lake Tahoe, and probably formed icebergs there. In its subsequent retreat it seems to have dropped more débris in its path and formed a more perfect terminal moraine than did Fallen Leaf Glacier.

EMERALD BAY GLACIER.

All that I have said of Fallen Leaf Lake and Cascade Lake apply, almost word for word, to Emerald Bay. This beautiful bay, almost a lake, has also been formed by a glacier. It also is bounded on either side by moraines, which run down to and even project into Lake Tahoe, and may be traced up to the rocky points which form the mouth of the canyon at the head of the bay.

Its eastern moraine, as already stated, is partly merged into the western moraine of Cascade Lake, to form a huge medial ridge which runs down to Lake Tahoe to form Rubicon Point. At the head of the bay, as at the head of Cascade Lake, there is a cliff about 100 feet high, over which the river precipitates itself and forms a beautiful cascade.

Over the lip of this cliff, and in the bed of the canyon above, and up the sides of the cliff-like walls, 1000 feet or more, the most perfect glaciation is found.

The only difference between this glacier and the two preceding is, that it ran more deeply into the main lake and the deposits dropped in its retreat did not rise high enough to cut off its little rock basin from that lake, but exists now only as a *shallow bar* at the mouth of the bay. This bar consists of *true moraine matter,* i.e., intermingled boulders and sand, which my be examined through the exquisitely transparent water almost as perfectly as if no water were present.

All that I have described separately and in detail, and much more, may be taken in at one view from the top of Mount Tallac. From this peak nearly the whole course of these three glaciers, their fountain amphitheaters, their canyon beds, and their lakes enclosed between their moraine arms, may be seen at once. The view from this peak is certainly one of the finest that I have ever seen. Less grand and diversified in mountain forms than many from peaks above the Yosemite, it has added beauty of extensive water surface, and the added interest of several glacial pathways in a limited space.

The observer sits on the very edge of the fountain amphitheaters still holding large masses of snow; immediately below, almost at his feet, lie glistening, gem-like, in dark rocky setting, the three exquisite little lakes; on either side of these, embracing and protecting them, stretch out the moraine arms, reaching toward and directing the eye to the great Lake, which lies, map-like, with all its sinuous outlines perfectly distinct, even to its extreme northern end, twenty-five to thirty miles away. As the eye sweeps again up the canyon beds, little lakes, glacier scooped rock basins, filled with ice-cold water, flash in the sunlight on every side. Twelve or fifteen of these may be seen.

From appropriate positions on the surface of Lake Tahoe, also, all the moraine ridges are beautifully seen at once, but the glacial lakes and the canyon beds, of course, cannot be seen.

CHAPTER IX

OTHER LAKES OF THE TAHOE REGION

Rich as our Sierra are in treasures, none are more precious than these. They give one pleasing surprises, often when least expected. For while the tree clusters, the mountain peaks, and the glowing snowbanks throw themselves into our view by their elevated positions, the retiring lakes, secluded, modest, hide their beauty from us until we happen to climb up to, or above them.

From the higher summits how wonderfully they appear. Let the eye follow a fruitful branch of an apple, pear or peach. How the leaves, the stem, the fruit occur, in sure but irregular order. It is just so with the glacial lakes of the Sierra. They are the fruit of the streams that flow from the glacial fountains. They lie on rude and unexpected granite shelves — as Le Conte Lake; under the shadow of towering peaks — as Gilmore Lake; on bald glacier gouged and polished tables — as those of Desolation Valley; embosomed in deep woods — as Fallen Leaf, Heather and Cascade; in the rocky recesses of sloping canyons — as Susie, Lucile and the Angoras; hidden in secret recesses of giant granite walls — as Eagle; or sprawling in the open — as Loon, Spider, etc.

What a variety of sizes, shapes and characteristics they present. There are no two alike, yet they are nearly all one in their attractive beauty, in the purity of their waters, and in the glory, majesty, sublimity and beauty mirrored on their placid faces.

In poetic fashion, yet with scientific accuracy, John Muir thus described their origin in his book, *Mountains of California.*

When a mountain lake is born — when, like a young eye, it first opens to the light — it is an irregular, expressionless crescent, inclosed in banks of rock and ice — bare, glaciated rock on the lower side, the rugged snout of a glacier on the upper. In this condition it remains for many a year, until at length, toward the end of some auspicious cluster of seasons, the glacier recedes beyond the upper margin of the basin, leaving it open from shore to shore for the first time, thousands of years after its conception beneath the glacier that excavated its basin.

The landscape, cold and bare, is reflected in its pure depths; the winds ruffle its glassy surface, and the sun thrills it with throbbing spangles, while its waves begin to lap and murmur around its leafless shores — sun spangles during the day and reflected stars at night its only flowers, the winds and the snow its only visitors.

Meanwhile, the glacier continues to recede, and numerous rills, still younger than the lake itself, bring down glacier mud, sand grains, and pebbles, giving rise to margin rings and plats of soil. To these fresh soil beds come many a waiting plant.

First, a hardy carex with arching leaves and a spike of brown flowers; then, as the seasons grow warmer, and the soil beds deeper and wider, other sedges take their appointed places, and these are joined by blue gentians, daisies, dodecatheons, violets, honey-worts, and many a lowly moss. Shrubs also hasten in time to the new gardens — kalmia with its glossy leaves and purple flowers, the arctic willow, making soft woven carpets, together with the healthy bryanthus and casiope, the fairest and dearest of them all. Insects now enrich the air, frogs pipe cheerily in the shallows, soon followed by the ouzel, which is the first bird to visit a glacier lake, as the sedge is the first of plants.

So the young lake grows in beauty, becoming more and more humanly lovable from century to century. Groves of aspen spring up, and hardy pines, and the hemlock spruce, until it is richly overshadowed and embowered. But while its shores are becoming enriched, the soil beds creep out with incessant growth, contracting its area, while the lighter mud particles deposited on the bottom cause it to grow shallower, until at length the last remnant of the lake vanishes — closed forever in ripe and natural old age. And now its feeding stream goes winding on without halting through the new gardens and groves that have taken its place.

The length of the life of any lake depends ordinarily upon the capacity of its basin, as compared with the carrying power of the streams that flow into it, the character of the rocks over which these streams flow, and the relative position of the lake toward other lakes. In a series whose basins lie in the same canyon, and are fed by one and the same main stream, the uppermost will, of course, vanish first unless some other lake-filling agent comes in to modify the result; because at first it receives nearly all of the sediments that the stream brings down, only the finest of the mud particles being carried through the highest of the series to the next below.

Then the next higher, and the next would be successively filled, and the lowest would be the last to vanish.

But this simplicity as to duration is broken in upon in various ways, chiefly through the action of side streams

Grass Lake, near Glen Alpine Springs.

OPPOSITE: Pyramid Peak and lake of the Woods, near Lake Tahoe.

Snow bank, Desolation Valley, near Lake Tahoe.

Lily lake (left) near Mt. Tallac.

Heather Lake, near Glen Alpine

that enter the lower lakes direct. For, notwithstanding many of these side tributaries are quite short, and, during late summer, feeble, they all become powerful torrents in springtime when the snow is melting, and carry not only sand and pine needles, but large trunks and boulders tons in weight, sweeping them down their steeply inclined channels and into the lake basins with astounding energy. Many of these side affluents also have the advantage of access to the main lateral moraines of the vanished glacier that occupied the canyon, and upon these they draw for lake-filling material, while the main trunk stream flows mostly over clean glacier pavements, where but little moraine matter is ever left for them to carry.

Thus a small rapid stream with abundance of loose transportable material within its reach may fill up an extensive basin in a few centuries, while a large perennial trunk stream, flowing over clean, enduring pavements, though ordinarily a hundred times larger, may not fill a smaller basin in thousands of years.

Many striking examples of these successive processes may be seen in the Tahoe region, as, for instance, Squaw Valley, which lies between the spurs of Squaw Peak and Granite Chief. This was undoubtedly scooped out by a glacier that came down from Squaw Peak and Granite Chief. The course of the ice sheet was down to the Truckee River.

When the glacier began to shrink it left its terminal moraine as a dam between the basin above and the river below. In due time, as the glacier finally receded to a mere bank of half-glacierized snow on the upper portions of the two peaks, the basin filled up with water and thus formed a lake. Slowly the sand and rocky débris from the peaks filled up the lake, and in the course of time a break was made in the moraine, so that the creek flowed over or through it and the lake ceased to exist, while the meadow came into existence.

Susie Lake, near Glen Alpine Springs.

Desolation Valley, looking toward Mosquito Pass

Gilmore lake, Pyramid Peak and the Crystal Range, in winter, from summit of Mt. Tallac.

The peaceful atmosphere of Donner Lake, where fishing and pleasure boating abound, belies the tragedy of the 1846 emigrant Donner Party which found itself stranded in the high Sierra with autumn storms approaching. Among the 81 people still in camp on October 31, 34 of them would soon perish, with most victims being children under 18, as well as those past 50 years of age. Every bachelor succumbed to the freezing weather.

CHAPTER X

DONNER LAKE AND ITS TRAGIC HISTORY

Closely allied to Lake Tahoe by its near proximity, its situation on the Emigrant Gap auto mobile road from Sacramento to Tahoe, and that it is seen from Mt. Rose, Mt. Watson, and many Tahoe peaks, is Donner Lake — lake of tragic memories in the early day pioneer history of this region.

It was in 1846 that James T. Reed, of Springfield, Ill., determined to move to California. This land of promise was then a Mexican province, but Reed carefully and thoroughly had considered the question and had decided that, for his family's good, it was well to emigrate. He induced two other Illinois families to accompany him, those of George and Jacob Donner.

Thursday, April 15th, 1846, the party started, full of high hopes for the future. The story of how they met with others bound for California or Oregon, at Independence, Mo., journeyed together over the plains and prairies to Fort Hall, where Lansford W. Hastings, either in person or by his "Open Letter," led part of the band to take his new road, which ultimated in dire tragedy, is well known.

The Oregon division of the divided party took the right hand trail, while the other took the left hand to Fort Bridger. It is the experiences of this latter party with which we are concerned. Misfortune came to them thick and fast from this time on. The wagons were stalled in Weber Canyon and had to be hauled bodily up the steep cliffs to the plateau above; some of their stock ran away, after heartbreaking struggles over the Salt Lake desert; mirages intensified their burning thirst by their disappointing lure. Indians also threatened them.

Finally, to add despair to their wretchedness, a quarrel arose in which Mr. Reed, in self-defense, killed one of the drivers, named Snyder. Reed was banished from the party under circumstances of unjustifiable severity which amounted to inhuman cruelty, and his wife and helpless children, the oldest of them, Virginia, only twelve years of age, had to take the rest of the journey without the presence of their natural protector.

Food supplies began to give out, the snow fell earlier than usual and added to their difficulties, and before they reached the region of the Truckee River they were compelled to go on short rations. Then, under suspicious circumstances one of the party, Wolfinger, was lost, and though his wife was in-

The Donner Monument at Truckee.

formed that he had been murdered by Indians, there was always a doubt in the minds of some as to whether that explanation were the true one.

On the 19th of October, an advance guard that had gone on to California for food, returned, bringing seven mules laden with flour and jerked beef. The story of this trip I have recounted more fully in the book *Heroes of California.* Without this additional food the party never could have survived. On the 22nd they crossed the Truckee River for the forty-ninth time.

Heavy snow now began to intercept their weary way. They were finally compelled to take refuge in an abandoned cabin near the shore of what is now known as Donner Lake, and there, under circumstances of horror and terror that can never fully be comprehended and appreciated, the devoted men, women and children were imprisoned in the snow until the first relief party reached them, February 19th, with scant provisions, brought in at life's peril on snowshoes.

A "Forlorn Hope" had tried to force its passage over the snowy heights. Fifteen brave men and women determined to see if they could not win their way over and send back help. Out of the fifteen seven only survived and reached the Sacramento Valley, and they were compelled to sustain life by eating the flesh of those who had perished.

The second relief party was organized by Mr. Reed — the banished leader — and thirty-one of the party were still in camp at Donner Lake when he arrived, with nine stalwart men to help, on March 1st. On the 3rd nine of them left, with seventeen of the starving emigrants, but they were caught in a fearful snowstorm as they crossed the summit, and ten miles below were compelled to go into camp.

Their provisions gave out, Mrs. Graves died, leaving an emaciated babe in arms and three other children, one a five-year-old, who died the next day. Isaac Donner died the third night. Reed and Greenwood, carrying Reed's two children, Mattie and James Jr., with one of the survivors who could walk, now struggled down the mountain in the hope that they could reach help to go back and finish the rescue work.

These met Mr. Woodworth who organized the third relief party, of seven men, who returned to "Starved Camp," to find the survivors begging piteously for something to eat. This relief party divided into two parts — one to go over the summit to give help to the needy there, the other to get the "Starved Camp" remnant to safety. The first section succeeded in their mission of mercy and a few days later caught up with the other section from Starved Camp.

Through privations and hardships untold the survivors were ultimately enabled to reach Sutter's Fort, only to find the most vile and fearful stories set in circulation about them. Four separate relief parties were sent from California, and their adventures were almost as tragic as those of the sufferers they sought to help.

Bret Harte, in his *Gabriel Conroy*, has told much — though in the exaggerated and unjust form the stories were first circulated — of the Donner tragedy, and it has been made the subject of much newspaper and other writing and discussion.

An unusual trip that can be taken from Tahoe Tavern is down to the foot of Donner Lake and then, turning to the left, follow the old emigrant and stage road. It has not been used for fifty years, but it is full of interest.

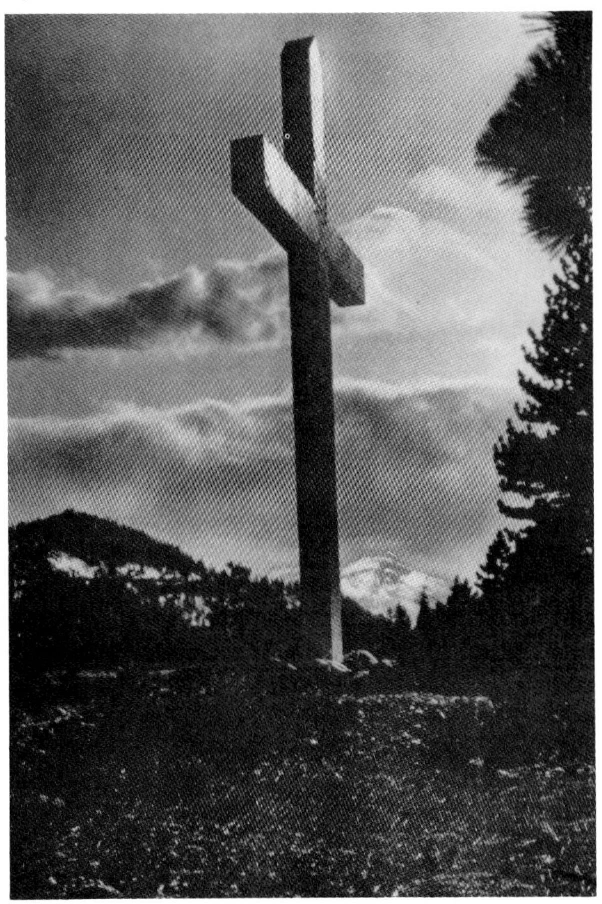

Memorial cross at Donner Lake.

There are many objects that remain to tell of its fascinating history. Over it came many who afterwards became pioneers in hewing out this new land from the raw material of which lasting commonwealths are made. Turning south to Cold Stream, it passes by Summit Valley on to Starved Camp. The stumps of the trees cut down by the unfortunate pioneers are still standing.

It was always a difficult road to negotiate, the divide between Mt. Lincoln and Anderson Peak being over 7500 feet high. But those heroes of 1848-49 made it, triumphing over every barrier and winning for themselves what Joaquin Miller so poetically has accorded them, where he declares that "the snow-clad Sierra are their everlasting monuments."

This road is now, in places, almost obliterated. One section for three miles is grown up. Trees and chaparral cover it and hide it from the face of any but the most studiously observant. When the road that takes to the north of Donner Lake was built in 1861-62 and goes directly and on an easier grade by Emigrant Gap to Dutch Flat, this road by Cold Stream was totally abandoned. For years the county road officials have ignored its existence, and now it is as if it never had been, save for its memories and the fragments of wagons, broken and abandoned in the fierce conflict with stern Nature, and suggesting the heartbreak and struggle the effort to reach California caused in those early days.

Passenger car on the automobile road near Donner Lake, as seen from the window of a Southern Pacific rail car.

Truckee, Calif., where travelers take trains for Lake Tahoe

Crossing the Truckee River near Dear Park Station

CHAPTER XI

LAKE TAHOE AND THE TRUCKEE RIVER

AS is well known, the Truckee River is the only outlet to Lake Tahoe. This outlet is on the northwest side of the Lake, between Tahoe City and Tahoe Tavern, and is entirely controlled by the concrete dam and head gates referred to in the chapter on "Public Uses of the Water of Lake Tahoe."

When Frémont came down from Oregon in 1844, he named the river "Salmon Trout River," from the excellent fish found therein, but the same year, according to Angel, in his *History of Nevada*, a party of 23 men, enthused by the glowing accounts they had heard of California, left Council Bluffs, May 20th, crossed the plains in safety, and reached the Humboldt River. Here an Indian named Truckee presented himself to them and offered to become their guide. After questioning him closely, they engaged him, and as they progressed, found that all his statements were verified. He soon became a great favorite among them, and when they reached the lower crossing of the river (now Wadsworth), they were so pleased by the pure water and the abundance of the fish to which he directed them, that they named the stream "Truckee" in his honor.

This Capt. Truckee was the chief of the Paiutes, and the father of Winnemucca (sometimes known as Poito), and the grandfather of Sarah Winnemucca Hopkins, long known in Boston and other eastern cities, where she lectured under the patronage of Mrs. Horace Mann, Mrs. Ole Bull, Miss Longfellow, and other prominent women, as the Princess Sallie. When I first went to Nevada, over 33 years ago, I soon got to know her and her father, Winnemucca, and met them constantly.

Sarah always claimed that Truckee and Frémont were great friends and that it was the Pathfinder who named the river after her grandfather, but nowhere in this *Report* of the 1843-44 Expedition does he mention Truckee, and he called the river the "Salmon Trout River"; and this name he retained both in the report and map published in his *Memoirs of My Life*, Vol. I, issued in 1887.

Hence Sallie is undoubtedly mistaken in this regard. But on several points she is correct, and too great emphasis cannot be laid upon these facts. They are, that Truckee guided several emigrant parties, even as far as Sutter's Fort, California (where Sacramento now stands); that he was always friendly, true and honest in his dealings with the whites; that had the emigrants and settlers in Nevada treated him as honestly as he did them there would never have been any conflicts between the Paiutes and the whites; that when the latter first came to the country he called councils of his people and bade them welcome the newcomers with open arms.

He died just as the wrongs inflicted upon the Paiutis were making them desperate and resolved on war. Though his son, Winnemucca, is well known never openly to have waged war against the whites, it was thoroughly understood that secretly he favored it. But had his father lived and retained his health and power there is little doubt but that the open conflict would have been averted, and many precious human lives on both sides saved.

The Truckee River has its rise in Lake Tahoe, flows northward and breaks through the Mount Pluto ridge in a narrow canyon, one to two thousand feet in depth. While the canyon is narrow and its slopes, especially on the east, are rocky and steep, it is not exactly gorge-like, except for about a mile or so, a short distance below Tahoe. For twelve miles the river follows a northerly course, and it is then joined by Donner Creek flowing from Donner Lake. The united streams then turn eastward and take a course across the northern end of the gravelly flat of Martis Valley, in a channel 200 to 250 feet below the level of the plain.

At Boca it cuts through the eastern range with a canyon 1000 to 3500 feet in depth and emerges on the plains of Nevada between Verdi and Reno. It returns again to the north below Wadsworth, having run 69 miles from Donner Creek, and then, flowing 16 more miles, it discharges into Pyramid Lake. At Tahoe the river begins at an elevation of 6225 feet above sea level; at Pyramid the level is 4890 feet, thus giving the river a fall of 1335 feet in 97 miles.

The Truckee River receives a number of large tributaries; the principal ones being Little Truckee River and Prosser Creek, the former heading in Webber Lake, the latter in the main range of the Sierra, most of its sources lying in small lakes held in hollows and basins excavated by glaciers.

Until it was contaminated by the refuse of civilization its waters were pure and healthful, but legal enactments have been necessary to protect the stream from sawdust and other pollutions.

As elsewhere explained the Truckee River being the only outlet of Lake Tahoe, and therefore its natural outflow channel, together with the facts that its origin is in California and it then flows into Nevada, and that part of Lake Tahoe is in each state, has helped complicate the solution of the question as to who is entitled to the surplus waters of the Lake. This is discussed in a later chapter.

It may be interesting to recall that in 1900 A.W. Von Schmidt, President of the *Lake Tahoe and San Francisco Water Works*, offered to sell to the City of San Francisco certain rights to the water of Lake Tahoe, the dam at the outlet, contract for a deed to 2-1/2 acres of land on which the outlet dam was constructed, a diverting dam in the Truckee River, a patent to the land (40 acres) on which this land stood, and the maps and surveys for a complete line conveying the water of Lake Tahoe to the city of the Golden Gate. He offered to construct this line, including a tunnel through the Sierra Nevada, and deliver thirty million gallons of water daily, for $17,960,000. If a double line, or a hundred millions of gallons daily, were required, the price was to be correspondingly increased.

This proposition aroused the people of Nevada, and R.L. Fulton of Reno, Manager of the State Board of Trade, wrote to the San Francisco supervisors, calling attention to the facts that there was no surplus water from Tahoe during the irrigation season, for the water had been diverted by the farmers living along the Truckee River to their fields; that flouring mills, smelting and reduction works, electric light plant and waterworks at Reno, immense sawmills, a furniture factory, box factory, water and electric light works, railroad water tanks, etc., at Truckee, half a dozen ice ponds, producing over 200,000 tons of ice annually, sawmills and marble-working mills at Essex; planing mills at Verdi, paper mill at Floristan, and other similar plants, were totally dependent for their water supply upon the Truckee River.

He also claimed (what was the well-known fact) that the Von Schmidt dam was burned out many years ago, and that Nevada would put up a tremendously stiff fight to prevent any such diversion of Tahoe water as was contemplated. Needless to say, the plan fell through.

CHAPTER XII

BY RAIL TO LAKE TAHOE

Lake Tahoe is 15 miles from Truckee, which is one of the mountain stations on the main line of the Southern Pacific Railway (Central Route), 208 miles from San Francisco, 35 miles from Reno, and 574 miles from Ogden, Utah. By the San Joaquin Valley route via Sacramento, the distance to Los Angeles is 580 miles, or by San Francisco and the Coast Line, 692 miles.

During the summer season trains run frequently, making Tahoe easily accessible.

From the east the traveler comes over what is practically the long known and historic overland stage road, over which so many thousands of gold seekers and emigrants came in the days of California's gold ex-citement. Every mile has some story of pioneer bravery or heroism, of hair-breadth escapes from hostile Indians or fortuitous deliverance from storm or disaster.

It was over this route the pilgrims came who sought in Utah a land of freedom where they might follow their own peculiar conceptions of religion and duty, untrammeled and uninterfered with by hostile onlookers and disbelievers. Here came the home seekers of the earlier day, when California was still a province of Mexico; those who had been lured by the glowing stories of the Land of the Sun Down Sea, where orange and lemon, vine and fig flourished and indicated the semi-tropic luxuriance and fruitfulness of the land.

From the west the railroad traverses, in the main, the continuation of this old overland road. After leaving the fertile valley of the Sacramento and rising into the glorious foothills of the Sierra, every roll of the billows of the mountains and canyons wedged in between is redolent of memories of the argonauts and miners.

Yonder are Yuba, Dutch Flat, the North Fork, the South Fork (of the American River), Colfax, Gold Run, Midas, Blue Canyon, Emigrant Gap, Grass Valley, Michigan Bluff, Grizzly Gulch, Alpha, Omega, Eagle Bird, Red Dog, Chips Flat, Quaker Hill and You Bet. Can you not see these camps, alive with rough-handed, full-bearded, sun-browned, stalwart men, and hear the clang of hammer upon drill, the shock of the blast, the wheeling away and crash of waste rock as it is thrown over the dump pile?

And then, as we look up and forward into the sea of mountain waves into the heart of which we ride, who

The transcontinental Southern Pacific traversed the entire length of the Truckee River canyon.

but Joaquin Miller can describe the scene?

Here lifts the land of clouds! Fierce mountain forms,
Made white with everlasting snows, look down
Through mists of many canyons, mighty storms
That stretch from Autumn's purple drench and
 drown
The yellow hem of Spring. Tall cedars frown
Dark-brow'd, through banner'd clouds that stretch
 and stream
Above the sea from snowy mountain crown.
The heavens roll, and all things drift or seem
To drift about and drive like some majestic dream.

And it is in the very bosom of this majestic scenery that Lake Tahoe lies enshrined. Its entrancing beauty is such that we do not wonder that these triumphant monarchs of the "upper seas" cluster around it as if in reverent adoration, and that they wear their vestal virgin robes of purest white in token of the purity of their worship.

Thoughts like these flood our hearts and minds as we reach Truckee, the point where we leave the Southern Pacific cars and change to those of the narrow-gauge Lake Tahoe Railway and Transportation Company. After a brief wait, long enough to allow transfer of baggage, we leave, from the same station, for the 15 miles' ride to Tahoe Tavern on the very edge of the Lake.

This ride is itself romantic and beautiful. On the day trains observation cars are provided, and the hour is one of delightful, restful and enchanting scenes. The Truckee River is never out of sight and again and again it reminds one in its foaming speed of Joaquin Miller's expressive phrase: "See where the cool white river runs."

Before 1900 this ride used to be taken by stage, the railway having been built in that year. It is interesting here to note that the rails, the locomotives, the passenger and freight cars were all transported bodily across the Lake from Glenbrook, on the Nevada side. There they were in use for many years mainly for hauling logs and lumber to and from the mills on the summit, whence it was flumed to Carson City.

In those days logging was carried on in the Truckee River Canyon and the visitor would often have the pleasure of seeing logs "shoot the chutes" into the river, by which they were floated to the mills at Truckee. Here is a picture:

"Tree, bush, and flower grow and blossom upon either side; and a little bird, with a throat like a thrush, warbles a canticle of exquisite musical modulations, so to speak. But the most stirring sight of all is the system of logging carried on by the mill companies. 'Look! Quick!' ejaculates the driver; and your gaze is directed to a monster log that comes furiously dashing from the summit down a chute a thousand feet in length with twice the ordinary speed of a locomotive.

"So rapid is its descent that it leaves a trail of smoke behind it, and sometimes kindles a fire among the slivers along its way. Ah! it strikes the water! In an instant there is an inverted Niagara in the air, resplendent with prismatic and transparent veils of spray." (John Vance Cheney in *Lippincott's*.)

The main portion of the canyon is walled in by abrupt acclivities, upon which majestic trees used to grow, but where now only the growth of the past twenty-five to fifty years is found, doing its best to hide the scars and wounds of the logging days.

The river, issuing from the Lake above, dashes down its wild way in resistless freedom. It is a rapid, all but savage stream, widening occasionally into sheltered pools exceedingly dark and deep. The boulders in its channel, and those crowding down into it from its farther bank, cause it to eddy and foam with fierce but becoming pride.

A few miles from the Tavern we pass the scene of the Squaw Valley mining excitement where the two towns of Knoxville and Claraville arose as if by magic, tent cities of thousands of inhabitants, lured hither by a dream of gold, too soon to fade away, leaving nothing but distress behind.

Deer Park station suggests the leaving point for that charmingly picturesque resort, snuggling in the heart of Bear Canyon. Now we pass the masses of tuffaceous

The Southern Pacific Railroad issued 75,000 copies of this descriptive pamphlet during the same summer in which author George Wharton James released *The Lake of the Sky*.

breccia that "Pap" Church, the old stage driver used to call the Devil's Pulpit, and the devil's this and that or the other, until many a traveler would wish they were all with the devil.

This is a remnant of the vast mass of volcanic rock that in long ago prehistoric times was poured out in molten sheets over the region, and that formed the range we shall shortly see at the north end of the Lake — the Mount Pluto range.

At some later period either earthquake convulsion started the break which ultimately eroded and disintegrated into the great gorge through which the railway has brought us, or grinding glacier cut the pathway for us.

Here, on the right, is a tiny swinging foot bridge over the river. This is the beginning, the suggestion, for the vast suspension bridges that have allowed the world to cross the great North River from New York to Brooklyn, and that span great rivers and gorges elsewhere in the world. Nay! scarcely the beginning.

That you find further up and deeper down in the High Sierra and their shaded and wooded canyons, where wild vines throw their clinging tendrils across from one shore to another of foaming creeks, and gradually grow in girth and strength until they form bridges, over which chipmunks, squirrels, porcupines, 'coons, coyotes, and finally mountain lions, bears, and even men cross with safety. There is the *real origin* of the suspension bridge. But this is a miniature, a model, a suggestion of the big bridges. It affords ready access to the house on the other side. In winter, however, the boards are taken up, as the heavy snows that fall and accumulate might wreck it.

It is hard to realize that, a few months from now, when winter begins, this railroad must perforce cease its operations. Snow falls, here, where the sun is now smiling so beneficently upon laughing meadows, dotted here and there with dainty flowers, to a depth of ten and even twenty feet.

The mail — necessarily much reduced in winter — is first of all carried in sleighs, then, as the snows deepen, on snowshoes, so that those who stay to preserve the "summer hotels" from winter's ravages may not feel entirely shut out from the living world beyond.

But there is nothing that suggests snow now. We are enjoying the delights of a summer day or evening, and know that we are near our journey's end. Suddenly there is a long call of the whistle, a short curve, and if in the daytime, the Lake suddenly appears, or, if at night, the lights of the Tavern, and our rail journey is done. We are deposited in Fairyland, for whether it be day or evening, the Lake or the Tavern, our senses are thrilled and charmed by everything that appears.

CHAPTER XIII

THE WISHBONE AUTOMOBILE ROUTE TO AND AROUND LAKE TAHOE

This is the name given to the 260 mile automobile route to and from Lake Tahoe, going in from Sacramento over the world-famed Emigrant Gap and Donner Lake road, around the western shore of Lake Tahoe, from Tahoe Tavern to Tallac, and thence back to Sacramento over the historic and picturesque Placerville road. While both of the two main arms of the "wishbone" carry the traveler over the Sierra, the roads are wonderfully different.

On the Emigrant Gap arm the road seems to have been engineered somewhat after the Indian fashion, viz., to allow the wildest and most expansive outlooks, while the Placerville route is largely confined to the picturesque and beautiful canyon of the South Fork of the American River.

Both have honored histories and both are fascinating from the scenic standpoint and the difference in the two routes merely accentuates the charm of the trip, when compared with the new portion of the road, the connecting link that binds them together and now makes possible the ride around the lake shore. Experience has demonstrated, however, that it is better to make the circuit as herein outlined.

A brief sketch of the history of the building of the Emigrant Gap portion of this road cannot fail to be of interest.

It was practically followed by a host of the emigrants who sought California during the great gold excitement of 1848-9. It was also one of the earliest routes used between Sacramento and the mines of the High Sierra. In 1849 it was established from Sacramento to Auburn, Grass Valley and Nevada City and today there is practically little deviation from the original route. In 1850 the mines on the Forest Hill Divide were discovered and a branch road from Auburn was built to that section. At Illinoistown (now Colfax) the road branched, one arm crossing the North Fork of the American River to Iowa Hill and other camps on that divide, while the main road continued up the Sierra to Gold Run, Dutch Flat and other points higher up.

Until the Central Pacific Railway was built in the 'sixties, Illinoistown was the junction for the different Camps in Nevada County and the Bear River and Iowa Hill Divides. The population of these regions in those early days was much greater than at the present time, yet the demands of the modern automobile have so improved the roads that they are much superior to what the large population of those days enjoyed.

In 1862 the California legislature authorized the supervisors of certain counties to call special elections to vote upon the question as to whether those counties should subscribe towards the building of the Central Pacific Railway, and to authorize them to issue bonds for the amounts they decided to expend. San Francisco County subscribed $1,000,000, Sacramento County $300,000 and Placer County $250,000.

In 1863 the Railroad Company began its work of grading the road bed at Sacramento, and yet, in 1865 it was only completed to Alta, a distance of 68 miles. At the same time it was making strenuous efforts to divert passenger and freight traffic for Virginia City and other Nevada points from the Placerville route.

This had become possible because of the fact that when the railway line was actually built as far as Newcastle the engineers realized that before they could build the rest of their railroad they would need to construct a highway of easy grade, which would enable them to haul the necessary supplies for constructing the tunnels, cuts and bridges. Accordingly, a survey was made up to Truckee, over the Nevada line into Reno and Virginia City, securing the best possible grade for a wagon road, and this was rushed to a hasty completion.

Naturally, they were anxious to gain all the paying traffic possible, and especially under the adverse conditions under which they were laboring. But, needless to say, this caused the fiercest hostility on the part of their competitors, laid them open to serious charges, which, later, were made, and that for a time threatened desperate consequences, as I will now proceed to relate.

In the last fall of 1864 the Sacramento Valley Railroad (the rival of the Central Pacific) arranged to make a record trip from Freeport to Virginia City by the Placerville route. Though the officials endeavored to keep the matter secret, it leaked out and immediately the Central Pacific planned to circumvent their aim. They stationed relays along their own line to compete, and Nature and Fate seemed to come to their aid.

A fierce storm arose the day before the start was to be made, and it fell heavier on the Placerville than on the other route. Though the drivers of each line did their utmost, feeling their own personal honor, as well as that of their company at stake, the heavy rains at Strawberry arrested the Placerville stage and made further progress impossible, while the other route was enabled to complete its trip on record time.

Mr. L.L. Robinson, the Superintendent of the Sacramento Valley Railroad, who himself accompanied the stage, wired from Strawberry, "Heavy rains, heavy roads, slow time" — reluctant to own a possible defeat. But the Sacramento *Union,* the organ of the Central Pacific, came out the next morning with glowing accounts of the successful run of the stages over the Emigrant Gap route and ridiculed Mr. Robinson's telegram, ironically comparing it with Cæsar's classic message to the Roman Senate: "Veni, Vidi, Vici."

It was such struggles for local business as this that led the San Francisco *Alta California,* a paper bitterly opposed to the Central Pacific, to denounce the railway, in 1866, as the "Dutch Flat Swindle." It claimed that the railway would never be built further than Alta and that it was built so far only for the purpose of controlling passenger and freight traffic over their wagon road to Virginia City and other Nevada points.

Other San Francisco papers joined in the fight and so energetically was it conducted, and so powerful became the opposition that they actually prevailed upon the people of San Francisco to repudiate their contract to purchase a million dollars' worth of Central Pacific stock and compromise by practically making the railroad company a present of $600,000 (which had already been expended) provided they would release the City and County from their pledge to raise the remaining $400,000.

The folly of this action is now so apparent that it is hard to conceive how even political and civic jealousy or hatred could have been so blinded to self-interest. The Central Pacific engineers had undertaken one of the most difficult pieces of railway engineering in the world, and the financiers of the company were having an equally desperate struggle. During the Civil War the financiers of the nation were at a low ebb and money was exceedingly difficult to secure.

Yet in spite of all obstacles the company had gone ahead in perfect good faith, and at that very time were hauling rails and track material from Alta, and soon from Cisco, to Truckee (then called Coburn Station on the old Emigrant Gap road), and had actually built the railroad from Truckee down into Nevada and as far east as Wadsworth, or a little beyond, before the tunnel at Summit was completed.

Thus in storm and stress was this road born, and in the winter time of our day it is still a road of storm and stress, as are all of the roads over the High Sierra. It must

The canyon of the Truckee River.

Automobiling along the picturesque Truckee River en route to Lake Tahoe.

Donner Lake, on the automobile highway from Sacramento to Truckee and Lake Tahoe.

be remembered that while the elevation at Sacramento is but thirty feet above sea level, at Summit it is 7018 feet, and even at Truckee, where the turn is made for Tahoe, it is 5819 feet.

Naturally such high altitudes receive considerable snow, which render the roads impassable during the winter season. In 1914 I went from Truckee to the Summit on the 10th of June, and save for two or three patches of snow which were rapidly melting, there were no serious obstacles that any good motor could not overcome.

FROM SACRAMENTO TO TAHOE ON THE EMIGRANT GAP AND DONNER LAKE ROUTE, 135 MILES.

From Sacramento the grade is easy and the country fairly open until Auburn is reached (25-1/2 miles). The roads are excellent, the disintegrated granite affording local material close at hand for perfect road building. The Sierra stretch away to the east in gently ascending billows, covered over with richest verdure of native trees of every variety, and of the thousands of orchard trees that are making this region as famous for its fruits as it used to be for its mines.

For from 1849 until the hydraulic mines were closed down by the anti-débris decision in the U.S. Supreme Court, this section and beyond was one of the richest gold mining regions of California, and historically, one of the greatest importance to the State. Such places as Auburn, Illinoistown (Colfax), Gold Run and Dutch Flat, were rich producing camps and branch roads reached to Yankee Jim, Todd's Valley, Forest Hill, Michigan Bluffs, Bath, and other towns on what is known as the Forest Hill Divide, a divide being a local term, to signify the rocky, mountainous mass — nearly always having a level grade on its summit — that separates two forks of the same stream, or two different streams.

From Colfax another road led to Grass Valley, Nevada City, and North Bloomfield in Nevada County, and Iowa Hill, Wisconsin Hill, Monona Flat, and Damascus on the Iowa Hill Divide. All these were centers of rich mining districts which were scenes of the greatest activity in the days of their productivity.

Now, however, most of them are abandoned, except Auburn, Colfax, and Nevada City which have other resources, and Grass Valley, which maintains its high standing owing to its rich quartz mines. Forest Hill, Iowa Hill, and Michigan Bluff have drift mines which maintain small and meager populations compared with those of the early and prosperous days. In the 'fifties Yankee Jim and its tributary mines had a population of 3000, while today it is entirely deserted. Todd's Valley, which was also a flourishing camp, had suffered the same fate.

Auburn to Colfax 16 Miles, Colfax to Emigrant Gap, 30-1/2 Miles. Leaving Auburn the road ascends more rapidly until Colfax (16 miles) is reached (elevation 2422 feet). Then 10 miles further one is in the heart of the most extensive hydraulic mining operations of California. Thousands of acres are passed which yet bear the scars of the "washing down" for the precious mineral hid away during the centuries until the Argonauts of '49 and later unearthed it by their gigantic hydraulic nozzles. Millions of dollars were extracted from these placers, but now the villages are deserted and all mining operations have ceased.

The time is not far distant when automobile parties will arrange to stop over in one of these little places, and with a competent guide, go over the deserted placers. It is hard to realize that by the mere power of water mountains were washed away, leaving the denuded country on the one hand, a land of mounds and hummocks, like the Bad Lands in miniature, and on the other hand of masses of débris, too heavy to be washed away into the streams.

The wildest portions of the Sierra are revealed in ascending from Dutch Flat to the Summit. The snowsheds of the Southern Pacific Railway come into sight, perched like peculiar long black boxes, with peep holes, along an impossible ledge of the massive granite cliffs, and the Sierran trees tower upright from every possible vantage ground in the granite beneath.

At Towle, three miles beyond Dutch Flat, the shipping point is reached from which much of the material was hauled for the building of Lake Spaulding dam. Hundreds of teams were employed in this work, and the road showed an almost unbroken procession for months. This was in 1912-13.

A side trip to this remarkable dam, impounding the waters of the High Sierra for the generation of electric power to be used not only in the Sacramento Valley but in far away San Francisco, cannot fail to be of interest. The area of the Lake, with the dam at its present

The turbulent Truckee River, near Lake Tahoe.

Automobiling along the Truckee River.

elevation, is such as to justify the assertion that it is next to if not the largest artificial lake in the world.

Emigrant Gap to Cisco, 14 Miles. Fourteen miles from Towle, after enjoying the rich blue haze of Blue Canyon, the road passes through the natural Sierra pass at Emigrant Gap which gives its name to the route. Here one who has not been over the road before must not fail to note the following: As he passes through the Gap the massive granite wall towers in dominant power to the right and leads one to feel that miles of rugged peaks are there.

Yet not more than a hundred yards farther on, the wall fades away, and if he Yet not more than a hundred yards farther on, the wall fades away, and if he stops here, and turns off the road slightly to the right, he will glimpse a vision of glory and sublimity that will take away his breath. Here, from 1000 or 2000 feet almost sheer above it, one gazes down to where in peaceful repose lies Bear Valley, a rich emerald green meadow, on the right side of which flows the South Fork of the Yuba River, and on the left heads Bear Creek, which empties into the Sacramento at Marysville. Ten, fifteen, twenty minutes are always spent here by those who know of this delectable surprise, yet many come over the road unheeding and are never aware of what they have missed.

Eight miles beyond Emigrant Gap, at Cisco, one sees a branch road which leads to the old Meadow Lake Mining District, which in the 'sixties had a population of several thousand. A large town was built there, which is now abandoned.

Cisco to Summit, 13 Miles. At Summit a marvelous view is had in both directions, east and west. Westward the fall of the Sierra into the Sacramento Valley is apparently so gentle and easy as to lead one to wonder that he has risen so high, but eastward the descent is much more steep and abrupt. The rude granite in many places is almost barren though Sierran trees abound. The grade is easy, and the new grade and tunnel under the Southern Pacific tracks makes an added improvements.

Almost immediately on emerging from this tunnel the full glory of the eastern view is forced upon the attention. At one's feet, apparently, lies the placid surface of Donner Lake, its pure blue giving one a premonitory foretaste of the richer blues that await him at Tahoe, while beyond are the mountains that overlook the Great Basin of Nevada.

Summit to Truckee, 11 Miles. Rapidly the road descends, well engineered and easy to negotiate to any responsible driver, and before one is aware he is bowling along on the level Donner Boulevard, which is as perfect a piece of country road as can be found anywhere on earth. The Monument erected by the Native Sons to the memory of the Donner Lake pioneers, and the Memorial Cross, erected on the spot where the unhappy party camped, are passed and in a few minutes Truckee is reached. This was once the scene of great lumber activities but now much reduced, although it is the shipping point for Hobarts Mills, which is one of the largest lumber camps of the West.

Here the road to Tahoe turns sharply to the south, and the fifteen miles run to the Tavern is made in the picturesque canyon of the Truckee River fully described in another chapter.

The elevations are Sacramento, 32 feet; Auburn, 1360; Colfax, 2422; Emigrant Gap, 5225; Cisco, 5940; Summit, 7018, Truckee, 5819; Tahoe Tavern, 6240.

FROM TAHOE TAVERN TO TALLAC

On Tuesday, June 9, 1914, I had the pleasure of making the first trip of the season over the new Tahoe Boulevard from Tahoe to Tallac. Let me here quote the account written at the time:

> It was a fine morning, clear and just cool enough to be pleasant, no wind, sun shining through the trees, the Lake glistening in its richest morning glory, the air like wine, birds singing everywhere, chipmunks chattering as they ran up and down the trees, and we as full of life as they, when we made the start. Our machine was a Chalmers 20, a first-class chauffeur at the wheel, with instructions to go slow, let us see all there was, and to run no risks if the winter's snows and storms had interfered with the safety of the road. We didn't even wear overcoats, though all the peaks were covered with snow.
>
> The first mile or two from the Tavern is through avenues of second growth timber just tall enough to be delightful. In turn we passed many of the choice residences that are making Tahoe growingly popular as a summer home, and then crossed Ward Creek and Blackwood Creek.
>
> This latter is one of the principal trout spawning streams of Tahoe, and to prevent fishermen from catching the fish that seek the stream at the spawning season the

On the automobile boulevard around Lake Tahoe.

Atlantic to Pacific automobile party, premier tour, 1914, stopping at Tahoe Tavern.

Looking toward the casino, Tahoe Tavern, Lake Tahoe.

Fish Commissioners have placed a buoy out in the Lake, some twenty-five hundred feet away, within which bound it is illegal to catch fish.

While many trees have been logged from this region there are still enough to make it forest-like, and as the road winds and turns it affords glimpses and full views, sometimes for only a moment or two, and again for a minute or more, of the placid-faced blue Lake on the left, or the snowy mountain summits straight ahead or on the right. What rich contrasts of color, what revelations of majesty and sublimity each new turn affords!

The first eight miles is fairly level road and close to the Lake, but eight miles out, just before reaching McKinney's, the new portion of the State Highway begins, and it has been engineered to give scenic and romantic effect all along the way. In road building no longer is it necessary to consider the cheapest and nearest way. "Give us the most scenic," cry the motorists, "we'll pay the bills and our machines will speedily eat up any extra distance we may be required to travel to obtain the best scenery of the country."

From now on the whole trip is one of carefully engineered surprises and revelations. Colwell's Moana Villa, and Pomin's new and beautiful place are passed and then we ascend, and suddenly Meek's Bay is revealed to us, a glorious symphony in blues, deepening and richening into pure amethyst, with lines, patches and borders of emerald and lapis lazuli. Beyond rise hill-studded slopes leading the eye higher and higher until, anchored in a sky as blue as is the Lake below, are the snowy white crowns of the Rubicon Peaks, with here and there a craggy mass protruding as though it were a Franciscan's scalp surrounded by pure white hair.

Up and down we glide, the soft purring of the motor as we run on the level changing to the chug-chugging of the up pulls, or the grip of the brake as we descend. Every few feet new vistas of beauty are projected before us. The moving pictures are all exquisite. Indeed, after many studies of this incomparable Lake Tahoe I verily believe there is no more beautiful spot on it that Meek's Bay seen from this road.

To get its full charm we stop the machine for a while. Looking back we discover that the curve where we rest is a marvelous outlook point. We have ascended to a good height and look down upon the Lake. There are light blue, emerald green, deep blue in patches and in long irregularly shaped points. Here are Como, Maggiore, Lugano and Windermere all in one, though as yet free from the houses and artificial gardens on the slopes. But Nature such as this needs none of man's adornment to make it perfect.

Starting the engine again we circle around the point and come immediately into another charming circlet of views. Between Meek's Bay and Rubicon Point is another little recess in the lake shore, Grecian Bay, a good second to the one I have just described. Here we particularly notice the effect of the many varieties of trees, their dark trunks, branches, and foliage set out almost in silhouette against the pure color of the Lake below. These elevated stretches of road are a constant joy and delight. They afford us glad surprises every few moments in such views of the Lake as we could not otherwise obtain.

Crossing Lonely Gulch, watched over by the serene pure loveliness of the snowy peaks above, a good climb up a steep stretch of road brings us to the shoulder of Rubicon Point. Winding in and out, twining and twisting around and around, we reach Rubicon Park, from which place we get a perfect view of the whole Lake from one end to the other.

Today there are a score or more of fishermen out in their little boats, and strange to say, all of them near enough to be seen, are fishing in a patch of deep blue. The water there must be deeper than elsewhere, for there is where they invariably get their best catches.

In marked contrast to the blue is a great finger of emerald thrust out from a nearby point, as if in warning not to dare pass its mysterious border.

Now we come to the wild and rugged scenery. We are hemmed in on the right by towering crags and walls of massive gray rock. Shattered and seamed, scarred and disintegrated, they look as though earthquake and lightning shock and the storms of a thousand years had battled with them. They give a new touch of grandeur and almost awesome sublimity to the scene.

For a mile or two we play at hide and seek with the Lake. It seems as though we were in the hands of a wizard. "Now you see it, now you don't." Query: "Where is the Lake?" Mountains, snowbanks, granite walls, trees galore, creeks flashing their white crests dashing down their stony courses toward the Lake, but only now and then do we catch fleeting glimpses of it.

All at once it bursts full and clear again upon our enraptured vision, but only to give us a full taste of its supernal beauty before we are whirled around a curve where the eye rests upon nothing but the rugged majesty of the Sierra. Change and contrast, the picturesque,

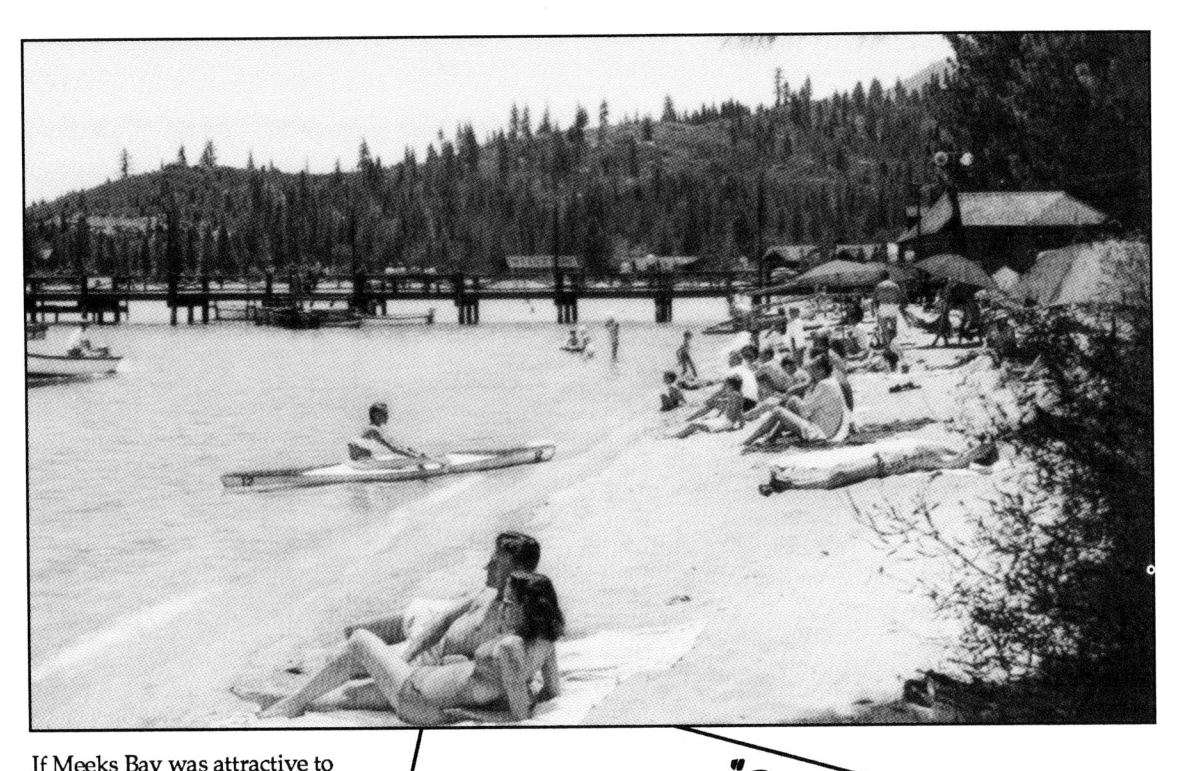

If Meeks Bay was attractive to author James in 1914, this resort soon gained even more prominence after 1919 as a family resort stressing an informal, family atmosphere. By mid-century Meeks Bay offered sunbathing, swimming, rowboats and kayaks. Besides a nifty restaurant, the resort was complete with service station, post office, and a beauty salon.

"GOOD MORNING"

MEEKS BAY RESORT WISHES YOU A HAPPY DAY

Breakfast Served from 8:00 – 11:00 A.M.

Juices

ORANGE . . . . .35 - .60
TOMATO . . . . .35 - .60
GRAPEFRUIT . . . . .35 - .60
APPLE . . . . .35 - .60
PINEAPPLE . . . . .35 - .60
GRAPEFRUIT-PINEAPPLE . . .35 - .60

Hot and Cold Cereals

ASSORTED CRISP CEREALS 75
With milk or cream
HOT CEREALS 85
With milk or cream
FRESH FRUIT in Season 75

Breakfast Suggestions

1. CHILLED JUICE, 2 EGGS (any style) – Ham, Bacon or Sausage . . 2.25
2. CHILLED JUICE, 2 EGGS (any style) 1.50
3. CHILLED JUICE, STACK of HOTCAKES, 1 EGG (any style) . . 2.00
4. 2 EGGS (any style) 1.25
5. PLAIN 3 EGG OMELET 1.75
6. 3 EGG OMELET with CHEESE, JELLY or DICED HAM 2.35

The above orders are served with:
Hash Brown Potatoes, Buttered Toast, Jam and Coffee

Built in 1934, the Kehlet Mansion is Meeks Bay's number one attraction. It has been owned by San Francisco Bay area millionaires, and today it is a summer rental. This fine two-story house is located just beyond the point shown below.

Cascade Lake, near the automobile boulevard, Lake Tahoe.

Mt. Tallac in storm, Lake Tahoe.

beautiful, delicate and exquisite in close touch and harmonious relationship with the majestic and the sublime. Travel the whole world over and nothing surpassing this can be found.

Now we curve around high up above Emerald Bay, that small glacial Lake, the eastern terminal moraine of which was unfortunately torn through, so that the *lake* disappeared and became a *bay* of the great Lake itself. Every moment of this portion of the ride is a delight. The senses are kept keenly alert, for not only have we the Lake, the bay and the mountains, but part of the way we have flowers and shrubs by the thousands, bees and butterflies flit to and fro, and singing streams come foaming white from the snowbanks above, eager to reach the Lake.

As our car wheels dash across these streamlets they splash up the water on each side into sparkling diamonds and on every hand come up the sweet scents of growing, living things. Now Mt. Tallac, in all its serene majesty, looms ahead. Snow a hundred or more feet deep in places covers its rocky sides. Here we can see where glaciers were born in the early days when Tallac was several thousand feet higher than it now is.

Below us is the emerald-ringed bay, with its romantic little island at the west end, and nearby the joyously shouting Eagle Creek as it plunges over the precipice and makes the foam-flecked Eagle Falls. Our road here was blasted through some fiercely solid and hostile rock. One boulder alone that stood in the way weighed (it was estimated by the engineers) from 800 to 1000 tons. Fifty cases of highly explosive powder were suitably placed all around it.

Excursion steamers took hundreds of people from all parts of the Lake to see the explosion, and at the proper moment, while everybody held his breath, the fuses were fired, the blasts took effect, the rock flew down to the level beneath, shattered into four great masses.

A new El Capitan now rises above us, though it lacks the smooth unbroken dignity of the great Yosemite cliff, yet it is sublime in its sudden rise and vast height. Nestling at its feet is Eagle Lake, and beyond are the Velmas and a score of other glacial jewels calling for visitors to rhapsodize over their beauty. Maggie's Peaks are to our right, Eagle Falls to our left, with Emerald Bay, the Island, the Point and the Lake beyond all calling upon us to enjoy them to the full.

We decide to stay here for lunch, and under the shelter of a giant sugar pine a thousand years old, listening to the eternally buoyant song of Eagle Falls, we refresh ourselves with the good lunch put up for us at the Tavern.

Again we push ahead and soon have our first adventure: The road gang was at work, and we did not expect to go much farther, but they assured us that, save for a few rough places here and there, which they would speedily correct, we need have no fear but that we could get through with ease. In a score of places, since we left the Tavern, we had crossed little streams of snow water that had come tumbling down from the banks above.

Suddenly we came to one with a larger volume than most of the others, and the road bed a little softer, so it had cut quite a deep little passage for itself. Easily our chauffeur dropped the front wheels into the cut, and to his surprise he found they stuck there. It did not take us long to jack up the wheels and put rocks underneath them, and we were about ready to get out when the road gang came along with a wagon and a pair of sturdy mules. As quickly as it takes me to tell it, the mules were attached to our back axle and we were pulled out. A few more rocks and a couple of planks placed over the cut and we were honking on our way with triumph.

Half a mile farther we came upon the ridge that separates Emerald Bay from Cascade Lake. Both are in clear view at the same time, while to the west we can hear the joyous song of Cascade Falls in its grand leap down from the foot of the snow banks of Mt. Tallac into the tree-clad stream-course below.

Now the road brings us almost directly above the Lake, with a rapid slope down, covered with dainty trees and shrubs of recent growth. From here we gain a fine view of the south end of the lake shore. Tallac, the Grove, Bijou, Al Tahoe and clear across to Lakeside, with the deep green of the meadows above, and the snowy crowns of Freel's, Job's, and Job's sister, with Monument Peak combine to give the proper setting to the Lake.

Soon we are racing across the level to the Fish Hatchery, between avenues of quaking aspens and young tamaracks and pines. Suddenly we come upon a mired car, the driver of which had just crossed the Sierra from Placerville, with little or no difficulty, but coming to a soft piece of road here when going a trifle faster than he should, and the side of the road having caught a lot of snow water, he had bogged and was working like a beaver to extract himself.

We had a stout rope along and it was the work of two or three minutes to get him out and we again pushed forward, gratified and smiling at the warmly

Cascade Lake, near the automobile boulevard, Lake Tahoe.

Tamarack and Echo lakes.

expressed thanks of himself and his three happy womenfolk who were enjoying their first trip into the Tahoe country, and already confessing their complete subjection to its thrall.

Passing the Hatchery we were only a few more minutes in reaching Tallac House, the first to complete the auto trip this season. Except for a few short stretches of scarcely completed road, it is in excellent condition, and the road gang now at work will have all the rough portions smoothed down in a few days.

It should here be noted that side trips may be made in automobiles to Glen Alpine Springs and Fallen Leaf Lodge. Both resorts use their own automobile stages daily during the season, hence keep the roads in good condition.

We made the return trip from Tallac House to the Tavern in two hours exactly. The distance is 26 miles. The road gang had already put a bridge over the place that had delayed us on coming out, and the road throughout was easy and safe. Naturally it is not as easy to negotiate as a San Francisco boulevard, but with the wheel in the hands of a careful chauffeur there is perfect safety and a trip that need give not a moment's fear to the most timorous.

THE "LAY OUT."

FROM TALLAC TO SACRAMENTO, BY THE PLACERVILLE ROUTE, 108 MILES

This is practically the first historic route into California, for, as I have shown in the chapter on Frémont's Explorations, it was the one the Pathfinder practically followed on his memorable trip that led to the discovery of Lake Tahoe.

Hence, when the gold excitement attracted its thousands to California, many of the argonauts took this road, following the Humboldt River and turning south at this Humboldt "Sink," crossing to the Carson "Sink" and then ascending to the headwaters of the Carson River, over into Hope Valley and thence down to Strawberry Valley and on to the mines.

This was the origin of the road, and it was in steady and continuous use until the startling news of the discovery of the Comstock Lode in Virginia City aroused the mining world. From every camp in California rude and stalwart men eagerly set forth to reach the new Camp. It was a genuine stampede. The chief question was: "Will the new Camp make good?" It answered this question by transcending the expectation of the most sanguine.

Silver and gold were taken out in fabulous quantities. Chunks of almost pure native silver, weighing scores of pounds, were hewed out of the chambers where they were found, and men went wild with excitement. Houses sprang up overnight. A vast population soon clung to the slopes of Mt. Davidson. Mining and milling machinery was needed, and demanded with tremendous urgency, to reap the richer harvest. There was no railroad, and the old Emigrant Road was not in condition to meet the needs.

Few people can realize the wild excitement that reigned and the string of teams, men riding on horseback, or afoot, stagecoaches, freight wagons, that poured in endless procession over the road. Nothing like it has been seen since, except during the Klondike rush.

As soon, however, as it was possible to secure the proper authority newer and easier grades were surveyed and private individuals undertook to build certain sections of the road under the condition that they were to be granted the right to collect toll for so many years. These rights have long since lapsed, and the road is now a part of the excellent system of El Dorado County, which, though a mountain county, boasts some of the best roads in California.

Tallac to Echo, 11-1/2 Miles. Leaving Tallac, an easy and pleasant eight-mile run on almost level roads through Tallac Meadows brings one to Celios, once Myers' Station (6500 feet). Now begins the upgrade, winding its way up the mountain side to the crest from which Starr King wrote his exquisite description, elsewhere quoted. This is one of the superb outlook points where the full sweep of Lake and encircling mountains is in full and complete view.

After a few minutes for gazing the journey is resumed, soon crossing a bridge, near which stand the remnants of the old toll house. On the right a foot trail or bridle path leads to Glen Alpine. A few miles of fairly rapid descent and Echo is reached, 49-1/2 miles from Placerville.

The stream here, during the snow melting season must be a dashing, roaring, sparkling mass of foam, for it is a boulder-strewn, rocky way suggesting the wild stream it becomes when the snows melt and spring's freshets come.

Echo to Strawberry, 7 Miles. The next mile and a half is a rapid descent, for elevation declines five hundred

The famous Strawberry Station on the Placerville route as depicted by J. Ross Browne during the Nevada silver boom at Virginia City in 1860.

feet, ere we reach Phillips, near which, in Audrian Lake, is the chief source of the South Fork of the American River.

The Water Company that controls the flow has here tampered with primitive physiography, in that it has cut a tunnel or channel from the Echo Lakes, tapping their water supply and conveying it to Audrian Lake. Hence strictly speaking the Echo Lakes are now the headwaters of the South Fork.

Soon we pass Hay Press Meadows, so called from the fact that hay was cut here in the old stagecoach days, baled with an old-fashioned press, and sold for $90 to $100 per ton, after being hauled to Virginia City.

Down we go into Strawberry Valley, where 42-1/2 miles from Placerville, we reach Strawberry, at 5700 feet elevation. This used to be a noted stopping place in the olden days, sometimes the whole flat area being covered with loaded wagons bound for the mines.

There is a rugged majesty about this Valley that has always made its impression on men. To the right is the southern end of the Crystal Range, and to the left the Yosemite-like cliff known as Lover's Leap, 6985 feet elevation. As the station at Strawberry is 5700 feet, this cliff is 1285 feet in sheer ascent.

Leading up it are strange columnar towers and structures of Egyptian appearance that remind us of those lines of Joaquin Miller's:

> Great Massive rocks that near us lay,
> Deep nestled in the grass untrod
> By aught save wild beasts of the wood —
> Great, massive, squared, and chisel'd stone,
> Like columns that had toppled down
> From temple dome or tower crown,

Along some drifted, silent way
Of desolate and desert town
Built by the children of the Sun.

We pass under the great cliff, and past a glacially polished dome on the left. The cliff is all cross-hatched and seamed with infiltrations of quartz. Ahead of us to the right is a canyon that is the southern extension of Desolation Valley.

Strawberry to Kyburgs, 10 Miles. A few miles below Strawberry we pass Georgetown Junction (where the road from Georgetown enters the main road), and ten miles brings us to Kyburgs, 4000 feet elevation, the canyon narrowing as we descend. On the right we pass Sugar Loaf (6500 feet).

At Kyburgs the water is taken out for the domestic and irrigation water supply of Placerville—8000 inches of water. The station is located at a break in the mountains where a cone-shaped rock, covered with trees, is a striking feature.

Kyburgs, Through Riverton, to Pacific House, 14 Miles. Passing the South Fork of the American on the left, nine and a half miles brings us to Riverton, a charming river resort where many visitors stop during the season for a day or a week, as this is a noted center for fishing and hunting. Here we cross over an excellent bridge, surrounded by a mountain amphitheater lined with trees, and our road follows the course of the boulder-strewn river bed. Yonder is the scene of a noted "hold up" in the old mining days.

If we cared to go over the files of the newspapers of the days when bullion was being shipped daily by stage to Placerville, how many accounts might we not find of "hold ups" by daring "road agents." And it does not take much imagination to picture in this secluded spot or that, the sudden appearance of a masked bandit, gun in hand, and to hear the sharp quick commands, "Halt! and Hands up!" and to hear the "squeesch" of the brake on the wheel, to see the hands of driver, express messenger, and passengers go up in helpless anger and furious impotence.

Then the "Stand down here!" or "Come off of that quick, and line up alongside!" and the immediate obedience of all concerned, and the sharp "keep *them* hands up, gentlemen, or somebody'll be gettin' hurt," or perhaps a fierce imprecation, if the bandit was less of the "Gentleman George" type than has so often been described.

And what a scene it would make for an artist — the most indignant passenger of them all made to hold the hat and collect the "swag," as the alert-eyed bandit stands by, gun in hand, ready to shoot down the first person who makes any show of resistance!

Then the permission given to get aboard, accompanied by the rude order, "Throw out that express box, and drive on, and don't look this way or some one'll have a hole blown through the top of his head!" and the mixture of dejection and relief shown in the faces of driver, messenger and passengers as the coach rolled on again.

What a panorama of quickly acted scenes it must have been, and how often it occurred on this road! Not even history has recorded a half of the times it happened.

Soon, almost hidden in the dense foliage of the tree-lined slopes, we pass Esmeralda Fall, whose waters dash in foam over 60 feet, to unite with the river far beneath.

As we near Pacific House, 4-1/2 miles further on, we come to where the new road diverges a little from the old one. It used to descend to the river, but we preserve a fairly even grade, solidly built, wide and well kept.

Pacific House to Placerville, 18-1/2 Miles. Then for a mile or so the road hangs over the yawning chasm of the river. It is wide and in fine condition so we dash along to where, on the up trip, the first glimpse is gained of the Crystal Range, its two chief peaks, Pyramid and Agassiz, dominating the landscape from this side as they do from Desolation Valley on the eastern side of the range.

In nine more miles Camino is reached, through clusters of pines, with perfectly level stretches for speeding and — dreaming. One's mind unconsciously goes back to the old days and he sees as in a moving-picture film the "days of '49." For this road is a road of memories, One shuts his eyes and muses, and immediately there troops before him a rushing, bustling, hurrying throng. These were the modern argonauts, the seekers for the Golden Fleece:

Great Horny-handed men and tall;
Men blown from many a barren land
Beyond the sea; men red of hand,
And men in love, and men in debt,
Like David's men in battle set —
And every man somehow a man.
They push'd the mailèd wood aside,
They toss'd the forest like a toy,

That grand forgotten race of men —
The boldest band that yet has been
Together since the Siege of Troy.

Some carried packs on their backs, with pick and shovel, drill and pan. Others rode, leading their burden-bearing burrows or mules. Wagon after wagon creaked along, laden to the full with supplies, food, or machinery.

As we push along and come to the river, Joaquin Miller's words make the memory pictures for us:

I look along each gaping gorge,
I hear a thousand sounding strokes
Like giants rending giant oaks,
Or brawny Vulcan at his forge;
I see pickaxes flash and shine;
Hear great wheels whirling in a mine.
Here winds a thick and yellow thread,
A moss'd and silver stream instead;
And trout that leap'd its riffled tide
Have turn's upon their sides and died.

Below Camino we pass near to Pino Grande, where the great cable railway carries loaded cars of logs across the deep canyon of the American River.

Rapidly we reach Smith's Flat, 4 miles, a famous mining camp in the days gone by, but now consisting of a general store, a few houses, and a gnarled old log fashioned into a glorious water trough fit for the Vikings.

Three more miles and Placerville is reached, the quaint old reminder of "the days of '49, the days of old, the days of gold," when men flocked to California from all parts of the earth eager with the lust for gold. In those memorable days it was called "Hangtown," a name some of its present-day citizens would fain forget, oblivious, in their own small-mindedness, that they are neither responsible for its history nor its nomenclature.

Built primarily in the somewhat shut-in walls of a small canyon, it winds and curves around in a happy-go-lucky fashion, and when the canyon widens out, spills over into irregular streets and up and down hills that were once clad with pines, firs, spruces and junipers.

Vineyard on the automobile highway between Lake Tahoe and Placerville.

That wealth and prosperity have smiled upon it in late years is evidenced by its comfortable lawn-girdled homes, its thriving orchards, its active business streets, and its truly beautiful, because simple, chaste and dignified, county courthouse.

Placerville to Sacramento, 47 Miles. This is a well-known road, via Diamond Springs, 2-1/2 miles; El Dorado, 6 miles; Shingle Springs, 11 miles, and Folsom, 25 miles.

The elevation at Tallac is 6225 feet; at Echo, 7500 feet; Strawberry, 5700 feet; Kyburgs, 4000 feet; Riverton, 3300 feet; Pacific House, 3400 feet; Sportsman's Hall, 3600 feet; Camino, 3000 feet; Smith's Flat, 2250 feet; Placerville, 1830 feet; El Dorado, 1610 feet; Folsom, 198 feet, and Sacramento, 32 feet.

A well equipped auto stage is run daily between Tallac House and Placerville. Experienced and careful drivers and first class cars only are used. They are owned by the Richardson Garage, of Pasadena, Calif., long known to the exacting population of that city as a thoroughly reliable, prompt and efficient house.

The famous Tahoe Tavern, located at the south end of the community of Lake Tahoe. While on an extended stay, George Wharton James wrote most of his famous book *Lake in the Sky*.

The launch *Catalina*, Lake Tahoe.

A steamer in dock at the wharf, Tahoe Tavern.

CHAPTER XIV

TAHOE TAVERN

Swinging around to the south from the course of the Truckee River on to the Lake, the railway deposits the traveler at Tahoe Tavern, prëeminently the chief resort for those who demand luxurious comfort in all its varied manifestations. Yet at the outset let it be clearly understood that it is not a fashionable resort, in the sense that every one, men and women alike, must dress in fashionable garb to be welcomed and made at home.

It is a place of common sense and rational freedom. If one comes in from a hunting or fishing trip at dinner time, he is expected to enter the dining room as he is. If one has taken a walk in his white flannels he is as welcome to a dance in the Casino, the dining room, or the social hall as if he wore the most conventional evening dress.

Indeed, visitors are urged to bring their old clothes that they may indulge to the full their *penchants* for mountain climbing, riding, rowing, fishing, horseback riding, botanizing in the woods, or any other out-of-door occupation where old clothes are the only suitable ones.

The building itself is completely embowered in pine, cedar, spruce and firs of differing ages, sizes and qualities of color. Though far enough from the Lake to allow of a large untrimmed grass plot where innumerable swing seats, reclining chairs, "lazy rests," etc., invite to lounging and loafing, the trees have been so trimmed out as to give exquisite glimpses of the dazzling blue of the water from every hand.

The Tavern is especially appropriate to its surroundings. It is three full stories high, with many gables relieving the regularity of the roof, which is steeply pitched, to throw off the winter's snows. The whole structure is covered with shingles, stained or oiled to a dark brown, and as climbing and clinging vines have wreathed themselves about every corner, and up many posts of the veranda, and there is a wealth of cultivated wild flowers banked up in beds around it, nothing could be more pleasing and harmonious.

Roads, walks and trails radiate from the Tavern in all directions, except directly across the Lake, and numerous boats and launches make this as accessible as any other direction. Near enough to be interesting is the wharf, with its daily bustle of the arrival and departure of trains, launches and steamers.

For all the indoor sports a Casino has been erected, far enough away so that the music, dancing, the sharp

The Tahoe Tavern, complete with casino and steamer pier, stood on a low bluff overlooking the northern end of Lake Tahoe, and was surrounded by tall pines and flower gardens. This multi-wooded hotel was admirably fitted to its surroundings. Tahoe Tavern was at once the terminus of the train from Truckee and the starting point for daily boat trips around the lake. This beautiful structure burned around 1925.

Ballroom in the casino, Tahoe Tavern.

The front of Tahoe Tavern from a table in the dining room.

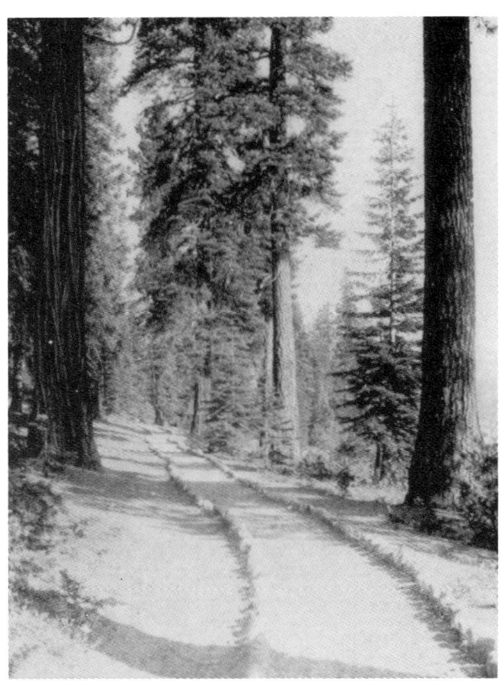

Path through the woods, adjacent to Lake Tahoe and Tahoe Tavern.

Morning service at the *Chapel of the Transfiguration*, Tahoe Tavern.

clangor of bowling, the singing of extemporized glee-clubs, and the enthusiasm of audiences at amateur theatricals and the like do not disturb the peaceful slumbers of those who retire early.

While Tahoe Tavern itself is *sui generis* in that it is the most wonderful combination of primitive simplicity with twentieth century luxury, the Casino is even more remarkable. Its interior finish is the work of a nature artist. Its porches immediately overlook the Lake, and

Ladies lounging room, in the casino of the Tavern.

when one has wearied of dancing there is a witchery as rare and subtle as it is delightful to sit in the subdued light overlooking the ripples of the moonlit water, sipping some liquid refreshment, eating an ice or chatting with a suitable partner.

Here a fine orchestra discourses sweet music, moving pictures are regularly shown, lectures and concerts occasionally provided, besides all the conveniences for private card parties and other pleasures that fashionable visitors expect for their entertainment.

Ruskin has somewhere brought out the idea in his finest phraseology that nowhere can man so readily worship God as in the presence of the most beautiful of His works in Nature. This is readily apparent at Tahoe, hence the summer visitors and others of religious trend will delight to learn that churches for both Catholic and Episcopal worshipers have been erected not far from the Tavern.

The Catholic Church was dedicated Sept. 10, 1911. It has a seating capacity of 175. Its location was chosen with an eye to the beautiful, being on Tahoe Heights, and is less than fifteen minutes' walk from the Tavern.

The Episcopal "Church of the Transfiguration" is unique in that it is an open air building, the altar only being roofed. Towering pines stand as aisles and the vaulted ceiling is the clear blue dome of heaven. Rustic and simple, it harmonizes exquisitely with its surroundings, and strangely insensible must that worshiper be who, as he kneels in this Nature shrine, and the organ peals forth its solemn notes, with a wonderful accompaniment of hundreds of singing birds, and the ascending incense of a thousand flowers, does not feel his own soul lifted into a higher and more spiritual mental frame.

One of the chief troubles about a hotel like Tahoe Tavern is that it is *too* tempting, *too* luxurious, *too* seductive to the senses. The cool, delicious breezes from the Lake make the nights heavenly for sleep. With Sancho Panza we cry aloud: "Blessed be the man that

Lady bathers and their friends at Tahoe Tavern.

invented sleep," and we add: "Blessed be the man that invented cool nights to sleep in." And I have no fault to find with the full indulgence in sleep. It is good for the weary man or woman.

It is well to make up arrears, to pay oneself the accumulated debts of insomnia and tossing and restlessness with an abundance of calm, dreamless, restful sleep. Nay, not only would I have men claim their arrearage, but lay in a surplus stock against future emergencies, future drafts upon their bank account of "restorer."

Nor would I find any fault with the allurements of the Lake, either for swimming, boating, "launching," canoeing or fishing. Indulge them all to your heart's desire and you will not only be none the worse, but immeasurably better for every hour of yielding. A plunge every morning is stimulating, invigorating and

The casino at Tahoe Tavern rose amid the shoreline pines as shown in this view from the pier. In a directly opposite view (below), from the casino, the steamer *Tahoe* is tied up to the pier. Casino gaming in California shut down before 1930.

jolly. It clears the brain, sets the blood racing up and down one's spine, arms, fingers, legs and toes, and sweeps the cobwebs out of the brain.

A row is equally good. It pulls on the muscles of the lower back, as well as the arms, chest and shoulders. It drives away Bright's disease and banishes asthma and lung trouble. It makes one breathe deep and long and strong, and when inbreathing, one can take in power from Tahoe's waters, forests, mountains and snow fields.

It means a purifying of the blood, a clearing of the brain, a sending of a fuller supply of gastric juices to the stomach, or digestive sauces to the palate, and a corresponding stimulus to the whole body, which now responds with vim, energy, buoyancy and exuberance to all calls made upon it by the spirit.

So with walking through the woods, by the Lake, along the River Trail, up the mountains. The results are the same until the man who hates and despises the poets shouts out with glee and exclaims: "*Them's* my sentiments!" when you throw out with fervor such lines as:

> Oh! the wild joys of living! the leaping from rock up to rock,
> The strong rending of boughs from the fir tree, the cool silver
> shock
> Of the plunge in a pool's living water ...
> How good is man's life, the mere living! how fit to employ
> All the heart and the soul and the senses forever in joy!

while all the conventional amusements are provided at Tahoe Tavern a large number of the guests, like myself, find much pleasure in feeding and making friends with the chipmunks, which have been so fostered and befriended that there are *scores* of them, most of them so fearless as to climb into the laps, eat from the hands, run over the shoulders, and even explore the pockets of those who bring nuts and other dainties for their delectation.

Children and adults, even gray-haired grandpas and grandmas, love these tiny morsels of animation, with their quick, active, nervous movements, their simulations of fear and their sudden bursts of half-timorous confidence. With big black eyes, how they squat and watch, or stand, immovable on their hind legs, their little forepaws held as if in petition, solemnly, seriously, steadily watch, watch, watching, until they are satisfied either that you are all right, or are to be shunned. For, with a shisk of the tail, they either dart toward you, or run in the other direction and hide in the brush, climb with amazing speed up a tree, or rush into their holes in the ground.

Some of them are such babies that they cannot be many months old, and they feel the friendly atmosphere into which they have been born. And it is an interesting sight to see a keen, stern, active business-man from "the city" saunter with his wife after lunch or dinner, sit down on the steps leading down to the water's edge, or on a tree stump, or squat down on his haunches anywhere on the walk, the lawn, or the veranda, fish some nuts out of his pocket and begin to squeak with his lips to attract the chipmunks. Sometimes it is a learned advocate of the law, or a banker, or a wine merchant, or the manager of a large commission house. It seems to make no difference. The "chips" catch them all, and everyone delights in making friends with them.

Here is a tiny little chap, watching me as I loll on the stairs. His black, twinkling eye fixes itself on me. He is making sure. Suddenly he darts toward my outstretched fingers where a peanut is securely held. He seizes it with his sharp teeth, but I hold on. Then with his little paws he presses and pushes, while he hangs on to the nut with a grip that will not be denied. If he doesn't get it all, he succeeds in snapping off a piece and then, either darting off, with a quick whisk of his tail, to enjoy it in his chosen seclusion, or, squatting down on his hind legs, he holds the delicious morsel between his fore-paws and chews away with a rapidity as astonishing as it is interesting and amusing.

Now a fat old fellow—he looks like a grandpa in age—comes up. He is equally suspicious at first, takes his preliminary reconnaissance, darts forward and just about reaches you, when he darts away again. Only for a moment however. On he comes, seizes the nut, and eats it then and there, or darts off with inconceivable rapidity, up the tree trunk to a branch twenty, forty feet up, and then sits in most cunning and *cute* posture, but in just as big a hurry and in equally excitable fashion to eat his lunch as if he were within reach.

Sometimes half a dozen or more of them, big and little, will surround you. One leaps upon your knee, another comes into your lap, while another runs all over your back and shoulders. Now and again two aim at the same time for the same nut, and then, look out. They are selfish little beggars and there is an immense amount of human nature in such tiny creatures.

The bigger one wants the morsel and chases the smaller one away, and he is so mad about it and gets so in earnest that sometimes he chases the other fellow so far that he forgets what it was all about. He loses the nut himself, but, anyhow, he has prevented the other fellow from getting it. How truly human!

Then the younger one, or the smaller one, or the older one, will whisk himself up a tree, perch on a branch and begin to scold, or he climbs to the top of a stump, or a rock, or merely stands upright without any foreign aid, and how he can "Chip, chip, chip, chip!" His piercing little shriek makes many a stranger to his voice and ways wonder what little bird it is that has so harsh a cry, and he keeps at it so persistently that again you say, How human! and you wonder whether it is husband scolding wife, or wife husband, or — any of the thousand and one persons who, because they have the power, use it as a right to scold the other thousand and one poor creatures who have to submit, or think they have (which is pretty much the same thing).

A trail party about to leave Tahoe Tavern.

These proceedings at Tahoe Tavern are diversified by the presence of a friendly bluejay. He is one of the smartest birds in the world. Some relation, no doubt, to the bird told of by Mark Twain in his *Tramp Abroad*. This bluejay has watched the visitors and the chipmunks until he has become extra wise. He has noticed that the latter toil not neither do they spin and yet neither Solomon Levi nor Kelly feed more sumptuously or more often than do they, simply because they have succeeded in beguiling the hearts of the guests who are so bored with each other that association with the "lower" animals is a great relief.

Pleasure party on the Wild Goose, *Lake Tahoe.*

So he has started the "friendly chipmunk" rôle. He stifles his raucous cry, he puts on a shy, timid and yet friendly demeanor. He flies conveniently near, and gives forth a gentle note, asking, *please,* your kind and favorable attention to the fact that he is a bluejay. As soon as he sees your eye upon him, he hops a little nearer; not too near, however, either to mislead you or to put himself in your hands, but just near enough to tempt you to try to tempt him.

You hold out a nut, and then, with a quick dart and a sharp peck with a bill trained to certain and sure work, your thumb and finger lose that which they held, and

On the trail returning from the summit of Mt. Tallac.

Mr. Bluejay is eating it in perfect security well beyond your reach. Oh, he is a fascinating creature is this bunch of beautiful blue feathers decorating the harshest voice of all bird-dom in the region of Lake Tahoe.

But birds, squirrels, flowers, scenery, sports, worship, fine music, the best kind of food, "air the angel's breathe," and sleep recuperative enough to revivify the old and decrepit, fishing, rowing, swimming and the like are not all that need fill one's days at Tahoe Tavern.

Hike out, afoot or horseback. Take the trails. Get Bob Watson, or one of his understudies, to pilot you to Watson Peak and lake, go to Ellis, Squaw or a score of other peaks, visit the various Sierran lakes, or take a camping out or hunting trip to Hell Hole, the Yosemite, or any one of the scenic spots, one, two, five, or ten days away. Then, my word for it, you will return home "a new man," life will put on a new meaning, and sensations long since lost will come back with unthought of force, for you will have "regained your youth" — the dream of the old of all the ages.

There are a number of interesting walks, drives and automobile trips which may be taken from the Tavern, besides the lake shore walks which are always interesting. Indian Camp is half a mile away; Tahoe City, a little further, and here the interesting Frémont howitzer, to whose history I have devoted a separate chapter, may be seen; Tavern Spring, a beautiful walk through the woods, one and a quarter miles; the Fish Hatchery, a mile away, where all the processes of hatching various kinds of trout before they are distributed to the different lakes and streams may be witnessed.

To those who prefer longer walks, or horseback rides, there are the Logging Camp, 3-1/3 miles; Idlewyld, 4 miles; Stanford Rock, 5 miles; Ward Peak, 6 miles; Blackwood Creek Dairy, 6 miles; Carnelian Bay, 6 miles; and Twin Peaks, 7 miles. Several of these interesting places can be reached also by automobile.

An especially delightful walk or horseback ride is by the Truckee River Trail to Deer Park Inn, 6-1/2 miles and thence 2 miles farther to Five Lakes, near which the waters divide, one stream flowing into the Rubicon, thence into the Sacramento and out by the Golden Gate into the Pacific Ocean; the other by Bear Creek into the Truckee River, thence into Pyramid Lake in the heart of the Nevada desert.

Automobile trips from the Tavern are numerous, depending entirely upon the length of time one can give to them. Chief of all is the Tahoe Boulevard trip around the Lake to Tallac, and thence on by Lakeside and by Cave Rock to Glenbrook, a distance of 50 miles. Hobart Lumber Mills, 22 miles, are well worth a visit to those who have never seen modern methods of making lumber; Independence Lake, 30 miles, is easily reached in two hours, and it is one of the charming spots of the High Sierra; Webber Lake, 43 miles, is another exquisite beauty spot, where there is an excellent Country Club House.

Reno is reached by three routes, all of them interesting, and each well worth traveling over. An excellent trip is to leave the Tavern after breakfast, ride on the Tahoe Boulevard to Glenbrook for lunch, then over to Carson City, where a brief visit can be made at the Capital of the State of Nevada, the Indian School and the prehistoric footprints, that for years have been the wonder of the scientists of the world.

Then on to Reno, where at the Riverside Hotel, mine host Gosse, one of the noted figures of the hotel world of the West, will accord a hearty welcome. Next morning Pyramid Lake can be visited and the return to the Tavern made by way of Truckee.

For those who enjoy motorboating on the Lake, excellent provision is made. The Lake Tahoe Railway and Transportation Company own several steam and gasoline launches, with varied capacities — from 6 to 250 passengers — full particulars of which can always be obtained.

Fishing boats in large numbers are to be had either with or without oarsmen, together with full equipment for fishing or hunting trips.

The Tavern stables are prepared to supply all reasonable demands for saddle horses, driving teams, and pack animals for hunting trips, and arrangements can be made for equipment and guides for mountain trips, of any duration, from a couple of days to three months or more. There is also a garage with first class cars and experienced chauffeurs for hire.

CHAPTER XV

TRAIL TRIPS IN THE TAHOE REGION

TO nature lovers, more or less active, the trails all around and about Lake Tahoe are a source of perpetual surprise and delight. I know of no region in California that possesses such a wealth of trails — not even the Yosemite or Mt. Shasta regions. The Lake is an ever present friend. From ridges, peaks, summits and passes, near at hand or scores of miles away, it never fails to satisfy the eye.

Again and again, when one is least expecting it, a turn in the trail, or a few steps forward or backward on a summit ridge brings it into sight, and its pure blue surface, now seen smooth and glossy as a mirror, again shining in pearly brilliancy in the sun, or gently rippled by a calm morning or evening zephyr, or tossed into white caps by a rising wind storm, pelted with fierce rain or hail, or glimpsed only through sudden openings in a snowstorm, at sunrise or sunset, each with its own dazzling brilliancies — it always gives one a thrill and warming sensation at the heart.

Then, too, the number of peaks to the summits of which trails have been cut, so that the walker, or the horseback rider may have easy access, are many and varied. In all there are not less than forty peaks, each of which is well worth a trip, each presenting some feature of its own that renders its personality worth cultivating.

In this and other chapters, I present my own experiences as illustrative to give the general reader an idea of what may be expected if he or she is induced to try one of the chief delights of a sojourn in this scenic region.

WATSON'S PEAK AND LAKE

Leaving Tahoe Tavern, crossing the bridge to Tahoe City, the trail leaves the main road on the left about a mile and a half further on, passing the horse pasture on the right. Near Tahoe City is the Free Camping Ground owned by the Transportation Company. This has a mile frontage overlooking the Lake, and scores of people habitually avail themselves of the privilege, bringing their own outfits with them, as, at present, there are no arrangements made for renting tents and the needed furnishings to outsiders.

The slope up which the trail now ascend with gradual rise is covered with variegated chaparral, making a beautiful mountain carpet and cushion *for the eye*. To the foot and body it is entangling and annoying, placing an effectual barrier before any but the most strenuous, athletic and determined of men.

Now the white firs, with their white bark, and the red-barked yellow pines begin to appear. They accompany us all the rest of the way to the peak and lake.

Soon we cross Burton Creek, a mere creek except during the snow-melting or rain-falling time. It empties into Carnelian Bay. Burton was one of the old-timers who owned the Island ranch near the Lake shore, and who came to the Tahoe region at the time of the Squaw Valley mining excitement.

When the "bottom fell out" of that he did a variety of things to earn a living, one of which was to cut bunch grass from Lake Valley and bring it on mules over the pass that bears his name, boat it across to Lakeside at the south end of the Lake, on the Placerville and Virginia City stage road, and there sell it to the stage station. Hay thus gathered was worth in those days from $80 to $100 per ton.

About 2-1/2 miles from the Tavern we come to a wood road, which is followed for half a mile. Years ago all these slopes were denuded of their valuable timber, which was "chuted" down to the Lake and then towed across to the sawmills at Glenbrook. The remnants were gathered up and used as fuel for the hotel and the steamboats.

Here and there are charming little nurseries of tiny and growing yellow pines and white fir. How sweet, fresh and beautiful they look — the Christmas trees of the fairies. And how glad they make the heart of the real lover of his country, to whom "conservation" is not a fad, but an imperative necessity for the future — an obligation felt towards the generations yet to come.

Of entirely different associations, and arousing a less agreeable chain of memories, are the ruined log cabins of the woodcutter's and logger's days. Several of these are passed.

As we reenter the trail, Watson's Peak, 8500 feet high, with its basaltic crown, looms before us. At our feet is a big bed of wild sunflowers, their flaring yellow and gold richly coloring the more somber slopes. Here I once saw a band of upwards of 2000 sheep, herded by a Basque, one of that strange European people who seem especially adapted by centuries of such life to be natural shepherds.

Few of them speak much American, but they all know enough, when you ask them how many sheep they have, to answer, "About sixteen hundred." The limit allowed on any government reserve in any one band is, I think 1750, and though a passing ranger may be sure there are more, he is nonplussed when, on his making question, the owner or the shepherd shrugs his shoulders and says, "If you don't believe, me, they're there. Go and count 'em!"

Before the officials treated some of the Basque shepherds with what seemed to be too great severity there were numerous forest fires on the reserve. These men were generally both self-willed and ignorant, and we passed by at this spot a clump of finely growing firs, which had been destroyed by a fire started by a shepherd the year before.

Watson assures me that he has personally known many cases where a tree had been blown across a trail, and the shepherd would stop his sheep, set fire to the "wind-fall" and then leave it to burn — sometimes allowing it to smolder for months, to the infinite peril of the forest should an arousing wind blow the fire into life and make it spread.

Fire notices, however, now are everywhere, and a few severe punishments have largely put a stop to all carelessness on the part of shepherds, let alone their culpable neglect. There are still campers and automobilists and others, of the so-called superior and educated race, who need as severe lessons as some of these ignorant Basque shepherds. They knock down the forest service placards, throw down matches, cigar and cigarette stumps, and often go off and leave a campfire burning.

The time is rapidly coming when severer and swifter penalties will be meted out to this class of culprits, for not only are their actions against the law, but they jeopardize all property in and near to the forests, as well as the lives, sometimes, of many innocent men, women and children, besides destroying the value of the mountains slopes as watersheds.

As our trail winds and ascends, the rotting stumps of trees cut years ago meet the eye on every hand, until at length, when at about 7000 feet altitude we see no more. The indications are clear that, though the timber is abundant above this elevation, for some reason or other cutting ceased. Careful observation reveals a possible reason for this. From this point on up the soil is both thin and poor, and though the trees seem to have flourished they are, in reality, gnarled, twisted, stunted and unfit for a good quality of lumber. Many of them are already showing signs of decay, possibly a proof that they grew rapidly and are rotting with equal or greater speed.

At this elevation, 7000 to 8000 feet, the red fir begins to appear. It is an attractive and ever-pleasing tree, its dark red bark soon making it a familiar friend.

Near by we found quite a nursery of graceful, dainty and attractive young firs; "Noah's ark trees," I always feel like calling them, for they remind one constantly of the trees found in the Noah's arks of childhood days, made by the Swiss during the long winter nights in their mountain chalets, where the trees are of a similar character to those of the Sierra.

Near to the point at which we turn to the left for Watson's Peak, and to the right for Watson's Lake, is a delicious, cool, clear spring, which I instinctively called, "the Spring of the Angels." When Bob asked the *why* of the name, the answer quickly came: "It is up so high and is so pure and good." The elevation is about 8000 feet. We take to the left.

Here also is found the mountain pine, its fine, smooth, black bark contrasting markedly with that of the firs and pines further down. It is generally found not lower than this elevation around Lake Tahoe.

Near by are some scattered hemlocks. This tree is found even higher than the mountain pine, and is seldom found lower than 8000 feet. In these higher elevations one sees what a struggle some of the trees have for mere existence. Again and again a mountain pine will be found, a tree perhaps fifty feet high, bowed over almost to the ground. This was done by snow.

Given the slightest list from the perpendicular when the heavy, wet snow falls upon it, it is bound slowly to be forced over. If it is a tough, strong tree it may sustain the weight until melting time comes, when it is released. But it never becomes upright again. On the other hand if a cold snap comes after the snow has bent it over, it is no uncommon thing for it to snap right in two, eight, ten or more feet from the ground.

Now we stand on the summit. This peak and its attendant lake were named after my incomparable guide, Robert Watson, and it is well that the name of so admirable a man should be preserved in the region through which he had intelligently and kindly guided so many interested visitors. The elevation is 8500 feet.

What a wonderful panorama is spread out before us. Close by, just across the valley in which nestles Watson's Lake, 7900 feet elevation, is Mt. Pluto, 8500 feet, the sides of which are covered with a dense virgin forest, thus presenting a magnificent and glorious sight. There is no trail through this forest though sheep are taken there to graze in the quiet meadows secluded on the heights.

Further to the east and north is Mt. Rose, 10,800 feet, on which is perched the Meteorological Observatory of the University of Nevada. Beyond is the Washoe Range.

Even before reaching the summit we gain a fine view, through the trees, of Castle Peak, 9139 feet, while further north is Mt. Lola, 9167 feet. Close at hand is a glorious specimen of red fir, fully four and a half feet in diameter. Below us to the west is a patch of vivid green, known as Antone Meadows.

It was named after a Switzer who lived there years ago and whose children now own it. Not far away is Round Meadow, locally known as Bear-Trap Meadow, for one may still find there an old bear-trap that hunters were wont to use thirty or forty years ago. In this meadow is the cabin of the Forest Ranger, which we shall see on the return trip.

Looking now over Lake Tahoe to the western horizon we see, over Tahoe Tavern, and a little west of north, Needle Peak (8920 feet), to the right of which is Lyon Peak (about 9000 feet). A trifle to the south of Needle Peak is Granite Chief, followed by Squaw Peak (8960 feet), Ward Peak (8665 feet), and Twin Peak (8924 feet) the one to the right having the appearance of a buffalo feeding.

While these peaks appear in a line, and as if belonging to the same range, a glimpse at the map will reveal that they are some miles apart.

As we look further south, across the head of Ward and Blackwood Creek Canyons, the mountains do not seem so high, though we discern Barker Peak (over 8000 feet).

Still further southward is Ellis Peak (8700 feet) apparently well timbered. It was named after Jock Ellis, who, on the further side, had a dairy ranch for a while. But when he found the cream would not rise in the colder periods of the year, he gave up his dairy, and went to raising sheep. In the summer months, however, he had no trouble in disposing of all the butter he could make, or milk and cream he cared to sell, for he was on the road from Georgetown which passed by Rubicon Springs to McKinney's on the Lake.

On the ridge to the left are the Rubicon Peaks (9199 feet), three of them apparently, all closely overlooking Lake Tahoe, and leading the eye down to Sugar Pine Point, which is at the south end of McKinney's Bay.

To the west of Rubicon Peaks is Phipps Peak (9120 feet), and a little farther back Mt. Tallac (9185 feet), while farther to the south is Ralston Peak (about 9500 feet), at this angle and distance appearing not unlike one of the domes of the Yosemite Valley. Near by, to the right, is Pyramid Peak (10,020 feet), though from here it presents a very different appearance from that it holds when viewed from Mt. Tallac. Still farther to the right is Tell's Peak (9125 feet), apparently at the end of a richly timbered ridge. Tell was an old Switzer who used to keep a dairy ranch on the slopes of the mountain bearing his name.

At the extreme south of Lake Tahoe stands Round Top (10,130 feet), to the left of which are the three great peaks of the Tahoe region, Freel's (10,900 feet), Job's (10,500 feet) and Job's Sister (10,820 feet). Freel was one of the old timers who used to have a cattle range on the slopes.

Then, allowing the eye to follow along the southeastern curve of the Lake up to the mountains on the eastern side, the first great depression is the pass over which the Placerville road goes down the Kingsbury grade to Genoa. At the foot of the grade, at the entrance to the Carson Valley is Van Sickle's old place, one of the early day stage stations on the Placerville road.

Van Sickle was a noted character, a fearless, rude pioneer, but well liked and highly respected. His fame was materially enhanced when he killed Sam Brown, one of the noted desperadoes of the Tahoe region in the days of the Virginia City mining excitement. Tradition says that Brown was a fire-eating southerner, from Texas, a man proud of his bad record of several murders.

He was notorious in Virginia City, and when the war broke out was one of the outspoken heralds and advocates of secession. He had trouble with Van Sickle and had threatened to kill him on sight. Coming to the place for this purpose he himself was killed, for Van Sickle secured a shotgun, "laid for him," and shot him.

A great sense of relief was felt by many people at this, what was then considered not only a justifiable but highly laudable act, for Brown was seeking to raise a body of men to go South and fight in the Civil War. This event had much to do with stopping too vigorous advocacy of the claims of the South from that time on in Virginia City and the immediate neighborhood.

The road around the Lake forks at a place originally known as Edgewood's, the branch to the left continuing along the eastern shore of Lake Tahoe, past Round Mound and Cave Rock to Glenbrook, where it swings over the grade to the east and over the summit, divides, one branch going down Clear Creek Canyon, and the other down King's Canyon to Carson City. It is 13-1/2 miles from Glenbrook to Carson by way of King's Canyon, and automobiles use this route, while stages run regularly over the other route via Clear Creek Canyon which is only 14-1/4 miles to Carson.

It was during the lumbering days at Glenbrook that the railway ran from the mills to the summit, nine miles, carrying carloads of lumber there, which were then unloaded and shot down the water flume to Carson City.

Letting the eye still follow the eastern shore of Lake Tahoe completing the circuit, northward, Snow Valley Peak and Marlette Peak are reached. Under the latter, to the southwest, is Marlette Lake, largely an artificial body over a mile long and half a mile wide, which is the reservoir for the water supply of Virginia City.

The course of the conveying flume may distinctly be traced, for part of its twenty-four miles of length. Both peak and lake were named after S.H. Marlette, once Surveyor General of Nevada, and a well-known character of the earlier mining days.

Just below Marlette Lake, almost directly facing Tahoe Tavern, are several scarrings, running almost parallel to each other and going in the most direct fashion to Lake Tahoe. These denote where the flume broke and the water made its own rude channels to the Lake beneath.

From this inadequate and imperfect description it can readily be imagined what a sublime and comprehensive view is afforded from Watson's Peak. Every visitor to Tahoe should take the trip, especially those who stay for a few days or longer at Tahoe Tavern.

WATSON LAKE

About half a mile northwest from the summit of Watson Peak is Watson Lake, 7900 feet. It is about 300 yards long by 250 yards broad, hence rudely oval in shape. While about fifty feet deep in the center, it shallows toward the edges, where lilies abound, and then becomes mere marsh. Practically it is surrounded by trees. Restocked with a variety of fish (trout) in large numbers each year, it is one of the best fishing lakes at the northern end of Lake Tahoe, and a most enjoyable day to the angler is to start early, take his lunch along, and spend the day there.

To those who are not anglers this same day can be spent in the quiet enjoyment of the trees, flowers, lake and sky.

The outlet from the lake is by Deer Creek, and thence into the Truckee not far from the site of the old mining camp of Knoxville.

The return trip to Tahoe Tavern is made through a virgin forest, on a ridge between Watson Lake and the Truckee Valley, the trail having been outlined only about five years ago. Later the Forest Rangers considerably improved it, until now it is a very easy and comfortable trail to traverse. One notices here the especial "blaze" on the trees, of the rangers. It consists of a perpendicular parallelogram with a square above *(as shown at right)* Wherever this blaze is found everybody in the region knows it for a ranger's blaze, denoting a trail leading to a ranger's cabin.

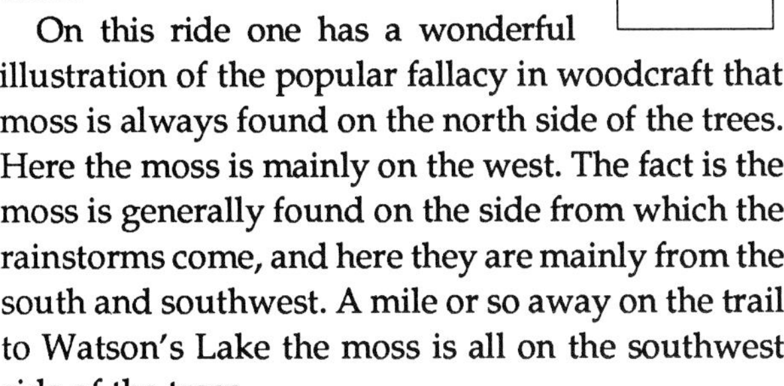

On this ride one has a wonderful illustration of the popular fallacy in woodcraft that moss is always found on the north side of the trees. Here the moss is mainly on the west. The fact is the moss is generally found on the side from which the rainstorms come, and here they are mainly from the south and southwest. A mile or so away on the trail to Watson's Lake the moss is all on the southwest side of the trees.

Most of the trees here are red fir and mountain pine, some of them being of large size, and noble specimens.

A little further on a fine opening reveals Deer Creek, through which the waters of Watson Lake flow to the Truckee. It was nearing the hour of sunset when I reached this point, and the trees were glowing with flaming gold, reminding one of the pictures John Enneking, the wonderful Boston artist, so loves to paint, while below the water gleamed like dazzling diamonds.

along here the side of the ridge below the trail seemed as if plowed into a number of rudely parallel lines. These were sheep trails made as the sheep followed each other over the softer soil of the mountain side.

A mile and a half from Watson Lake we came to a telephone box. This was the signal box of the Forest Rangers connecting with Lake Tahoe, five miles away, Truckee, eight miles, Shaffer's Mills, five miles and thence to Brockway, six miles. In the direction we were going it was but one mile to the ranger's log cabin in Round Meadow.

In the wintertime the ranger often finds it difficult to keep the line in operation. The damp snow falling upon the wire, clings to it, freezes and keeps receiving additions until it is bigger than a man's arm, and the weight breaks it down.

As we rode along we saw a fat porcupine, weighing full 25 pounds and deliberately walking up the slope near by, as if going to its den in the rocks, but, though we yelled and shouted, it scorned to notice us and indifferently went its way. A horned owl now and then hooted and bade us begone, while a badger came out form his hole, but hurried back when he saw or smelled who we were.

Now and again we caught marvelous sunset reflections on Lake Tahoe through the trees, and on the eastern mountains was a peach glow more soft and beautiful than the famous Alpen glow.

Soon the sun was gone, and then, as we rode through the dark aisles of the trees the stars came out and shone with dazzling splendor overhead. Just as we left the ranger's cabin a long dark corridor of majestic trees framed in a patch of black velvet in the upper sky, and there, in the very center, shining in resplendent glory, was Venus, the evening star.

The wind began to blow a regular cyclone from the north, so the roaring of the trees told us, but we were largely sheltered, and as we looked up through the dancing and whirling tree tops there was not a cloud in the sky.

Thus we returned to the Tavern, dramatically and gloriously bringing our delightful and easy trip to an end.

I have been rather prolix, and have entered much more fully into detail than some may deem necessary in the account of this trip, for two important reasons. It is a trip that none should fail to take, and I have made it a sort of general account, giving in broad outline what the visitor may expect of any of the peak trips in the vicinity of Tahoe Tavern. It goes without saying that, constantly, from a score or more outlook points, the eye finds its resting place upon Lake Tahoe, each view being different and more charming than the one that preceded it.

TO SQUAW VALLEY, GRANITE CHIEF PEAK, FIVE LAKES AND DEER PARK SPRINGS

Leaving Tahoe Tavern we cross the Truckee River and ride down on the north side. The flowing Truckee is placid and smooth, save where eager trout jump and splash. The meadows are richly green and the mountain slope on the further side is radiant with virgin tree life in joyous exuberance. Jays are harshly calling, chipmunks are excitedly running, the pure blue of the sky over-arches all, the wine of the morning is in the air, and we are glad we are alive. A spring of pure cold water on the right, about a mile out, tempts us to a delicious morning draught.

A little further down is "Pap" Church's "Devil's Playground," "Devil's Post," and devil's this, that and the other, out of which he gained considerable satisfaction while driving stagecoach between Truckee and Tahoe in the days before the railroad.

It is well carefully to observe these singular laval pudding-stone masses, for, according to the theory of John Le Conte, the eminent physicist, recounted in another chapter, these were the restraining masses that made the Lake at one time eighty or a hundred feet higher than it is today.

Four miles from the Tavern we pass Engineer Von Schmidt's old dam, for the history of which see the chapter on "The Truckee River."

Near Deer Park Station is another spring on the right. In the old stage days "Pap" Church always stopped here and gave his passengers the opportunity to drink of the water, while he made discourse as to its remarkable coldness. Five years ago a land slide completely buried it, and the road had to be cut through again. Ever since the spring has been partially clogged and does not flow freely, but it is cold enough to make one's teeth ache.

In the winter of 1881-2 a land-and-snow-slide occurred a little beyond Deer Park Station. Watson was carrying the mail on snowshoes at the time and saw it. There had been a five foot fall of snow in early March, and a week or two later came a second fall of seven feet. Something started the mass, and down it came, rushing completely across the river and damming it up, high on the other side, and the course of the slide can clearly be seen today.

It is now, however, almost covered with recent growth of chaparral, and thus contributed to one of the most beautiful effects of light and shade I ever saw. The mountain slope on one side was completely covered with a growth of perfect trees. Through these came pencillings of light from the rising sun, casting alternate rulings of light and shadow in parallel lines on the glossy surface of the chaparral beyond. The effect was enhanced by the fleecy and sunshiny clouds floating in the cobalt blue above.

Near the mouth of Bear Creek the river makes a slight curve and also a drop at the same time, and the road, making a slight rise, presents the view of a beautiful stretch of roaring and foaming cascades. Here the canyon walls are of bare, rocky ridges, of white and red barrenness, with occasional patches of timber, but very different from the tree-clad slopes that we have enjoyed hitherto all the way down from the Tavern.

Beyond is a little grove of quaking aspens. Their leaves, quivering in the morning breeze, attract the eye. Crossing the railway, the road makes a climb up a hill that at one time may have formed a natural dam across the river. Here is a scarred tree on the left where Handsome Jack ran his stage off the bank in 1875, breaking his leg and seriously injuring his passengers.

Crossing the next bridge to the left at the mouth of Squaw Creek, six miles from the Tavern, on a small flat by the side of the river is the site of the town of Claraville, one of the reminders of the Squaw Valley mining excitement.

Just below this bridge is an old log chute, and a dam in the river. This dam backed up the water and made a "cushion" into which the logs came dashing and splashing, down from the mountain heights above. They were then floated down the river to the sawmill at Truckee.

At Knoxville we forded the river at a point where a giant split boulder made a tunnel and the water dashed through with roaring speed. Retracing our steps for a mile or so we came to the Wigwam Inn, a wayside resort and store just at the entrance to Squaw Valley. To the right flows Squaw Creek, alongside of which is the bed of the logging railway belonging to the Truckee Lumber Co. It was abandoned about 1911, when all the available logs of the region had been cut. Most of the timberland between Squaw Creek and Truckee, on both sides of the river, was purchased years ago, from its locators, by the Truckee Lumber Company. But Scott Bros. purchased 160 acres from the locators and established a dairy in Squaw Valley, supplying the logging camps with milk and butter for many years past.

For 40 years or more this region has been the scene of active logging, the work having begun under the direction of Messrs. Bricknell and Kinger, of Forest Hill. This company, after the railway removed from Glenbrook and was established between Tahoe and Truckee, lumbered along the west side of Tahoe as far as Ward Creek.

Entering the valley we find it free from willows, open and clear. The upper end is surrounded, amphitheater fashion, by majestic mountains, rising to a height of upwards of 9000 feet. Clothed with sagebrush at the lower end and rich grass further up, even to the very base of the mountains, it is, in some respects, the prettiest valley in the whole of this part of the Sierra Nevada.

The upper meadows are full of milk cows, quietly grazing or lying down and chewing their cuds, while just beyond the great dairy buildings is the unpretentious cottage of the Forest Ranger. Remnants of old log chutes remind one of the logging activities that used to be carried on here.

One of the most observable features of Squaw Valley is its level character. This is discussed in the chapter on glacial action.

On the right the vein of quartz which outcrops at Knoxville is visible in several places and the various dump piles show how many claimants worked on their locations in the hope of finding profitable ore.

Halfway up the valley is an Iron Spring, the oxydization from which has gathered together a large amount of red which the Indians still prize highly and use for face paint.

How these suggestions excite the imagination—old logging chutes, mining claims and Indians. Once this valley rang with the clang of chains on driven oxen, the sharp stroke of the ax as it bit into the heart of the tree, the crash of the giant trees as they fell, the rude snarl of the saw as it cut them up into logs, the shout of the driver as he drove his horses alongside the chute and hurried the logs down to the river, the quick blast of the imprisoned powder, the falling of shattered rocks, the emptying of the ore or wastebucket upon the dump—all these sounds once echoed to and from these hillsides and mountain slopes.

Now everything is as quiet and placid as a New England pastoral scene, and only the towering mountains, snow clad even as late as this in the fall, suggest that we are in the far away wilds of the great West.

But Squaw Valley had another epoch, which it was hoped would materially and forever destroy its quiet and pastoral character. In the earlier days of the California gold excitement the main road from Truckee and Donner Lake went into Nevada County and thus on to Sacramento. In 1862 the supervisors of Placer County, urged on by the merchants, sent up a gang of men from Placerville to build a road from Squaw Valley, into the Little American Valley, down the Forest Hill Divide, thus hoping to bring the emigrant travel to Forest Hill, Michigan Bluff, and other parts of Placer County.

It was also argued that emigrants would be glad to take this new road as all the pasture along the other road was "eaten off." Over this historic road we are now about to ride.

As we look up it is a forbidding prospect. Only brave men and sanguine would ever have dared to contemplate such a plan. The mountain cliffs, separated and split, arise before us as impassable barriers. Yet one branch of the old trail used to pass through the divide to the right, over to Hopkins Springs, while the one that was converted into the wagon road took the left hand canyon to the main divide.

We now begin to ascend this road at the head of Squaw Valley, and in five minutes, or less, are able to decide *why* it was never a success. The grade is frightful, and for an hour or more we go slowly up it, stopping every few yards to give our horses breath. All the way along we can trace the blazes on the trees made over sixty years ago. It is hard enough for horses to go up this grade, but to pull heavily ladened wagons — it seems impossible that even those giant-hearted men, used to seeing so many impossible things accomplished, could ever have believed that such a road could be feasible.

What wonderful, marvelous, undaunted characters they must have been, men with wills of inflexible steel, to overcome such obstacles and dare such hardships. Yet there were compensations. Squaw Creek's clear, pellucid, snow-fed stream runs purling, babbling or roaring and foaming by to the right. These pioneers with their women and children had crossed the sandy, alkali and waterless deserts. For days and weeks they had not had water enough to keep their faces clean, to wash the sand from their eyes.

Now, though they had come to a land of apparently unscalable mountains and impassable rock barriers, they had grass for the stock, and water — delicious, fresh, pure, refreshing water for themselves. I can imagine that when they reached here they felt it was a new paradise, and that God was especially smiling upon them, and to such men, with such feelings, what could daunt, what prevent, what long stay their onward march.

As we ascend, the mountains on our right assume the form of artificial parapets of almost white rock, outlined against the bluest of blue skies. There is one gray peak ahead, tinged with green. The trail is all washed away and our horses stumble and slide, slip and almost fall over the barren and rough rocks, and the scattered boulders, a devastating cloudburst could not wash away.

Here is a spring on the left, hidden in a grove of alders and willows, and now new and more fantastic spires arise on the right. Higher up we see where those sturdy road builders rolled giant rocks out of their way to make an impassable road look as if it could be traversed.

Reaching the point at the foot of Squaw Peak at last we look back over Squaw Valley. In the late summer tints it is beautiful, but what must it be in the full flush of its summer glory and perfection? Then it must be a delight to the eye and a refreshment to the soul. How interesting, too, it is to rehabilitate it as a great glacial lake.

One can see its pellucid waters of clear amethystine blue and imagine the scenes that transpired when the ancestors of the present Indians fished, in rude dugouts, or on logs, or extemporized rafts, upon its surface. Now it is covered with brown, yellowish grass, with tree-clad slopes rising from the marge.

Turning to the right we find ourselves in a country of massive boulders. They seem to have been broken off from the summits above and arrested here for future ages and movements to change or pass on.

The road grows severer than ever, and we cannot help again picturing those old heroes driving their wagons up, while the women and children toiled painfully on foot up the steep and rocky slopes. Could anything ever daunt them after this? any obstacle, however insurmountable, discourage them? any labor, however severe, compel them to turn back?

Though there is a deep pathos in all these memories, the heroism of it makes our blood tingle with pride that such men and women belonged to us, that we are privileged to live in the land their labors, loves and lives have sanctified.

We turn to the right. A tiny waterfall, which in the season must be quite a sight, trickles down near by. We are now advancing directly upon the serrated ridge of fantastic spires that have long accompanied us. We now find those white-seeming pinnacles are of delicate pinks, creams, blues, slates and grays.

In one place, however, it seems for all the world as if there were a miniature Gothic chapel built of dark, brownish-black lava. Another small patch of the same color and material, lower down, presents a gable end, with windows, reminding us of the popular picture of Melrose Abbey in the moonlight.

Now we are lined on either side by removed boulders, but the road! Ah the road! Who could ever have traveled over it? Trees twenty feet high have now grown up in the roadway. To the left Squaw Peak (8960 feet) towers above us, while we make the last great pull through the rocky portion ere we come to the easier rise to the shoulders of Granite Chief. Here the road was graded out from the side of a granite mountain, blasted out and built up, but it is now sadly washed out.

Further up, a broad porphyritic dyke crosses our path, then more trees, and we come to the gentle slope of a kind of granitic sand which composes the open space leading to the pass between Granite Chief on the right, and a peculiar battlemented rock, locally known as Fort Sumpter, on the left. This was named by the Squaw Valley stampeders who came over the trail in the early days of the Civil War, when all patriots and others were excited to the core at the news that Fort Sumpter had been fired upon.

On one of the highest points stands a juniper on which a big blaze was cut by the early road makers, so that there need be no doubt as to which way the road turned. Other nearby trees, in their wild ruggedness and sturdy growth, remind us of a woman whose skirts are blown about by a fierce wind. Their appearance speaks of storms braved, battles of wind and snow and ice and cold fought and won, for they have neither branch nor leaf on the exposed side, and on the other are pitiably scant.

As we cross the sandy divide, over which a wagon could drive anywhere, we find white sage in abundance. Expansive vistas loom before us, ahead and to the right, while Squaw Peak now presents the appearance of a vast skyline crater. We seem to be standing on the inside of it, but on the side where the wall has disappeared.

Across, the peak has a circular, palisaded appearance, and the lower peaks to the right seem as if they were the continuation of the wall, making a vast crater several miles in diameter. The plateau upon which we stand seems as if it might have been a level spot almost near the center of the bowl. Fort Sumpter is a part of this great crater-like wall and Granite Chief is the end of the ridge.

As a rule there is a giant bank of snow on the saddle over which the trail goes between Ft. Sumpter and Granite Chief, but this year (1913) it has totally disappeared. It has been the driest season known for many years.

Looking back toward the Lake a glorious and expansive view is presented. Watson Peak, Mt. Rose, Marlette Peak, Glenbrook and the pass behind it, are all in sight and the Lake glistening in pearly brilliancy below.

At the end of the squaw Peak ridge, on the right, is a mass of andesite, looking like rude cordwood, and just above is a mass of breccia very similar to that found in the Truckee Valley a few miles below Tahoe Tavern.

Below us, at the head of Squaw Creek is a small blue pond, scarcely large and important enough to be called a lake, yet a distinctive feature and one that would be highly prized in a less-favored landscape.

On the very summit of the ridge we get fine views of Mounts Ralston, Richardson, Pyramid Peak and the whole Rock Bound Range, while close at hand to the north is Needle Peak (8920 feet), and to the south, Mt. Mildred (8400 feet). To our left is Fort Sumpter, to the right the Granite Chief, and between the two a stiff breeze is blowing.

Have you ever stood on a mountain ridge or divide when a fierce gale was blowing, so that you were unable to walk without staggering, and where it was hard to get your breath, much less speak, and where it seemed as if Nature herself had set herself the purpose of cleansing you through and through with her sweetening pneumatic processes? If not, you have missed one of the blessed influences of life.

Rough? harsh? severe? Of course, but what of that, compared with the blessings that result. It is things like that that teach one to love Nature. Read John Muir's account—in his *Mountains of California*—and see how he reveled in windstorms, and even climbed into a tree and clung to its top "like a bobolink on a reed" in order to enjoy a storm to the full.

Immediately at our feet lie the various mazes of canyons and ravines that make the diverse forks of the American River. In one place is a forbidding El Capitan, while in another we can clearly follow for miles the Royal Gorge of this many branched Sierran river. To the right is Castle Peak (9139 feet) to the north and west of Donner Lake, while nearby is Tinker's Knob (9020 feet) leading the eye down to Hopkins' Soda Springs. Beyond is Donner Peak (8135 feet) pointing out the location of Summit Valley, just to the left (west) where the trains of the Southern Pacific send up their smoke-puffs and clouds into the air.

At our feet is the Little American Valley, in which is the road, up the eastern portion of which we have to toilsomely climbed. With a little pointing out it is possible to follow the route it followed on the balance of its steep and perilous way.

Crossing the valley beneath it zigzagged over the bluff to the right, through the timber to the ridge between the North and Middle Forks, then down, down, by Last Chance to Michigan Bluff. The reverent man instinctively thanks God that he is not compelled to drive a wagon, containing his household goods, as well as his wife and children, over such roads nowadays.

Just before making the descent we succeed in getting a suggestive glimpse of what is finely revealed on a clear day. Slightly to the south of west is Mount Diablo, while northwards the Marysville Buttes, Lassen's rugged butte, and even stately Mt. Shasta are in distinct sight. At this time the atmosphere is smoky with forest fires and the burning of the tules in the Sacramento and other interior valleys, hence our view is not a clear one.

It did not take us long to reach the old stage station in the Little American Valley. Here Greek George — he was never known by any other name — had a station, only the charred logs remaining to tell of some irreverent sheepherder or Indian who had no regard for historic landmarks.

The pile of rocks which remain denote the presence of the chimney. When the new stage road was built and travel over this road — always very slim and precarious — completely declined, Greek George removed, but his log hotel and bunkhouse remained until a few years ago.

We lunch by the side of the old chimney and ruminate over the scenes that may have transpired here in those early days.

On our way back we pass the stumps of two large firs which were undoubtedly cut down to supply George's houses with shakes. At the base of Ft. Sumpter we leave the trail down which we have come, with the intention of going—without a trail—down Whisky Creek, over several interesting meadows to Five Lake Creek, and thence up by the Five Lakes, over the pass into Bear Creek Canyon, past Deer Park to the Truckee River and thus to the Tavern.

With such an excellent guide as Bob Watson we have no hesitation in striking out in any direction and in a short time Mt. Mildred (8400 feet) is on our right.

Great groves of willows and alders cover immense areas of the canyon's sides, while we pass a giant red fir with a diameter of fully six feet.

When about half a mile from Five Lake Creek the largest portion of the canyon is taken up with irregular masses of granite over which a glacier, or glaciers, have moved. The striation and markings are down the valley, and looking up from below the canyon for a mile or more it has the appearance of a series of irregular giant steps, each step gradually sloping back to the step above.

From above the course of the glacier seems clear. It must have flowed downwards, polishing and smoothing each step in turn, then falling over the twenty, thirty or fifty feet high edge to the next lower level, to ascend the next slope, reach the next precipice, and so on.

At the point where we strike Five Lake Creek, in a large expanse of meadow, we pass a camp, where in the distance we can clearly see three men and a woman. Deer hunters probably. We give them a cheery Halloo! and pass on.

Five Lake Creek here makes a sharp bend into the canyon which is a continuation of the canyon down which we have been traveling, and enters the Rubicon River at Hell Hole. We, however, turn *up* the Creek to the northeast, here striking the regular Hell Hole trail built a few years ago by Miss Katherine Chandler, of Deer Park.

Just ahead of us, appearing through a grove of trees near to where the Five Lakes are nestling, is a perfectly white cloud, absolutely startling in the vividness of its contrast to the deep blue of the sky and the equally deep green of the firs and pines.

A wilderness of boulders compels the winding about of the trail, but we hear and see Five Lake Creek, roaring and dashing along, for it has a large flow of water and its course is steep and rocky. We pass through groups of willows, wild currants and alders, enter a sparsely wooded meadow and in a few moments see the first of the Five Lakes. There is but little difference in their levels, though their sizes vary considerably.

The first one is the largest. Here is a log cabin and two or three boats. These are downed by the Deer Park Springs resort, and are for their fishing and hunting patrons. They also own 160 acres here, which include the area of the lake. The two first or lower lakes are the largest and the deepest. It is their flow which makes Five Lakes Creek. The three upper lakes are smaller and shallower.

It is said that a divide used to separate the two lower from the three upper lakes, and the flow from the latter descended through Bear Creek, past Deer Park, into the Truckee River and thence into faraway Pyramid Lake in Nevada.

From this point the trail is clear and well defined, being traveled constantly during the season by guests of Deer Park Springs. Passing through a fine nursery of beautiful and exquisite red firs we drop into the canyon of Bear Creek. To the left are great andesite crowns on the mountain tops.

Here also are more glacially polished masses and cliffs of granite, clearly indicating great glacial activity in the upper part of this canyon. The trail is ticklish in a few places, with steps up and down which our horses take gingerly, but nothing which need excite an extra heartbeat to one used to mountain trails.

In less than half an hour we are at Deer Park Springs, drinking its pleasant waters, and while we still have six and a half miles to go to the Tavern it is over easy and ordinary road, and therefore our pleasant trip is practically at an end.

TO ELLIS PEAK

Homewood is the natural starting point for Ellis Peak (8745 feet) as the trail practically leaves the Lake highroad at that point, and strikes directly upon the mountain slope. Hundreds make the trip on foot and it is by no means an arduous task, but many prefer to go horseback or burro back.

In its upward beginnings the trail follows the course of an old logging chute for a distance of some two miles, the lake terminus of which is now buried in a nursery of white fir and masses of white lilac. There are a few cedars and pines left untouched by the logger's ax, but they are not prime lumber trees, or not one of them would now be standing.

To the right is Dick Madden Creek, which, like all the streams on the eastern slopes of the great western escarpment of Lake Tahoe, comes dashing and roaring down steep and rocky beds to the Lake.

When at about 7000 feet we find few other than red firs and mountain pines. Here is a wonderful nursery of them that have secured a firm hold upon life. Throughout the whole region the year 1913 seems to have been a most kindly one for the untended, uncared for baby trees. There has been comparatively little snowfall for three successive years, and this has given the young trees a chance.

As soon as their heads appear above the snow and they are not battered down by storm they can make their way, but if the heavy snow falls and remains upon them too long, they are either smothered, or so broken down, that life becomes a fearful struggle and scores of them succumb. Yet in spite of this fact hemlocks and red firs seem to prefer the north or shady slopes of the mountains and invariably thrive much better there than where there is sunnier exposure.

When about three miles up from the Lake we reach a richly grassed meadow, about five acres in extent, confined in a bowl-shaped rim, broken down at the east side, through which a rivulet, which flows across the meadow, finds outlet. This is undoubtedly one of the many mountain lakes of the region, too shallow and with too sluggish a flow of water into it to clear itself of the detritus washed down from the disintegrating slopes above, hence it ultimately filled up and entered upon a new life as a meadow.

On the upper side of the meadow the trail passes through a glorious grove of hemlocks, the clean and clear "floor" of which leads one to the observation that hemlocks generally seem to be hostile to other and lesser growth coming in to occupy the ground with them.

Sierran heather of purple color now appears here and there in patches and we find quantities of it further along. There are also several peculiar puff-balls, and close by a remarkable fungus growth like a cauliflower, fully a foot in diameter.

Nearing the summit we come to another meadow followed by another grove, where scarcely any trees but hemlocks are to be seen. Here also we see great beds of the California primrose which grows with a straight upright stem crowned with blood-red or deep scarlet flowers above a rich cluster of leaves.

These flowers generally can be found blooming quite late in the season, following the snowline as the summer's sun makes it climb higher each day. When the winter's snows have been extra heavy the plants are covered and no flowers appear, as the snow melts too late, but when there is a lesser amount they bloom as freely as ever, apparently none the worse for their dormant period.

Over the peak billowy white clouds are tossing, like giant cradles built of the daintiest and most silvery cloud-stuff to be found in the heavens for the rocking of the cloud-babies to sleep.

On a sister peak to Ellis Peak, just to the south, is to be seen a remarkable and strikingly picturesque cluster of hemlocks. It is almost circular in form, with eight trees in the center, and twenty-three on the outer rim, which is over a hundred feet in circumference. Seldom does one see so interesting a group of trees anywhere, even when planted, and these, of course, are of native growth.

The summit itself is of broken and shattered granite, which has allowed a scraggly mountain pine to take root and grow close to the U.S. Geological Survey monument. A fierce gale was blowing from the west, and turning toward the tree-clad slopes of the east, we stood in the wind, with the everlasting blue above and the glorious and never-failing green beneath.

Unconsciously there sprang to my lips Joaquin Miller's lines:

> And ever and ever His boundless blue,
> And ever and ever His green, green sod,
> And ever and ever between the two
> Walk the wonderful winds of God.

Braving the wind and looking over the steep precipice to the west we see, some four hundred or five hundred feet below us, so that it seems that we might almost throw a stone into it, a small lake. This is Bessie Lake, named after Mrs. C.F. Kohl, of Idlewyld. It discharges its surplus waters into Blackwood Creek, and has several times been stocked with fish.

In the mid-distance is Loon Lake, which is the headwaters of the California Ditch, which follows over the

Georgetown Divide, carries water some forty to fifty miles, and is distributed by its owners, the Reno Water and Electric Power Co., for mining, irrigation and domestic purposes.

East of Loon Lake are Spider and Pleasant Lakes, all of which we are told are connected with one another and controlled by the same company. Another lake, Bixly or Bixby, slightly to the north of Pleasant, is also connected.

To the east of Pleasant Lake, Buck Island and Rock Bound Lakes were dazzlingly brilliant in the mid-day sun.

One has but to look at the map to realize what a comprehensive survey is possible in every direction from Ellis Peak. There is no wonder that it is so popular. The panorama is unobstructed — the outlook practically complete and perfect. Though the whole of the Lake is not revealed, there is sufficient of it to make a transcendent picture.

Every peak to the north and on the eastern side is in sight, while the Tallac range, and the nearby mountains make one long for an aeroplane that he might step from peak to peak without the effort of journeying by land to their elevated summits.

On the left side of Tinker's Knob is a peak, unmarked on the map, to which the name of Lion Peak has been given, for the following reason: Some years ago former Governor Stanford's nephew, who has been a visitor for many years at Hopkins' Spring, was climbing, together with a companion, over this peak, when they came to a cave. Lighting a rude torch they thoughtlessly entered it and had barely got well inside before they saw the two fierce eyes of a mountain lion glaring at them. Surprised and startled, they were about to turn and run, when the astonished animal sprang past them and disappeared before they recollected they had a gun.

It should not be overlooked that Ellis Peak is the most eastern mountain of the Sierran divide. East, its drainage empties into Lake Tahoe and thus eastward into the Big Basin; west, into the Rubicon, thence to the American, the Sacramento and finally out by the Golden Gate to the Pacific.

To the west of the Rubicon Peaks is a chain of lakes in the valley below known as the Rock Bound Lakes. There are nine of these in all, though several of them are practically unknown except to the few guides and the sheepmen who range over the surrounding mountains.

As far as the eye can see, westward, there are distinct glacial markings, a wonderful revelation of the widespread and far-reaching activity of these glaciers borne on the highest crests of the Sierra. The canyon in which the Rubicon River flows is definitely outlined, as is also the deep chasm known as Hell Hole. Nearby is Bear Lake, about the same size and appearance as Watson Lake, its overflow emptying into the Rubicon.

Close at hand to the north and west are Barker's Peak, Barker's Pass, and Barker's Creek, and these decide us to go home by way of Barker's Pass instead of the way we came. Accordingly we drop down, returning a short distance to the south, over the western slope of Ellis Peak to Ellis Valley. Both peak and valley receive their name from Jock Ellis, a Squaw Valley stay-behind, who entered the cattle and sheep business, and pastured his animals in this rich and well watered region.

On our way we pass thorough the most remarkable white fir nursery we have yet seen. Not far away were a few hoary monarchs from the still hanging but burst open cones of which winged seeds were flying before the breeze. These potential firs were carried in many cases over a mile before they found lodgement. It was a beautiful and delightful demonstration of Nature's lavish method of preserving this useful species of tree alive.

Sweeping now to the north and east we make a rapid descent of some six hundred or seven hundred feet to Barker's Pass, the elevation of which is about 7000 to 7500 feet, the nearby Peak having an elevation of about 8500 feet. It is a round, bare mountain, and seems as if it ought to be marked higher (on the map) than it is.

Rapidly dropping we come to a peculiar mass of stratified rock, acutely tilted, unlike any found elsewhere in the region except on Five Lake Creek on the way to Hell Hole. Just before reaching Blackwood's Creek the trail passes through rude piles of breccia similar to that of the Devil's Playground near the Truckee River.

It may be perfectly possible that one of the volcanic flows that covered large portions of the High Sierra, after the Cretaceous degradations had taken place, came from a vent, or volcano, nearby, and slowly flowed down Blackwood Creek, leaving vast masses behind which have rapidly disintegrated until these are all that remain.

These conjectures occupy our brain until we reach the Lake again, alongside of which the road soon brings us back to our starting point, after another most enjoyable, instructive, healthful and delightful day.

CHAPTER XVI

CAMPING OUT TRIPS IN THE TAHOE REGION

There are many trips in the Tahoe region which can be made, with greater or lesser ease, on foot or horseback, in one day, so that one can sleep in his hotel each night. On the other hand there are some highly desirable trips that can be taken only by camping out, and to these I wish to commend those of my readers of both sexes who are strong enough to care for such intimate contact with God's great out of doors.

To me one of life's greatest delights, appealing alike to body, mind and soul, is a camping out trip. Breathing day and night the pure air of mountain and forest — occasionally swept by breezes from desert and ocean — exercising one's body into vigorous healthfulness, sweating in the sun with life-giving labor — even though it be only tramping or riding up and down trails — sauntering over meadows, rambling and exploring untrailed spaces, under giant sky-piercing trees; lying down at night on the restful brown mother earth; sleeping peacefully and dreamlessly through delicious starlit and moonlit nights, cooled and refreshed by the night winds, awakening in the morning full of new life and vigor, to feel the fresh tang of the air and the cool shock of the wash (or even plunge) in the snow- or spring-fed stream; companioning with birds and bees, chipmunks and squirrels, grouse and quail, deer and antelope, trees and plants, shrubs and flowers, lava and granite, lakes and creeks, rivers and ponds; smelling the sweet fragrance of the trees, shrubs, plants and vines; bathing in an atmosphere of calm and quiet that seems almost Divine; covered with a sky as cloudless and pure blue as the dome of heaven itself, and which, at night, changes into a rich blue-black velvet, studded with silvery emblazonments, that dance and dazzle in the pellucid air; listening to the varied voices of Nature, each eager to give tongue to its joy; eating healthful, simple food with appetite and relish; absorbing the assurance that Nature means good and nothing but good to man, thus coming nearer to the heart of God; losing the fret and worry of money-getting and all other of life's lower ambitions and strivings; feeling the inflow of strength — physical, mental and spiritual; gaining calmness, serenity, poise and power — is there any wonder that a man so blessed should speak and write with radiant and exuberant enthusiasm of that which has been so lavish to him. This is what camping out means to me.

Hence, when I leave home for a mountain trip I

always put into my trunk an extra blue flannel shirt, riding boots and breeches (or a pair of overalls), a cap, and a bottle of Vaseline. The hunter and fisherman, of course, will bring his special equipment, as, also, will the geologist or botanist.

The first essentials of a successful camping out trip are personal. One must have the receptive and acceptive spirit. No matter what comes it is for the best; an experience worth having. Nothing must be complained of. The grouch has no place on a camping trip, and one who is a grouch, a sissy, a faultfinder, a worrier, a quitter, or who cannot or will not enter fully into the spirit of the thing had better stay at home.

If experiences are met with that are disagreeable, meet them as a man should; a woman always does — or always has on trips taken with me. The self-pitier, the self-indulgent, the fearful also had better stay at home.

The next essentials are a good guide — such as is suggested by the Dedication of this book — and good saddle and pack animals, good bedding, good food and the proper season. Then if the spot you have chosen contains anything worthwhile, you cannot fail to have an enjoyable, interesting, educative, health giving and generally profitable time.

In outfitting for such a trip always put into your pocket (and in the pack a reserve supply) a few crackers, a handful of malted milk tablets, and a cake of chocolate. With these you are safe for a whole day or two, or more, if anything should happen to separate you from your pack animal, or you should desire to ride on without stopping to prepare a noon, or later, camp meal.

The Tahoe region offers scores of just such trips, where for one or two months each year for a dozen years a visitor may camp out in some new region. For instance, every student of God's handiwork should go up to Deer Park, camp out at Five Lakes, and study the evidences of lava flows at the head of Bear Creek.

Go to the Lake of the Woods and spend a week there, tracing the glacial movements that made Desolation Valley. Take such a trip as I enjoyed to Hell Hole on the Rubicon, but take more time for it than I could give; cross the range to the Yosemite, and thus link the two sublimest parts of the Sierra in your memory; follow the old trails that used to echo to the voices of pioneers from Michigan Bluff, Last Chance, Hayden Hill, etc.; go out with one of the forest rangers and get a glimpse into his wonderful life of activity, independence and solitude.

Thus you will come in contact with larger conceptions, fuller ideas, deeper sympathies, higher aspirations than is possible where you follow the ordinary routine of the ordinary, mediocre, self-contented man. Thank God for the spark of discontent, of ambition, of aspiration, of desire to see beyond, to know more, to climb higher, to solve the mysteries, to abolish the unknown.

Then, if you dare the perils and joys of winter, get some expert on snowshoes to go with you over Tahoe's wild wastes of snow. Emulate Snowshoe Thompson, a short sketch of whose life and adventures will be found in my book, *Heroes of California*, and henceforth the days and nights of spring, summer, fall and winter will never seem quite the same to you.

Merely as a sample, the balance of this chapter is devoted to the trip made in the fall of 1913 with Bob Watson from Tahoe Tavern.

TO HELL HOLE AND THE RUBICON RIVER

I certainly think I can conjecture with accuracy the way it received its name. The trails in and out were first made and used by the wild animals — bear, deer, antelope, mountain lions, etc., then by the first Americans — the Indians, and at last, by the white man. Undoubtedly the first whites to come over the trails were miners from the Georgetown and Placerville districts, lured by the marvelous discoveries of the Comstock lode in Virginia City.

then in 1862-3 came the Squaw Valley stampede and this "strike" being so much nearer than the Comstock naturally attracted much attention, especially as the California mines of the Sierra Nevada were becoming less profitable. One of these old miners, whose language was more luridly picturesque than refined, on coming into the region or going out of it — when he struck the rough, rugged, uncertain, rocky, and exceedingly steep grade, must have called it a "hell of a hole" to get into or out of, and in future references the name stuck until, at last, it was passed down to future ages on the maps of the U.S. Geological Survey as the true and correct name.

But if the reader thinks the name in the slightest degree characteristic of the place itself he never made a greater blunder. Instead, it is a paradise of delightful surprises. A large, fairly level area — hundreds of acres at least — through which runs the clear and pellucid waters of the Rubicon River on their way to join those of the American, and dotted all over with giant cedars, pines, firs and live oaks, with tiny secluded meadows, lush with richest grasses, it is a place to lure the city dweller for a long and profitable vacation. Whether he hunts, fishes, botanizes, geologizes or merely loafs and invites his soul, it is equally fascinating, and he is a wise man who breaks loose from society — spelled with either a capital or small letter — the bank, the office, the countinghouse, the store, the warehouse, the mill, or the factory, and, with a genial companion or two, buries himself away from the outer world in this restful, peaceful, and God-blessed solitude.

When I first saw it I exclaimed: "Hell Hole? Then give me more of it," and instead of hastening on to other places of well-known charm, I insisted upon one day at least of complete rest to allow its perfection to "seep in" and become a part of my intimate inner life of remembrance.

It was under Bob Watson's efficient guidance I left Tahoe Tavern, for a five day trip. We took a pack horse well laden with grub, utensils for cooking and our sleeping bags. Riding down the Truckee, up Bear Creek, past Deer Park Springs, I was struck more forcibly than ever before by the marvelous glacial phenomena in the amphitheater at the head of the canyon through a portion of which the trail passes, and also with the volcanic masses that rest upon the granite, mainly on the right hand side of the pass. Its first appearance shows a cap of from two hundred to three hundred feet in thickness; later on two other patches of it appear, the upper one presenting the granite and superposed granite on the same level, clearly indicating a channel of early erosion filled up by the later flow of volcanic matter.

Passing by Five Lakes and down Five Lake Creek to its junction with the canyon down which we had come from the Little American Valley, we were soon headed down the creek for the Rubicon. To the right towered Mt. Mildred (8400 feet), on the other side of which is Shank's Cove. Shank was a sheepman who for years ran his sheep here during the summer, taking them down to the Sacramento Valley in winter.

After passing several grassy meadows, cottonwood groves, and alder thickets, we reached Bear Pen Creek, a rocky, bone-dry crossing, nine miles form the divide. To the left, Powder Horn Creek comes in, which heads on the northwestern slope of the ridge, on which, on the southern side, Barker Creek has its rise. It received this peculiar name from the fact that General Phipps, from whom Phipps Peak is named, was once chasing a bear, when suddenly the infuriated animal turned upon him, made a savage strike at him with his paw and succeeded in knocking the bottom out of his old-fashioned powder horn.

Further down we came suddenly upon a hawk who had just captured a grouse, and taken off his head. As the bird dropped his prey on our approach we took it as a gift of the gods, and next morning, with two or three quail, it made an excellent breakfast for us.

Nearing the descent into Hell Hole we gained striking glimpses of a great glacially formed valley in the mountains on the farther side, while a ridge to our left revealed a cap of volcanic rock apparently of columnar structure and extending form the eastern end halfway the length of the ridge.

Watson assured me that here he has found herds of sixteen and nineteen deer, on separate occasions. They seem to follow, in the early spring, the line of the melting snow. At this time they are tame and fearless, and will stand and look at you with surprise and impatience. They seldom run away.

On one occasion he came upon a doe and two fawns not far from the brink or ridge of Hell Hole. He was close upon them before he was aware, but stopped suddenly. The doe saw him, but instead of turning to flee she stood and impatiently stamped her foot several times. Then as he seemed to pay no attention and to be harmless, she and her young began to graze again, and shortly disappeared.

Before long we arrived at what may be called the "jumping-off place." In reality it is a steep descent into the depths of a wide canyon, but earth has so lodged in the rocky slopes that they are covered with dense growths of trees and chaparral, so that it is impossible to see very far ahead. Down, down, down we went, winding and twisting, curving around and dodging, but getting deeper with every zigzag until almost as suddenly as we began the steep descent we found ourselves on a fairly level platform. Hell Hole was reached.

The day spent here was a delightful one. While Watson fished I wrote, loafed, rambled about, studied the rock formations, and wished for a week or more instead of a day.

Next morning we struck into the canyon of the Rubicon River, for Soda Spring, half a mile away, where salt and soda exude in such quantities as to whiten the rocks. Here the deer, bear, grouse, quail, groundhogs, and other creatures come for salt. Indeed, this is a natural "salt lick," and there are eight or ten piles of rock, behind which Indian and white hunters used to watch for the coming of the game they desired to kill.

Years ago one could get game here practically every day. The Washoes used to descend the western slope as far as this; the men for deer, the women for acorns, though they had to be on the alert as the Sierra Indians resented their intrusion.

Right and left as we rode on there were great "islands" of granite, fifty to one hundred feet high, masses that either had been hurled from the heights above in some cataclysm, or planed to their present shape by long-forgotten glaciers. These granite masses alternate with flower and shrub-bestrewed meadows that once were glacial lakes. At times we found ourselves in a dense forest where the trees were ancient monarchs, whose solitudes had never been disturbed by stroke of ax, or grate of saw.

Clumps of dogwood and chaparral of a dozen kinds confuse the tyro, and he loses all sense of direction. Only the instinct that makes a real mountain and forest guide could enable one successfully to navigate these overgrown wilds, for we were now wandering up a region where trails had been abandoned for years. Here and there, when we came to the rocky slopes, "ducks" — small piles of stone so placed as to denote the course of the trail — in confusing variety were found but scarce a sign of a trail, and the "blazes" on the trees were more confusing than if we had been left to our own devices.

Yellow jackets' nests hung from many branches, and we were now and then pestered by the flying creatures themselves. Then we had a good laugh. Our pack horse, Shoshone, got between two trees. His head could pass but his pack couldn't, and there he stood struggling to pull through. He couldn't do it, but stupidly he would not back up. Take about horse sense! A burro would have backed up in a minute, but most horses would struggle in such a place until they died.

Near here there came into sight a granite ridge between the Rubicon and Five Lake Creek. This grows higher until it becomes quite a mountain, between Five Lake Creek and Barker Creek. On the right McKinstry Peak (7918 feet) towered up, with its double top, leading the eye along a ridge of red granite rock to Red Peak.

About three miles up the canyon we found a number of rocky basins in the course of the Rubicon with water, eight, ten and more feet deep in them, temptingly suggesting a plunge. I didn't need much tempting, and as quickly as I could disrobe I had plunged in. What a cold, invigorating shock it was. There's nothing like such a plunge for thoroughly arousing one and sending the blood quickly coursing through his veins.

Nearby were great beds of brake ferns, four and five feet high, groves of immense alders, sugar pines, some of which were fully eight feet through and the trunks of which were honeycombed with woodpecker holes. I saw and heard several woodpeckers at work. They had red top knots, and the noise they made echoed through the woods more as if a sledge hammer had struck the tree than the bill of a bird. How they climb up the trunk of the trees, holding on in a mysterious fashion and moving head up or down, as they desire, with jerky little pulls, bobbing their heads as if emphasizing some remarks they were making to themselves.

And what ideal spots for camping out we passed, shady trees, nearby meadows, to give abundant feed for the horses, the pure waters of the Rubicon close by, with scenery, trees, flowers, animals, birds — all the glory of nature — surrounding one with objects of delight, interest and study.

One large area was strewn with hundreds of thousands of the big long cones of the sugar pine. When one wishes to pack and ship home specimens of these and other cones, it is well to soak them in water. They then close up and carry safely, opening up as before, as they dry out.

Then we passed some giant "wind falls," mainly spruces. The roots of these monarchs of the forest had twined themselves around rocks of every size and shape, some of them massive boulders, but when the storm came, the purchase, or leverage of the tall trees was so great that these heavy rock masses were pulled out of place and lifted up as the trees crashed over to their fall.

Now we came to a stretch of perfect virgin forest. No ax, no saw, no log chutes, no wagons, no dragging of logs, no sign of the hand of man. Nature was the only woodsman, with her storms and winds, her snows and rains, to soften the soil and uproot her growing sons and daughters. There was confusion in places, even rude chaos, but in and through and above it all a cleanness, a sweetness, a purity, a grandeur, harmony, glory, beauty and majesty — all of which disappear when destroying man comes upon the scene.

About five miles up, we left the Rubicon and struck up toward Barker Creek. Here was another of the great, tempting granite basins, full of clear cool water. We also passed patches of belated scarlet larkspur, shooting stars, and glaring goldenrod.

Half a mile up we reached Barker Creek, now a boulder-strewn arroyo which aroused my covetousness to high degree. How I would love to build, with my own hands, a cottage, bungalow or house of some kind with these great boulders, of varied sizes and colors, shapes and material.

Just above the junction of Barker Creek and the Rubicon is "Little Hell Hole," a camping place almost as famous as its larger namesake, and noted for the fact that half a mile away is a small canyon full of mineral springs—sulphur, iron, soda, magnesia, etc. Naturally it is a "deer lick," which makes it a Mecca during the open season to hunters. The springs bubble up out of the bed of the stream, the water of which is stained with the coloring matter. When the stream runs low so that one can get to the springs he finds some of them as pleasant to the taste as those of Rubicon and Glen Alpine.

As we got higher we left the spruces behind, and the junipers, covered with berries, began to appear. Then we came to open spaces where the wind began to sing in the tops of the pines.

About a mile up Barker Creek, Watson showed me the course of one of his trails back to the Tavern. It ascends a formidable ridge and leads quickly to Idlewyld, but we were bound for Rubicon Springs. The old trail was inaccessible, but Mr. Colwell of the Springs had lately marked out a new trail, so we took our chances on finding our way somehow. Over windfalls, up and down and around rocky promontories, we came to West Meadow Creek Wash, its rude boulder-strewn course striking directly across our path.

Here we struck beds of brakes nestling in the shade of giant trees. On the left side of the creek where we were, we ran into dense clumps of wild cherry which prevented further progress. Scouting found us an outlet on the other side of Barker Creek. The divide on the left towered up with rugged majesty, reddish in color, and split into gigantic irregular terraces, the taluses of which were all crowded with dense chaparral growths.

On this side the slopes were all more open, nothing but rugged boulders clinging on the bare surfaces.

How enjoyable was this forcing our way along through these solitary wilderness places, so that I was really sorry when we finally dropped over a forested slope into the Rubicon Springs and McKinney's Road. A mile away we found the hotel. The buildings are old but all nature is gloriously grand and beautiful.

Though cordially invited to stay overnight, we pushed on over the Rubicon River, up the hill on part of the Georgetown road for a mile and a half — from which we had a fine view of Buck Island Lake — struck the trail for another mile and in the early afternoon made camp at Rock Bound Lake. Here we rowed and swam, studied the country from the nearby hills, and then slept the sleep of the healthfully weary under the blue vault of heaven.

Though Rubicon Springs was not far away there was such an air of quietude in this spot that we felt as if we were in one of Nature's choicest retreats.

Returning to Rubicon we followed the road back to where we had struck it the day before. The old trail from McKinney's used to come over the divide form the east and strike the Rubicon near where we then stood, pass by the Springs and then follow the river, but to avoid the steep grades the road had to be constructed around by Buck Island Lake.

Those who ride into Rubicon Springs from McKinney's, just as they make the last descent, have a wonderful view of Georgetown Mountain before them. Its sloping side is glacially planed off at a steep angle, and it reveals the vast extent the great ice field must have covered in the days of glacial activity. Many boulders near the Springs are very strongly marked by glacial action.

About a mile from the Springs we came to a tree on which a cut-off sign was placed. When the road was being constructed the builders started a new grade at this point and after going for a mile or so found it was so steep that it had to be abandoned and a lesser grade found by going around.

From the summit we could clearly follow the course of the Little Rubicon, and also secured an excellent view of the sharp point of Rubicon Peak (9193 feet).

A stiff and cool breeze was blowing from the west so we were not sorry to find shelter from the wind as we entered a wooded park, where the song of the pines cheered us on our way. Soon we struck the road and followed it until we came to the headwaters of Miller's Creek on the right.

Miller used to run sheep up in the meadows, which afford a smooth grade for the road for some distance. There are many alders here, which bear mute though powerful testimony, in the shape of their gnarled and bent over ground-groveling trunks, of the heavy winters' snows.

These meadows clearly were once glacial lakes, now filled up, and Miller's Creek was the instrument of their destruction. Crossing the last of the meadows we came to Burton's Pass, so called from H.D. Burton, another Placerville pioneer who used to cut hay here, pack it on mules to McKinney's, and then ship it across to Lakeside, where he sold it for $80 to $100 a ton. We then passed McKinney's old cabin, the place he built and occupied in 1863, before he went to live at the Lake. Only a few fragments remain, time and storms having nearly completed the work of destruction.

Nearby was a beautiful lily pond, soon to be a meadow, and just beyond this we stood on the actual divide between the Great Basin and the Pacific. We were at the head of Phipps Creek, named on the map General Creek, from General Phipps. At the mouth of the creek this pioneer located on 160 acres, which, when he died about 1883, was sold to M.H. de Young, of the *San Francisco Chronicle.* After holding it for many years he sold it in turn to I. Hellman, the banker, who now uses it as his summer estate, having built a fine residence upon it.

Near here we lunched at a sheepherder's camp and heard an interesting story of the relocation of an old mine that had helped create the Squaw Valley excitement forth years before. Owing to new and improved methods of extracting the precious metal it is now deemed that this may soon develop into a paying property.

Returning to the road we passed Jock Ellis's cabin, in a similar state of ruin to that of McKinney. Ellis Peak (8945 feet) is named after him. He was a Squaw Valley stampeder. Nearby we saw the largest tamarack I have yet found in the Sierra. It was fully five feet through and fluted in an interesting and peculiar fashion.

From here we made a mile detour to visit Hank Richards Lake, a beautiful crystal jewel in an incomparable wooded setting. Then back to Phipps Creek, over a perfect jumble of granite boulders and tree-clad slopes until we finally struck the trail and followed it to the Lake, and thence home to the Tavern.

CHAPTER XVII

HISTORIC TAHOE TOWNS

There have been only three towns on the immediate banks of Lake Tahoe — Tahoe City, Glenbrook and Incline — though Knoxville was located on the Truckee River only six miles away.

Tahoe City. Tahoe City as founded in 1864 at the collapse of the Squaw Valley mining excitement. Practically all its first inhabitants were from the deserted town of Knoxville. They saw that the lumbering industry was active and its permanence fully assured so long as Virginia City, Gold Hill and other Nevada mining camps remained profitable.

The forests around the Lake seemed inexhaustible, and there was no need for them to go back to an uncertainty in the placer mines of El Dorado County, when they were pretty sure to be able to make a good living here. They, also, probably exercised a little imagination and saw the possibilities of Lake Tahoe as a health and pleasure resort. Its great beauty must have impressed them somewhat, and the exploitation of these features may have occurred to them.

Anyhow, in 1864, the Bailey Hotel was erected, and, later, a man named Hill erected the Grand Central. The Squaw Valley excitement had attracted a number from the Nevada camps, and when these men returned they took with them glowing accounts of the beauty of Lake Tahoe, and of the fishing and hunting to be enjoyed there. Thus the Lake received some of its earliest resort patronage.

During lumbering days it was an active, bustling place, being the nearest town to which the loggers, drivers, treefellers, millmen and others could flee for their weekly recreation and periodic carouses. Yet it must not be though that the town was wholly given over to roughness. Helen Hunt Jackson, a widely traveled and observant woman of finest susceptibilities, say of the Lake Tahoe House, which she visited in stagecoach days, that it was "one of the very best in all California." It was the stopping place of the *élite* who came to see and enjoy Tahoe, and until later and more fashionable hotels were built around the Lake enjoyed great popularity.

As soon as the logging industry declined Tahoe City began to decline, and only the fishing and tourist interests kept it alive.

When the railway was moved over from Glenbrook and the shops and yard of the Transportation Company were established here it regained some of its former activity and life, and is now the chief business

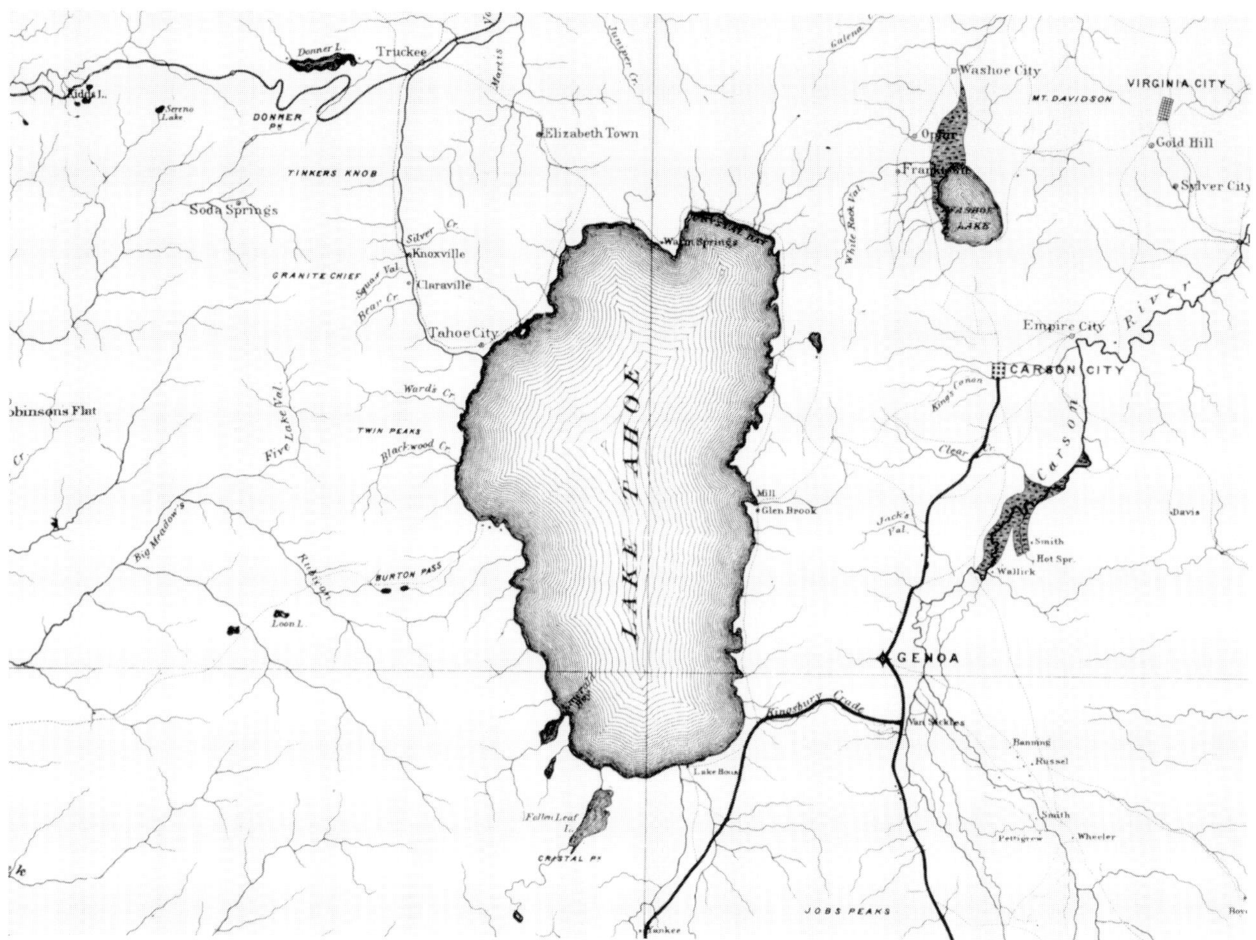

Map of Lake Tahoe region as it appeared in 1862, from Elliot Lord's book *Comstock Mining and Miners.*

center on the Lake. It is the headquarters of the campers who come for pleasure each year, and its store does a very large and thriving business.

New cottages are being erected and it is destined ere long to be a stirring pleasure resort town, for, as the delights of Tahoe become more widely known, every available piece of land will increase in value and where there is now one summer home there will be a hundred.

Glenbrook. On the Nevada side of the Lake, Glenbrook used to be one of the most active, busy, bustling towns in the west. It scarcely seems credible to one who visits the quiet, placid resort of today that when I first saw it, some thirty years ago, it had three or four large sawmills in constant operation, day and night. It was then regarded, and so designated in the *History of Nevada,* published in 1881, as "the great lumber manufacturing town of the state."

The town was begun in 1860, the land being squatted upon by G.W. Warren, N.E. Murdock, and R. Walton. In 1861 Captain A.W. Pray erected a sawmill, run by water power, but as water sometimes failed, when the demand for lumber increased, he changed to steam power. He also secured a thousand acres, much of it the finest timber land, from the government, using in its purchase Sioux Scrip.

Up to 1862 the only way to travel from California to Carson and Virginia City, south of Lake Tahoe, was by the Placerville road which came by Bijou and Lakeside and then over the Kingsbury Grade, via Friday's Station, afterward called Small's, by which latter name it is still known on the maps of the U.S. Geological Survey.

In 1862, however, a new road was projected, branching off to the northwest (the left) from Small's, and following the eastern shore of the Lake, passed Zephyr Cove and Cave Rock to Glenbrook, thence by Spooner's and down King's Canyon to Carson. This was called the Lake Bigler Toll Road (notice the fact that "Tahoe" was then officially designated in Ne-

The pioneer industry on the east shore of Lake Tahoe was Captain A.W. Pray's sawmill, built in 1861.

vada as "Bigler"), and was completed in 1863.

This demanded the opening of a better class of hotel for travelers and others in Glenbrook, and in the same year the road was finished Messrs. Winters and Colbath erected the "Glenbrook Hotel," which finally came into the hands of Messrs. Yerington and Bliss, who, later, were the builders of the railway, the owners of most of the surrounding timberlands, and who had practical control of the major portion of the lumber interests.

But prior to this a lumber mill was built by J.H.F. Goff and George Morrill in the northern part of the town. This did a good business, for even in those early days common lumber was worth $25. per thousand feet, and clear lumber, $45. The mill was soon destroyed by fire, but the site was bought by A.H. Davis and Son, who erected a new mill, which they operated for a while and then sold to Wells, Fargo & Co.

It was not until 1863 that Yerington & Bliss came to Glenbrook. They revolutionized the lumber industry. While Captain Pray had long used a steam tug to raft logs across Lake Tahoe, the lumber itself was hauled down to Carson and Virginia City. Now, owning large areas of timberland, operating two and then three sawmills in Glenbrook, and several others in the nearby mountains, Messrs. Yerington and Bliss sought easier means of transportation for their merchandisable product.

They constructed dams and reservoirs, with V flumes in a number of places, making them converge as near as possible at the Summit, some six miles east of Glenbrook. To this point they built a narrow gauge railway for the purpose of transporting the millions of feet of lumber sawn at their mills.

Bliss Brothers' store at Glennbrook, 1893.

From Summit a large V flume was constructed down Clear Creek Canyon into Carson City, and into this flume a constant stream of water was poured from the reservoirs which carried upon its bosom another stream of boards, timber, studding, joists and sheathing, the two streams emptying simultaneously just outside of Carson City at a point on the Virginia & Truckee Railway, where the lumber was loaded and thence shipped to its place of consumption.

That tremendous amounts of lumber were being manufactured is shown by the fact that the official records of Douglas County, Nevada, for 1875, given 21,700,000 feet as the product for that year.

Sawmill at Glenbrook, shown here about 1892.

One department of the lumber business should not be overlooked in this connection. As the timber disappeared from the mountain slopes nearest Glenbrook, the operators were compelled to go further afield for their logs. These were cut on the mountain slopes north, south, east and west, and sent down the "chutes" into the Lake.

Where the ground was level great wagons, drawn by ten, sixteen, twenty oxen, hauled the logs to the shore, where they were dumped into the water. Here they were confined in "booms," consisting of a number of long, thin poles fastened together as the ends with chains, which completely encircled a "raft" of logs arranged in the form of a V.

The raft was then attached, by strong cables, to a steamer and towed to Glenbrook, where the mills were so located that the logs were drawn up from the Lake directly upon the saw carriages. The size of some of the rafts may be imagined when it is known that they yielded from 250,000 to 300,000 feet of lumber.

The principal vessel for this purpose at the time I first visited Lake Tahoe in 1881 was an iron tug, called the *Meteor.* It was built in 1876 at Wilmington, Delaware, by Harlan, Hollingsworth & Co., then taken apart, shipped by rail to Carson City and hauled by teams to Lake Tahoe. It was a propeller, eighty feet long and ten feet beam, and cost $18,000.

The first store erected in Glenbrook was placed on piles over the water. This was built in 1874, by J.A. Rigby and A. Childers. One morning the latter partner disappeared, and it was surmised that he had fallen into the water and was drowned. New partners were taken into the firm, but in January, 1877, the store was burned, and it was not re-erected on its original site.

When the lumber interests and the railway were removed, Glenbrook declined until it was the most deserted looking place possible. Then the sons of Mr. Bliss, one of whom was born there, cleared away all the evidences of its former lumbering activities, built a handsome and commodious modern hotel on the most scenic point, and re-established the place as a choice resort on the Nevada shore, as described elsewhere.

Incline. It will be a source of interest, even to many who know Lake Tahoe well, that there used to be a town named Incline on its shores. In the curve of Crystal Bay, a few miles from where the scars show where the water escaped from Marlette Lake flume, this town was located in 1882. It was the source of supplies for the lumbering interests of the Sierra Nevada Wood and Lumber Company, and received its name from a sixteen-hundred feet incline up which lumber was hauled.

The incline was operated by an endless cable, somewhat after the style of Mount Lowe, in Southern California, the car on one side going up, and on the other coming down one trip, and *vice versa* the next. The lumber thus raised was thrown into the flume, carried therein around to Lake View, on the line of the Virginia and Truckee railway, there loaded on cars and shipped to Carson and Virginia, largely for use in the mines.

When the logging interests were active the place had quite a population, had its own post office and was an election precinct. When the logging interests waned the town declined, and in 1898 the post office was discontinued. Now nothing remains but the old incline, grown up with weeds and chaparral. New towns are springing up at Al Tahoe, Lakeside and Carnelian Bay.

Team hauling stripped logs to the lakeshore, where they were boomed to Glenbrook, in about 1893.

The steamer *Tahoe*, at the Tahoe Tavern wharf, just before starting around the lake.

The *Tahoe* was among the more popular steamers on the lake, transporting freight and passengers around Tahoe before the advent of automobile roads.

CHAPTER XVIII

BY STEAMER AROUND LAKE TAHOE

The ride around Lake Tahoe is one of varied delights, as the visitor sees not only the Lake itself from every possible angle, but gains an ever shifting panorama of country, and, more remarkable than all, he rides directly over that wonderful kaleidoscope of changing color that is a never ceasing surprise and enchantment.

Tahoe Tavern is the starting point of the ride, the train conveying the passenger directly to the wharf from which he takes the steamer. Capt. Pomin is in control.

Not far from where this, the most beautiful and charming hotel of the Lake is erected, there used to be a logging camp, noted as the place from which the first ties were cut for that portion of the Central Pacific Railroad lying east of the summit of the Sierra. A number of beautiful private residences line the Lake for some distance, the area having been portioned out in acre and half acre lots. Chief of these are the summer home of Professor W.T. Reid, for a time President of the State University of California, and Idlewyld, the residence of Mr. and Mrs. Frederick Kohl, of San Francisco.

One of the oldest villas of this portion of the Lake used to be owned by Thomas McConnell, of Galt, and it was his daughter, Mary, who first made the ascent of one of the peaks now known as Maggie's Peaks, as a marble tablet placed there testifies.

In the mountains beyond are Ward's Peak (8665 feet) to the right, and Twin Peak (8924 feet) to the left, from the first of which heads Ward's Creek and the second Blackwood Creek, both entering the Lake two miles or so apart. Just beyond Twin Peak are Barker's Peak (8000 feet), and nearer to the Lake, Ellis Peak (8745 feet), the waters from the former making the South Fork of Blackwood Creek. Ellis Peak, being easily reached by a good trail, is the common point of ascent from Homewood, McKinney's, Tahoe Tavern and other resorts.

Six miles out from the Tavern, the first stop is made at Homewood, one of the newer resorts.

Three and one-half to four miles further along is McKinney's, one of the oldest, best known and well established resorts on Lake Tahoe. It was founded by J.W. McKinney, who was first attracted to this region by the Squaw Valley excitement. For a time in 1862-3 he sold lots on the townsite of Knoxville, then when the bottom dropped out of the "boom" he returned to Georgetown, engaged in mining, but returned to Tahoe in or about 1867, located on 160 acres on the present site and in 1891-2, after having erected two or three cottages, embarked fairly and fully in the resort business.

For several years his chief patronage came from the mining camps of Nevada — Gold Hill, Virginia City, Silver City, Dayton, Carson City, Genoa, etc. They came by stage to Glenbrook and thence across the Lake, on the small steamer that already was doing tourist business in summer and hauling logs to the lumber mills in winter and spring. Thus this resort gained its early renown.

The bottom of the Lake may be seen at a considerable depth near McKinney's, and looks like a piece of mosaic work. The low conical peak, back of McKinney's is about 1400 feet above the Lake and used to be called by McKinney, Napoleon's Hat.

The next stop of the steamer is quite close to McKinney's, Moana Villa, and a mile or so further on at Pomin's, the former an old established resort, and the latter an entirely new one.

After passing Sugar Pine Point, Meek's Bay and Grecian Bay are entered. These two shallow indentations along the shore line are places where the color effects are more beautiful than anywhere else in the Lake, and vie with the attractions of the shore in arresting the keen attention of the traveler. Meek's Bay is three miles long, and, immediately ahead, tower the five peaks of the Rubicon Range, some 3000 feet above the Lake. Beyond, a thousand feet higher, is snow-crowned Tallac — *the* mountain — as the Washoe Indians called it, the dominating peak of the southwest end of the Lake.

Rubicon Point is the extension of the Rubicon Range and it falls off abruptly into the deepest portion of the Lake. The result is a marvelous shading off of the water from a rich sapphire to a deep purple, while the shore on either side varies from a bright sparkling blue to a blue so deep and rich as almost to be sombre. Well, indeed, might Lake Tahoe be named "the Lake of ineffable blue."

Here are shades and gradations that to reproduce in textile fabrics would have pricked a king's ambition, and made the dyers of the Tyrian purple of old turn green with envy. Solomon in his wonderful temple never saw such blue as God here has spread out as His free gift to all the eyes, past, present and to come, and he who has not yet seen Tahoe has yet much to learn of color glories, mysteries, melodies, symphonies and harmonies.

Soon, Emerald Bay is entered. This is regarded by many as the rich jewel of Lake Tahoe. The main body of the Bay is of the deep blue our eyes have already become accustomed to, but the shore line is a wonderful combination of jade and emerald, that dances and scintillates as the breeze plays with the surface of the waters.

A landing is made at Emerald Bay Camp, one of the most popular resorts of the Lake, and while at the landing the curious traveler should take a good look at the steep bank of the opposite shore. This is a lateral moraine of two glaciers, one of which formed Emerald Bay, as is explained in Chapter VIII, and the other formed Cascade Lake, which nestles on the other side of the ridge.

At the head of Emerald Bay, also, is Eagle Falls, caused by the outflow of water from Eagle Lake, which is snugly ensconced at the base of the rugged granite cliffs some three miles inland.

Four miles beyond Emerald Bay is Tallac, one of the historic resorts on the Lake.

Tallac was originally Yanks. Yank was really Ephraim Clement, originally a Yankee from Maine, a stout, hearty, bluff man, who homesteaded his land, added to it until he owned about a thousand acres, and finally sold out to E.J. (Lucky) Baldwin.

Baldwin had come over from Virginia City and seeing the great havoc made in the fine timber, of which he was very fond, exclaimed with an oath: "Someone will be cutting this (the timber of Yanks) next," and then and there he began to bargain for the place. In 1878 he bought, changed the name, and thenceforward Tallac became known. Little by little, as Yank had done, so Baldwin bought from sheepmen, squatters, and others until he had quite a holding.

The hotel was built and in 1879 Sharp Brothers ran it. In 1880 Capt. Gordon was manager for a year, and in 1881 Baldwin gave a lease to Messrs. Lawrence & Comstock who held it until 1914.

Baldwin was a great lover of trees, and when the present hotel and cottages were built, not a single tree was cut without his express permission. Yet he had no foolish sentiment about the matter as is proven by the fact that all the buildings were constructed form local lumber produced in his own sawmill, except the redwood used for finishing. The hotel as it now stands was completed in 1900.

McKinney's and Moana Villa, with Rubicon Peaks in the distance, Lake Tahoe.

Steamer landing, McKinney's, Lake Tahoe

Gulls, pelicans and mudhens can generally be seen in large numbers around the piers at Tallac, and the fleet of fishing boats, each with its one or more eager anglers, is one of the sights.

The steamer stops here long enough to allow a few minutes ashore, and the visitors ramble over to the hotel, chat or chaffer with the Washoe Indian squaws who have their baskets for sale, or enjoy the grassy and shaded grounds.

From the wharf at Tallac visitors for Glen Alpine, Fallen Leaf Lodge, and Cathedral Park take their respective stages. These three resorts are within a few miles and afford additional opportunities for lovers of the region to add to their knowledge of its scenic, botanic, arboreal and geologic features. Indeed such glacial experts as Joseph Le Conte, John Muir, and David Starr Jordan have united in declaring that the region around Glen Alpine gives a better opportunity for the study of comparatively recent glacial phenomena than any other known area.

Adjoining Tallac on the east is the private residence of W.S. Tevis, of San Francisco. His beautiful yacht, the *Consuelo,* may generally be seen anchored here, when not in actual service.

Half a mile from Tallac is The Grove, close to the Upper Truckee River, the main feeder of Lake Tahoe, and four miles further is Al Tahoe, a new and well-equipped hotel, standing on a bluff commanding an expansive view of the Lake. It practically occupies the site of an old resort well known as "Rowland's." It is near to Freel's Peak (10,900 feet), which in olden days was known as Sand Mountain, on account of its summit being composed of sand.

A mile and a half further along is Bijou, a pleasant and comfortable stopping place, while three miles further a picturesque rustic pavilion on the end of the pier denotes Lakeside Park, a well-known and long-famous resort. Forty-five years ago, or more, Capt. W.W. Latham built the famous State Line House at this point, and twenty years ago it came into the hands of its present owners.

This is the most easterly of all the resorts and settlements at the south end of Lake Tahoe. It is in California, in El Dorado County, though its post office is Stateline, the dividing line between California and Nevada. The Park is over 2000 acres in extent and has already become the nucleus for a choice summer residence section.

Leaving Lakeside Park the steamer now turns northward and follows the eastern or Nevada shore, until Cave Rock is passed and Glenbrook is reached. This is the only resort on that side of Lake Tahoe. Once the scene of an active, busy, lumber town, where great mills daily turned out hundreds of thousands of feet of timber for the mines of Virginia City and the building up of the great historic mining camps of Nevada, the magic of change and of modern improvements has swept away every sign of these earlier activities and left Glenbrook a quiet, delightful, restful resort, nestling in its own wide and expansive meadows at the foot of towering mountains that give a rich and contrasting background for the perennial beauty of the Lake.

Practically all that remains to remind one of the old days are the remnants of the logging piers and cribs, the schoolhouse, the quiet "City of Those who are Gone," and further up the hills, the old railroad grade on which the logs were carried to the mill and the lumber taken through the tunnel, which still remains, to the flume by which it was further conveyed to the railroad at Carson City.

Immediately to the right of Glenbrook, as the steamer heads for the wharf, can be seen the celebrated Shakespeare Rock. John Vance Cheney, the poet, thus describes it:

> No sooner had the steamer been made fast than a ledge of rocks was pointed out to us, rising precipitously some distance from the pier. "Can't you see it?" again and again asked our guide, renewing his endeavor to dispel our distressing stupidity. At length "it" appeared to us, and we stood mute with astonishment. There, on the front of a bold cliff, graven with all the care of the best copies with which we are familiar, looked down upon us the face of Shakespeare!
>
> As if in remembrance of her favorite son, here in this far wild region, nature had caused his features, cut in everlasting rock, to be hung on high, a fitting symbol of his intellectual sovereignty over the world. The likeness needs no aid from the imagination: it is life-like, recognized instantly by the most careless observer, and, let it be added, never forgotten. The beard is a trifle longer than we are accustomed to see it, but this deviation does not detract from the majesty of expression becoming the illustrious original.
>
> The spacious forehead, the nose, even the eyes, all are admirably represented. A more astounding surprise it has

Steamer *Tahoe* rounding Rubicon Point, Lake Tahoe.

Steamer *Tahoe* off Cave Rock, Nevada side, Lake Tahoe

Rubicon Point, Lake Tahoe.

not been the writer's fortune to experience. The portrait looks as if it were made by moss growing upon the smooth flat surface of a huge rock; but we were informed that the face is all of stone, and has undergone no perceptible change since its discovery about five years since. [This was written in 1882.] A lady tourist from Massachusetts has, it is believed, the honor of first pointing it out. Nature cannot forget Shakespeare. So we all mused, and, musing, would have forgotten our dinners, had we not been summoned inside the hotel. The repast was not peculiarly relishable; consequently, we had all the more opportunity to feed spiritually upon the masterpiece on the cliff — the rock portrait of Avon's, of England's, of the World's immortal bard.

As the steamer leaves Glenbrook one may gain clear and distinct views of the four prominent peaks of the Nevada side. Above Lakeside, at the southeast end, is Monument Peak, then, about midway between Lakeside and Glenbrook is a sharp-pointed bare mass of rock known as Genoa Peak. Immediately behind Glenbrook is Dubliss Mountain (8729 feet), so named after Duane Bliss, father and son, both of whom have done so much to make Tahoe known to the world.

Marlette Peak is to the northeast, 8864 feet, with Snow Valley Peak, 9214 feet, a little to the South. These both overshadow Marlette Lake, a full description of which is given elsewhere. All these peaks afford excellent views of Lake Tahoe on the one side and of the valleys and mountains of western Nevada on the other.

The steamer now continues along the Nevada shore, past the scars caused by the breaking of the Marlette Lake flume, by Crystal Bay and the site of the old town of Incline, around State Line Point to Brockway.

This resort has been long and favorably known for its famous hot mineral springs. The hot water is piped to all rooms and private baths of the hotels and cottages, and is a great source of pleasure as well as health-giving comfort to the guests.

We are now on the home stretch, and soon after leaving Brockway (1-1/2 miles away) and 45 minutes (8 miles) from Tahoe Tavern, we reach Tahoe Vista. Here one is afforded a perfect view of the Lake and its snow-capped ranges east and south.

Crossing Agate and Carnelian Bays the steamer's last stop is at Carnelian Bay. Here there is great building activity going on and many neat and commodious cottages and bungalows are being erected.

Observatory Point is the last object passed before the Tavern is again reached. This name was given because of the fact that it was once the chosen site, by James Lick, for the observatory he contemplated building. This plan, however, was never carried out, as it was shown to the philanthropist that the cold weather of winter would work exceeding hardship upon the astronomers without any compensating advantages. The result was the Observatory was finally established on Mt. Hamilton, and it is now a part of the great California University system.

Thus the complete circuit of Lake Tahoe is made daily in summer by the steamer, and no matter how often the trip is taken it never palls upon the intelligent and careful observer. New glories and wonders are constantly springing forth as pleasant surprises and one soon learns to realize that here Nature indeed has been most prodigal in her scenic gifts to mankind.

CHAPTER XIX

DEER PARK SPRINGS

While in one sense *all* the resorts of the Tahoe region are *mountain* resorts, a difference should be noted between those that are located directly on the shores of Lake Tahoe, or some lesser lake, and those that are away from immediate proximity to a lake.

The latter type is more correctly designated mountain resorts, and of these are three in the Tahoe region, viz., Deer Park Springs, Rubicon Springs and Glen Alpine. All these resorts were discovered by following the trails of animals which were visiting them for "salt licks" that existed in connection with their mineral waters as related in the chapter on Glen Alpine.

Deer Park is a private estate of approximately 469 acres, in two sections, one the Mineral Springs Section, consisting of nearly 309 acres, and on which the celebrated springs—two of soda, one of sulphur, and one of iron — are located, and the other, the Five Lakes Section, of 160 acres.

The former begins a mile from the Truckee River, up Bear Creek Canyon. This was originally taken up from the Government as timber claims, but the timber has never been cut, and the great pines, first and junipers remain as the original settlers found them. The Five Lakes section is a fascinating and attractive location two miles away, over the first divide of the mountains, and therefore 1000 feet higher than the Inn, where five glacial lakes nestle in their granite basin.

Four of these, and a large part of the fifth, are included in the estate, while all surrounding is government land of the Tahoe National Forest. If a dam were built to restrain the flow of water into Five Lake Creek, it would need only to be ten feet high to convert the five lakes into one, so near are they to the same level.

As it is the flow from these lakes forms Five Lakes Creek, which empties into the Rubicon and thence into the South Fork of the American.

Five Lakes afford excellent fishing and a log cabin, three boats and fishing tackle are kept here throughout the season for the pleasure of guests. Those who disdain the ordinary accommodations of a hotel can here camp out, rough it, and make it their headquarters while climbing the adjoining peaks or exploring the ravines and canyons at the head of the American River.

In 1914 a student from Stanford University was h*ost* at the Five Lakes log cabin. He cooked for those who desired it, helped gather fir boughs for camp beds, prepared fishing tackle for women anglers, rowed

Summer snowballing near the summit of "The Crags," Deer Park Springs, five miles west of Tahoe City.

them to and fro over the lakes, and accompanied parties to the nearby summits.

There are full accommodations at the cabin for seven persons, and the rule of the camp is that guests stay only one night, moving on to make room for the next comer, unless arrangements for a longer stay are made beforehand. Thus all the guests at Deer Park Inn may enjoy this novel experience if they so desire.

In the region of Five Lakes, Basque and other foreign shepherds may be found tending their flocks, and prospectors, with queer little pack burros, who climb the mountains seeking the elusive gold, as they did in the days of '49.

It was from Deer Park that the trail into the famous Hell Hole was recut by Miss Katherine Chandler, owner of the Inn and estate, in 1908, after having been lost for many years. Arrangements for this trip, and other famous hunting and fishing trips may be made at the Inn and many people who have gone over the mountains to the Yosemite have outfitted and secured their guide here.

One of the finest trail trips of the Tahoe region is that afforded over the trail, back of Deer Park Inn, to the rugged pile known as The Crags, over Inspirational Ridge to Ward's Peak. In the early part of the season great snow banks are encountered, and when the flowers begin to bloom there are great fields covered with Sierran primroses, with many patches of white heather and beautiful cyclamens. This is but one of many fine trail trips that may be made.

Deer Park Inn is one of the oldest and best established resorts of the Tahoe region. The house that I occupied on my short visit was a solid log cabin, full of romantic interest, for it was quaint, old-fashioned, and appropriate to the surroundings.

The keynote of the place is comfort. Under its present management a large number of wild New England flowers have been planted to add their beauty to that of the native California flower, and each year, about the third week in July, the guests wander over the sun-kissed slopes, climb the snowy heights and ramble through the shady woods gathering Sierran flowers of every hue, form and variety for an annual flower show. This is one of the distinctive features of the life at Deer Park Inn.

It is an interesting fact here to notice that, when Miss Parsons, chief author of *Flowers of California*, was preparing that volume, she found such a wealth of mountain flora in the Deer Park region that she spent about as many weeks as she had planned for days. Other botanists have found it equally productive.

To those who come early in the season tobogganing and snow shoeing are not unusual experiences. The shady sides of the mountains offer these winter sports as late as June and early July, and many Californians who have never enjoyed the frolic of snow-balling come here to gain their first experience in this common eastern enjoyment.

Elsewhere I have referred to the many evidences of glacial action found about a mile above Deer Park Inn. Still further up the canyon, on the trail going to Five Lakes, are interesting deposits of volcanic rock — andesite — so that these two geological phenomena may be studied close at hand.

Having its own rich meadows on Bear Creek, the Deer Park Spring tables are always supplied with good milk and cream from its own dairies, while fresh fruit and vegetables are supplied daily. Fish and game in season are frequent, and the table being under the direct and personal supervision of the management has gained an enviable reputation.

Living water flows in marvelous abundance through Deer Park all throughout the year. Springs and melting snow send four different streams, tributary to Bear Creek, coursing across the property. The domestic water supply of the Inn is gained from springs on the mountainside, 800 feet above the Inn, and it is piped all over the place and to every cottage.

CHAPTER XX

RUBICON SPRINGS

One of the oldest and most famous resorts of the High Sierra is Rubicon Springs. It is nine miles from Lake Tahoe, at McKinney's, over a mountain road built many years ago, engineered so as to afford marvelously entrancing glimpses of the Lake and of the mountain scenery on either hand. Here are primeval forest, flower-strewn meadows of emerald, crystal streams and placid-faced glacial lakes in which snow-clad mountain summits are mirrored in quiet glory. The Rubicon River is one of the feeders of the American River, and the springs are located not far from its head waters.

The Rubicon Springs were originally discovered and located upon by the Hunsaker brothers, two genuine explorers and adventurers whose names deserve to be preserved in connection with the Tahoe region. They were originally from the Hoosier state, coming to California in 1849, across the plains, by Fort Hall, the sink of the Humboldt, Ragtown, and by Carson Canyon to old Hangtown (now Placerville). They mined for several years. Then came the Comstock excitement. They joined the exodus of miners for the Nevada mountains and were among the earliest to help to construct the Georgetown trail. Thus it was they discovered Rubicon. In 1869 they located upon 160 acres, built a log house and established a stopping station which they called Hunsaker Springs. In the winter they rested or returned to Georgetown, making occasional trapping trips, hunting bear and deer, and the meat of which they sold. In those days deer used to winter in large numbers almost as far down as Georgetown (some fifteen miles or so), so that hunting them for market was a profitable undertaking in the hands of experts.

They and John McKinney, the founder of McKinney's, were great friends, having worked together in the Georgetown mines. They soon made their places famous. Their mining friends came over from Virginia City, Gold Hill, Silver City, Carson, etc., by way of Glenbrook, where they were ferried across Lake Tahoe by the old side-wheel steamer, *Governor Stanford,* to McKinney's. Then by pack trail over to Hunsakers.

For many years they used to cut a great deal of hay from the nearby meadows. A natural timothy grows, sometimes fully four feet high. A year's yield would often total fully thirty tons, for which the highest price was paid at the mines.

There was another spring, beside Hunsakers', about a mile higher up, owned by a friend of the Hunsakers, named Potter. In time he sold this spring to a Mrs. Clark, who finally sold it back to him, when it was bought by Mr. R. Colwell, of Moana Villa. When the Hunsakers grew too old to run their place they sold it to a man named Abbott, who, in due time wished to sell out.

But, in the meantime the railroad had surveyed their land, granted by Congress, and found that the springs and part of the hotel building were on their land, so that while Abbott sold all his holdings to Mr. Colwell, he could not sell the main objects of the purchaser's desire. An amicable arrangements, however, was made between all the parties at interest.

For countless centuries the Indians of both west and east of Tahoe were used to congregate in the Rubicon country. They came to drink the medicinal waters, fish, catch deer and game birds, and also gather acorns and pine nuts.

How well I remember my own visit to the Springs in the fall of 1913. Watson and I had had three delightful days on the trail and in Hell Hole, and had come, without a trail, from Little Hell Hole up to Rubicon. The quaking aspens were dropping their leaves, the tang of coming winter was in the air, mornings and evenings, yet the middle of the day was so warm that we drank deeply of the waters of the naturally carbonated springs. No, this statement is scarcely one of fact. It was warm, but had it been cold, we, or, at least, I should have drank heartily of the waters because I liked them. They are really delicious, and thousands have testified to their healthfulness.

We saw the station of the water company, where a man remains through the year to register the river's flow and the snowfall. Then we passed a large lily lake to the left—a once bold glacial lake now rapidly nearing the filled-up stage ere it becomes a mountain meadow—and were fairly on the Georgetown grade, the sixty mile road that reaches from McKinney's to Georgetown.

It is a stern road, that would make the "rocky road to Dublin" look like a "flowery bed of ease," though we followed it only a mile and a half to leave it for the steep trail that reaches Rock Bound Lake. This is one of the larger of the small glacial lakes of the Tahoe region, and is near enough to Rubicon Springs to be reached easily on foot.

From a knoll close by one gains an excellent panorama of Dick's, Jack's and Ralston's Peaks. Tallac and Pyramid are not in sight. The fishing here is excellent, the water deep and cold and the lake large enough to give one all the exercise he needs in rowing.

On the summit of the Georgetown road one looks down upon the nearby placid bosom of Buck Island Lake. It received this name from Hunsaker. The lake is very irregular in shape, about a third of a mile long, and a quarter of a mile wide in its widest part. Near one end is a small island. Hunsaker found the deer swam over to this island to rest and sleep during the heat of the day, hence the name.

The Little Rubicon river flows into Buck Island Lake and out again, and about two miles below Rubicon Springs the Georgetown road crosses the river at the foot of the lake.

With these two lakes, and others not far away, fine hunting and fishing, with several mountains nearby for climbing, the hot springs, a fine table and good horses to ride, it can well be understood that Rubicon Springs makes a delightful summer stopping-place.

One great advantage that it possesses, under its present proprietorship, is that guests may alternate between Moana Villa and the Springs and thus spend part of their time on the Lake and the other part in the heart of the mountains. The Colwells are hearty and home-like hosts, and are devoted to living their many guests the greatest possible enjoyment, pleasure and health that a summer's vacation can contain.

CHAPTER XXI

EMERALD BAY

Situated near the southwest corner of Lake Tahoe is Emerald Bay, by many thousands regarded as the choicest portion of Lake Tahoe. Surrounded by so many wonderful scenes, as one is at Tahoe, it is difficult to decide which possesses surpassing power, but few there are who see Emerald Bay without at once succumbing to its allurement.

Its geological history has already been given in Chapter VIII, in which it is clearly shown by Dr. Joseph Le Conte that it was once a glacial lake, and that the entrance to the main lake used to be the terminal moraine that separated the two bodies of water. As a natural consequence, therefore, visitors may expect to find evidences of glacial action on every hand. They are not disappointed. The walls of the Bay, on both north and south, are composed of glacial detritus, that of the south being a pure moraine, separating the once glacial lake of Emerald Bay from Cascade Lake.

Emerald Bay is about three miles in length, with a southwesterly trend, and half a mile wide. The entrance is perhaps a quarter of a mile wide and is formed by a triangular spit of sand, on which grows a lone pine, on the one side, and a green chaparral-clad slope, known as Eagle Point, on the other.

The Bay opens and widens a little immediately the entrance is joined. The mountains at the head of the Bay form a majestic background. To the southwest (the left) is Mount Tallac, with a rugged, jagged and irregular ridge leading to the west, disappearing behind two tree-clad sister peaks, which dominate the southern side of the Bay's head. These are known as Maggie's Peaks (8540 and 8725 feet respectively, that to the south being the higher), though originally their name, like that of so many rounded, shapely, twin peaks in the western world gained by the white man from the Indian, signified the well-developed breasts of the healthy and vigorous maiden.

Emerging from behind these the further ridge again appears with a nearer and smoother ridge, leading up to a broken and jagged crest that pierces the sky in rugged outline. A deep gorge is clearly suggested in front of this ridge, in which Eagle Lake nestles, and the granite mass which forms the eastern wall of this gorge towers up, apparently higher than the nearer of Maggie's peaks, and is known as Phipps' Peak (9000 feet). This is followed by still another peak, nearer and equally as high, leading the eye further to the north, where its pine-clad ridge merges into more ridges striking northward.

Between Maggie's and Phipps' Peaks the rocky masses are broken down into irregular, half rolling, half rugged foothills, where pines, firs, tamaracks and cedars send their pointed spires upwards from varying levels. In the morning hours, or in the afternoon up to sunset, when the shadows reveal the differing layers, rows, and levels of the trees, they stand out with remarkable distinctness, each tree possessing its own perfectly discernible individuality, yet each contributing to the richness of the clothing of the mountainside, as a whole.

Down across the lower portion of Maggie's Peaks, 100 to 200 feet above the level of the Bay, the new automobile road has ruled its sloping line down to the cut, where a sturdy rustic bridge takes it over the stream which conveys the surplus waters from Eagle Lake to the Bay. On the other side it is lost in the rolling foothills and the tree-lined lower slopes of Cathedral Peak from whence it winds and hugs the Lake shore, over Rubicon Point to Tahoe Tavern.

But Emerald Bay has other romantic attractions besides its scenery. In the early 'sixties Ben Holladay, one of the founders of the great Overland Stage system that reached from the Pacific Coast to the Missouri River, built a pretentious house at the head of the Bay.

Naturally it was occupied by the family only part of the time, and in 1879, a tramp, finding it unoccupied, took up his lodgings therein, and, as a mark of his royal departure, the structure burned down the next morning. The site was then bought by the well-known capitalist, Lux, of the great cattle firm of Miller & Lux, and is now owned by Mrs. Armstrong.

As the steamer slowly and easily glides down the Bay, it circles around a rocky islet, on which a number of trees find shelter. This island was inhabited at one time by an eccentric Englishman, known as Captain Dick, who, after having completed a cottage to live in, carried out the serious idea of erecting a morgue, or a mausoleum, as a means of final earthly deposit upon dissolution.

This queer looking dog house might have become a sarcophagus had it not been for one thing, viz., Captain Dick, one dark and stormy night, having visited one of the neighboring resorts where he had pressed his cordial intemperately, determined to return to his solitary home. In vain the danger was urged upon him. With characteristic obstinacy, enforced by the false courage and destruction of his ordinarily keen perception by the damnable liquor that had "stolen away his brains," he refused to listen, pushed his sail boat from the wharf and was never seen again. His overturned boat was afterwards found, blown ashore.

EMERALD BAY CAMP

Emerald Bay is made accessible to regular summer guests by Emerald Bay Camp, one of the choice and highly commendable resorts of the Tahoe region. The Camp is located snugly among the pines of the north side of the Bay, and consists of the usual hotel, with nearby cottages and tents.

Less than five minutes' walk connects it with the picturesque Automobile Boulevard, which is now connected with the Camp by an automobile road. The distance is four-fifths of a mile and hundreds of people now enjoy the hospitality of Emerald Bay Camp who come directly to it in their own machines.

Its location suggests many advantages for the angler, the famous Indian fishing grounds being located at the mouth of the bay. Cascade, Eagle, and the unfished Velma Lakes are easily accessible to trampers, the outlets from these furnishing sporty brook trout fishing. These streams and lakes are all stocked with Eastern brook, Loch Levin and cutthroat. The protected waters of the bay make boating safe and bathing a comfortable delight.

But not all the beauty of nature and the advantages of excellent location can make a popular camp. There is much in the individuality of those who own or "run" it. Emerald Bay Camp is owned by Mr. Nelson L. Salter, for many years so favorably known in the Yosemite Valley. Such is its growing popularity that Mr. Salter has recently (1921) purchased another ten acres of adjoining land, thus enlarging his frontage on the Bay to about 1000 feet, and giving him many more cottages for the entertainment of his guests.

EAGLE LAKE

From Emerald Bay Camp there are quite a number of interesting trail and climbing trips, one of the commonest of which is that to Eagle Lake.

Taking the trail west, one zigzags to the north until the Automobile Boulevard is reached. A half mile's walk brings one to the bridge over Eagle Creek. Here a few steps lead to the head of the upper portion of Eagle Falls, which dash down a hundred feet or so to the rocky ledge, from whence they fall to their basin, ere they flow out to join the waters of Emerald Bay.

A few yards beyond the bridge the trail starts. It is a genuine mountain trail, now over rough jagged blocks of granite, then through groves of pines, firs, tamaracks and spruces, where flowers, ferns, mosses and liverworts delight the eyes as they gaze down, and the spiculae and cones and blue sky thrill one with delight as they look above, and where the sunlight glitters through the trees as they look ahead.

To the right Eagle Creek comes noisily down, over falls and cascades, making its own music to the accompaniment of the singing voices of the trees. Now and again the creek comes to a quiet, pastoral stretch, where it becomes absolutely "still water." Not that it is motionless, but noiseless, covered over with trees and vines, that reflect upon its calm surface and half hide the trout that float so easily and lazily through its clear, pure, cold stream.

There is enough of climbing to call into exercise long unused muscles, the granite blocks are rough, angular and irregular enough to exercise eyes, hands and feet to keep one from falling, and the lungs are filled with balsam-ladened mountain air, fresh from God's own perfect laboratories, healing, vivifying, rejuvenating, strengthening, while the heart is helped on and encouraged to pump more and more of its blood, drawn from long almost quiescent cells into the air chambers of the lungs, there to receive the purifying and life-giving oxygen and other chemical elements that multiply the leucocytes vastly and set them at work driving out the disease germs that accumulate and linger in every city-living man's and woman's system.

Suddenly from a little rise the lake is revealed. Eagle Lake, or Pine Lake, or Spruce Lake, or Hidden Lake, or Granite Lake, or Sheltered Lake — any of these names would be appropriate. Almost circular in form — this is if you are not expected to be too rigidly exact in geometric terms — it is literally a jewel of lapis lazuli in a setting of granite cliffs.

Here one may sit and rest, enjoying the placid waters of the lake, the rugged grandeur of the immediate cliffs, or the slopes of the towering mountains that encircle the horizon.

Eagle Lake is but one of the hundred of glacially made Sierran lakes of the Tahoe region, but a study of its idiosyncrasies would reveal distinctive and charming characteristics.

CATHEDRAL PEAK

There are two Cathedral Peaks at Tahoe, one above Cathedral Park on Fallen Leaf Lake, the other at the rear of Emerald Bay Camp. Early in the season, 1914, three girls decided to climb this peak from the camp although there was no trail. One of them wrote the following account of the trip:

> The most interesting peak of the Rubicon ridge is Cathedral. The mountain rises directly back of Emerald Bay, some three thousand feet above the Lake. About six hundred feet above the camp there is a meadow where larkspur grows four and five feet high. But from Eagle Creek the aspect is quite different. There are no soft contours.
>
> Huge rocks pile up — one great perpendicular surface adding five hundred feet to the height — into spires and domes for all the world like some vast cathedral which taunts the soul with its aloofness. If, on some sunshiny afternoon you look up from the camp and see a ghost moon hanging, no more than a foot above the highest spire, you must surely be "citified" if you do not pause to drink in its weird sublimity and wild beauty.
>
> Many winters of storm and snow have loosed the rocks and carried them down the mountain. Those thrown down years ago are moss-covered and have collected enough soil in their crevices to nourish underbrush and large trees.
>
> But there are bare rocks along Eagle Creek today large enough for a man to hew a cabin from. Standing in awe of their size one surely must look curiously up the mountain to find the spaces they once occupied. Then, taking in the size of the peak it is equally natural that one should be filled with a desire to climb it and look down the other side and across the vista to the neighboring ranges.
>
> While we were getting used to the altitude we stood below admiring. Every evening we went out on the wharf, gazed up at its grandeur and discussed the best way to go, for though we knew we should have to break our own trail, we had decided to attempt the climb. We set a day and the hour for rising; the night before laid out our tramping clothes and religiously went to bed at eight. I doubt if any of us slept, for we were used to later

hours and excitement kept us awake.

As it was the first trip of the season, we lost some time at the start, admiring each others' costumes. Two of us adhered to the regulation short skirt and bloomers, but the third girl wore trousers, poked into the top of her high boots. This proved, by far, the most satisfactory dress before the day's tramping was done.

We got started at four-thirty. The first awakened birds were twittering. The shadows of the moraine lay reflected in the unruffled surface of the Bay. Gradually rosy flushes showed in the east. By the time we reached the meadow the sun rose suddenly above the Nevada mountains and some of the chill went out of the atmosphere.

The meadow was flooded with snow water. Beyond, the mountain rose by sheer steps of rock with slides of decomposed granite between. We avoided the underbrush as far as possible, preferring to take back and forth across the loose granite. The wind came up as we left the meadow, grew in force as we climbed. Some one suggested breakfast, and then there began a search for a sheltered place.

A spot sided by three boulders away from underbrush was decided upon. By the time the fire was built the wind was a gale sending the flames leaping in every direction — up the rocks and up our arms as we broiled the bacon. Breakfast was a failure, as far as comfort was concerned. It was a relief when we finally tramped out the embers and resumed our journey.

The top of a long snowdrift was a previously chosen landmark. It was seven when we reached the top of it. Someone came out on the Bay in a rowboat — we were too high for recognition — though better of it and went back. Towards the top we left the decomposed granite and underbrush behind, climbing the rocks in preference to the snow, where the choice was allowed us. The wind howled and shrieked, and blew with a force great enough to destroy balance, while its icy touch brought the blood tingling to our cheeks.

At last we reached the summit. And oh! the joy of achievement.

All Rubicon ridge and its neighbors, as far as the eye could see, were white with snow; the lakes in the valley below were still frozen — only one showing any blue. Clouds came up rapidly from the west, rushed by to the Nevada side where they piled up in great cumulus heaps. The apex of Pyramid was cloud-capped all day.

Shifting gusts drove the waters of Tahoe scurrying first this way, then that. Where in the early morning every tree had viewed her image among the reflected tints of sunrise, at 10:30 whitecaps flashed and disappeared to flash in a different place among the ever-changing eddies. Cascade and Fallen Leaf Lakes presented a continuous procession of whitecaps to the east, while Eagle lay black and sinister in the shadow of Maggie's Peaks.

After lunch, the wind blowing too cold for comfort, we started home, straight down — over snow, granite and underbrush — till we hit the State Highway. Here we found a sheltered place by a creek and talked over the day's happenings.

Along the roadside we drew up a resolution on the satisfaction of the trip. The girl who had been cold all day didn't ever want to see snow again, but already the others were discussing a possible ascent from the Eagle Creek side — so great is the lure of the high places.

CHAPTER XXII

AL TAHOE

AL Tahoe, four miles east of Tallac, is one of the newer, better and more fashionable and pretentious resorts recently established at the south end of the Lake. Its projectors saw the increasing demand for summer residences on the Lake, and realizing to the full the superior advantages of this location, they divided their large holding into suitable villa and bungalow sites, and other lots, and readily disposed of a number of them to those who were ready to build.

To further the colonizing plans of these chosen and selected purchasers a fine, modern, well-equipped hotel was erected, replete with every convenience and luxury that progressive Americans now expect and demand in their chosen resorts. The result is quite a settlement has grown up, and Al Tahoe sees ahead an era of rapid growth and prosperity. Its homes are substantial and beautiful and indicate that John Le Conte's prophecy, elsewhere quoted, is already coming to pass. Pasadena capitalists are behind the hotel and town project.

Being advantageously located on the State and National automobile boulevard, and near to all the choice mountain, lake and other resorts of the southern end of Tahoe, is appeals to those who wish to combine equally ready access to civilization with the wild ruggedness and infinite variety of many-featured Nature.

It is situated on a high plateau, gently sloping from the bluff, with a Lake frontage of about three quarters of a mile. The land rises with a gentle slope to the edge of the terrace facing the stream, meadow, and mountains on the south.

With no stagnant water, there are practically no mosquitoes, and it is confessedly one of the most healthful spots of all this health-giving region. Being on a lea shore, the cold air from the snowy summits of the mountains tempered by the warm soil of the foothills and level area, there is no place on the Lake better adapted for bathing and boating, especially as the beach is sandy and shallow, sloping off for some distance from the shore.

The accompanying photographs give some idea of the hotel and its cottages, together with some Al Tahoe homes. The water supply for the town and hotel is gained from beautiful and pure Star Lake, 3000 feet higher than Lake Tahoe, and where snow may be seen during the entire year. The Al Tahoe

Company owns its own electric generating plant and supplies all the cottages with electric light.

The hotel itself is conducted on the American plan, and in every modern way meets the requirements of the most exacting patrons. Amusements of every kind are provided, and there is a good livery stable and automobile garage.

The town itself is being built up with a select class of summer residents. No saloons are allowed. There are still desirable lots for sale, and the Al Tahoe Company, or L.H. Bannister, the Postmaster, will be glad to correspond with any who contemplate purchasing or building.

Mount Tallac, Rubicon Peaks, from long wharf at Al Tahoe.

Murphey cottage, Al Tahoe

Al Tahoe Inn and cottages. This early 20th century inn was a precursor to several other fashionable resorts built at the south end of Lake Tahoe.

E.S. Brown cottage, Al Tahoe.

Porterfield cottage, Al Tahoe.

Whispering pines, Al Tahoe.

CHAPTER XXIII

GLEN ALPINE SPRINGS

The earliest of all the resorts of the Tahoe region away from the shores of Tahoe itself, Glen Alpine Springs still retains its natural supremacy. Located seven miles away from Tallac, reached by excellent roads in automobile stages, sequestered and sheltered, yet absolutely in the very heart of the most interesting part of the Tahoe region, scenically and geologically, it continues to attract an increasing number of the better class of guests who annually visit these divinely-favored California Sierra. John Muir wrote truthfully when he said:

> The Glen Alpine Springs tourist resort seems to me one of the most delightful places in all the famous Tahoe region. From no other valley, as far as I know, may excursions be made in a single day to so many peaks, wild gardens, glacier lakes, glacier meadows, and Alpine groves, cascades, etc.

The drive from Tallac around Fallen Leaf Lake under trees whose boles form arch or portal, framing pictures of the sunny lake, is a memorable experience; then on past Glen Alpine Falls, Lily Lake, and Modjeska Falls, up the deep mountain glen, where the road ends at the hospitable cottages, log houses and spacious tents of Glen Alpine.

Here is the world-famous spring, discovered in the 'fifties by Nathan Gilmore (for whom Gilmore Lake is named). Mr. Gilmore was born in Ohio, but, when a mere youth, instead of attending college and graduating in law as his parents had arranged for and expected, he yielded to the lure of the California gold excitement, came West, and in 1850 found himself in Placerville.

In due time he married, and to the sickness of his daughter Evelyn, now Mrs. John L. Ramsay, of Freewater, Ore., is owing his discovery of Glen Alpine. The doctor ordered him to bring the child up into the mountains. Accompanied by an old friend, Barton Richardson, of the James Barton Key family of Philadelphia, he came up to Tallac, with the ailing child and its mother. Being of active temperament he and Mr. Richardson scaled Mt. Tallac, and in returning were much entranced by Fallen Leaf Lake.

Later Mr. Gilmore came to Fallen Leaf alone, wandering over its moraines and lingering by its shores to drink in its impressive and growingly overpowering beauty. In those days there was no road at the southern end of Fallen Leaf and the interested explorer was perforce led to follow the trails of bear, deer and other wild animals.

Rambling through the woods, some two miles above the lake he came to a willow-surrounded swampy place, where the logs and fallen trees were clearly worn by the footprints of many generations of wild animals. Prompted by curiosity he followed the hidden trail, saw where a small stream of mineral-stained water was flowing, observed where the deer, etc., had licked the stones, and finally came to the source in what he afterwards called Glen Alpine Springs.

Scientific observation afterwards showed that the water had an almost uniform temperature, even in the hottest days of summer, of 39.6 degrees Fahr., and that there was free carbonic acid gas to the extent of 138.36 cubic inches. The analysis revealed that each U.S. gallon contained grains as follows:

Sodium Chloride	21.17
Sodium Carbonate	32.75
Potassium Carbonate	trace
Ferrous Carbonate	1.8
Alumnia	1.43
Borates	trace
Magnesium Carbonate	9.96
Calcium Carbonate	45.09
Calcium Sulfate	4.10
Silica	2.50
Organic Matter	trace
TOTAL SOLIDS	118.80

The water is pleasant to the taste, and, as has been shown, highly charged with carbonic acid gas; its action is diuretic, laxative and stimulative to the entire digestive tract. Eminent physicians claim that it is beneficial in dyspepsia, torpid liver, kidney and bladder irritation, and is also a tonic.

Whether this be true or not I cannot say, but I do know that every time I go to Glen Alpine I drink freely and abundantly of the water, to my great physical pleasure and satisfaction. It is one of the most delicious sparkling waters I have ever tasted, as gratifying to the palate and soothing to the fevered mucous membranes as Apollinaris or Shasta water, and I am not alone in the wish I often express, viz., that I might have such a spring in my backyard at home.

One result of this discovery was that Mr. Gilmore decided to located upon the land. As soon as the first claim was made secure a rude one-roomed cabin was built and Mr. Richardson was the first guest.

Preparatory to bringing his family, Mr. Gilmore added two more rooms, and to render ingress easier he built a road to intersect with the Tallac road at the northern end of Fallen Leaf Lake. As this had to be blasted out with black powder — it was before the days of dynamite — Mr. Gilmore's devotion to the place can be well understood.

When his daughters grew up, they and their friends came here to spend their summers, and by and by, almost unconsciously, but pleasantly and agreeably, the place became a public resort. Though Mr. Gilmore has long since passed on, having died in Placerville, Calif., in the year 1898, Glen Alpine Springs is still in the ownership of his family, and its management and direction is entirely in their hands.

As in the beginning they have ever sought to preserve its character of simplicity. It is their aim that everything should be as primitive as possible, consonant with healthfulness, privacy and comfort. While no sanitary precautions are neglected, and water, hot and cold, is extravagantly provided, with free shower baths, there are none of the frills and furbelows that generally convert these — what should be — simple nature resorts into bad imitations of the luxurious hotels of the city.

There are positively no dress events. Men and women are urged to bring their old clothes and wear them out here, or provide only khaki or corduroy, with short skirts, bloomers and leggings for the fair sex. Strong shoes are required; hob-nailed if one expects to do any climbing. Wraps for evening, and heavy underwear for an unusual day (storms sometimes come in Sierran regions unexpectedly), are sensible precautions.

Sleeping out-of-doors is one of the features of the place, an invigorating, rejuvenating joy, which Mark Twain affirmed was able to destroy any amount of fatigue that a person's body could gather. Visitors are given their choice of a comfortable bed in the open, in a cottage, tent, or one of the main buildings.

There are practically no rules at Glen Alpine save those that would operate in any respectable home.

No liquors are sold, and visitors are frankly told that "If they must have liquid stimulants they must bring them along." In order that those who desire to sleep may not be disturbed by the thoughtlessness of others, music is prohibited after ten o'clock.

One of the delights of the place is the nightly campfire. Here in a large open space, close to the spring, surrounded by commodious and comfortable canvas seats, that will easily hold eight or ten persons, the blazing fire is started every evening. Those who have musical instruments — guitars, banjos, mandolins, flutes, cornets, violins, and even the plebeian accordion or the modest Jew's harp — are requested to bring them. Solos, choruses, hymns and college songs are indulged in to the heart's content. Now and again dances are given, and when any speaker arrives who is willing to entertain the guests, a talk, lecture or sermon is arranged for.

Three things are never found at Glen Alpine. These are poison oak, rattlesnakes and poisonous insects. The rowdy, gambling and carousing element are equally absent, for should they ever appear, they speedily discover their lack of harmony and voluntarily retire.

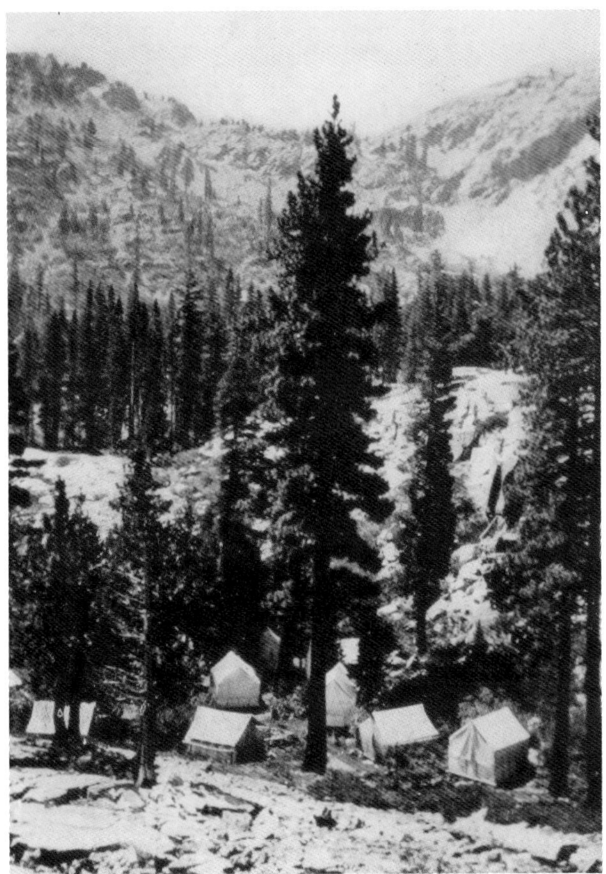

Cluster of tents at Glen Alpine Springs.

Glenn Alpine Falls.

While the Glen Alpine resort is not situated directly on one of the lakes, it owns over twenty boats on eight of the nearby lakes, and the use of these is freely accorded to its guests. That it is in close proximity to lakes and peaks is evidenced by the following table, which gives the distance in miles from the hotel:

MILES	
2-1/2	Angora Lake
4	American Lake
6	Avalanche Lake
3-1/4	Alta Morris Lake
7	Azure Lake
5	Center Lake
5-1/2	Crystal Lake
5-3/4	Crater Lake
6	Cup Lake

4-3/4	Cathedral Lake
5-1/2	Echo Lake
2	Fallen Leaf Lake
5-1/4	Floating Island Lake
4-1/4	Forest Lake
6	Fontinalis Lake
1-1/4	Glen Alpine Falls
1-1/4	Grass Lake
4-3/4	Grouse Lake
3-1/2	Gilmore Lake
3-1/4	Heather Lake
3-1/4	Half Moon Lake
5	Kalmia Lake
1	Lily Lake
2-1/4	Lucile Lake
3-3/4	Le Conte Lake
2-1/2	Margery Lake
1/4	Modjeska Falls
3-1/2	Observation Point
4-1/4	Olney Lake
4-1/4	Pit Lake
6	Pyramid Lake
4-3/4	Rainbow Lake
2-3/4	Susie Lake
3-1/2	Susie Lake Falls
2-3/4	Summit Lake
6	Snow Lake
4-1/2	Tamarack Lake
6	Tallac Lake
7	Tahoe Lake
6-1/2	Velma Lakes
3-1/4	Wood, Lake of the
3-1/2	Angora Peak
5-1/4	Dick's Peak
5-1/2	Jack's Peak
2-1/2	Keith's Dome
7	Pyramid Peak
6-1/2	Ralston Peak

As the proprietors of Glen Alpine ask: "Where else outside of Switzerland is there a like region of lakes (forty-odd) and world of Sierran grandeur, such air with the tonic of altitude, mineral spring water, trout fishing, and camaraderie of kindred spirits!"

While the foregoing list gives a comprehensive suggestion of the wide reach of Glen Alpine's territory there are several especial peaks and lakes that are peculiarly its own. These are Pyramid, Agassiz, Dick's, Jack's, Richardson's, Ralston, and the Angora Peaks, Mount Tallac, Mosquito Pass, and Lakes Olney, Le Conte, Heather, Susie, Grass, Lucile, Margery, and Summit with Lake of the Woods and others in Desolation Valley, Gilmore, Half Moon, Alta, Morris, Lily, Tamarack, Rainbow, Grouse, and the Upper and Lower Echo.

Desolation Valley and all its surroundings is also within close reach. This is some four miles westward of Glen Alpine Springs, and is reached by way of easy mountain trails under sweet-scented pines and gnarled old junipers; beside singing streams; across crystal lakes, through a cliff-guarded glade where snowbanks linger until midsummer, ever renewing the carpet of green, decking it with heather and myriad exquisite mountain blossoms. On, over a granite embankment, and lo! your feet are stayed and your heart is stilled as your eyes behold marvelous Desolation Valley.

Greeting you on its southern boundary stands majestic Pyramid Peak, with its eternal snows. Lofty companions circling to your very feet make the walls forming the granite cradle of Olney, the Lake of Mazes. The waters are blue as the skies above them, and pure as the melting snows from Pyramid which form them. He who has not looked upon this, the most remarkable of all the wonder pictures in the Tahoe region, has missed that for which there is no substitute.

The whole Glen Alpine basin — which practically extends from the Tallac range on the north, from heather Lake Pass (the outlet from Desolation Valley) and Cracked Crag on the west and southwest, Ralston Peak and range to the south and the Angora Peaks on the east — is one mass of glacial scoriations.

Within a few stone-throws of the spring, on a little-used trail to Grass Lake, there are several beautiful and interesting markings. One of these is a finely defined curve or groove, extending for 100 feet or more, above which, about 1-1/2 feet, is another groove, some two to four feet wide. These run rudely parallel for some distance, then unite and continue as one. Coming back to the trail — a hundred or so feet away — on the left hand side returning to the spring, is a gigantic sloping granite block, perfectly polished with glacial action, and black as though its surface had been coated in the process.

In the "good old days" — Glen Alpine stage approaching office at Glen Alpine Springs.

Near here the trail *ducks* or markers are placed in a deep grooving or trough three or four feet wide, and of equal depth, while to the right are two other similar troughs working their winding and tortuous way into the valley beneath.

In Chapter VIII an idea is given of the movements of the great glaciers that formed Desolation Valley and all the nearby lakes, as well as Glen Alpine basin. These gigantic ice sheets, with their firmly wedged carving blocks of granite, moved over the Heather Lake Pass, gouging out that lake, and Susie Lake, in its onward march, and then, added to by glacial flows from Cracked Crag, the southern slopes of the Tallac range, and the Angora Peaks, it passed on and down, shaping this interestingly rugged, wild and picturesque basin as we find it today.

How many centuries of cutting and gouging, beveling and grooving were required to accomplish this, who can tell? Never resting, never halting, ever moving, irresistibly cutting, carving, grinding and demolishing, it carried away its millions of millions of tons or rocky débris in boulders, pebbles, sand and mud, and thus helped make the gigantic moraines of Fallen Leaf Lake. The ice flow itself passed along over where the terminal moraine now stands, cutting out Fallen Leaf Lake basin in its movement, and finally rested in the vast bowl of Lake Tahoe.

To the careful student every foot of Glen Alpine basin is worthy of study, and he who desires to further the cause of science will do well to make a map of his observations, recording the direction, appearance, depth, length and width of all the glacial markings he discovers. On the U.S. Government maps the stream flowing through Glen Alpine basin is marked as Eau Claire Creek.

To the proprietors of Glen Alpine, and the visitors, the French name is absurd and out of place. No Frenchman has ever resided here, and if it was desired to call it Clear Water Creek, why not use good, understandable, common sense English. At the request of those most intimately concerned, therefore, the name has been changed on the map that accompanies this volume, to Glen Alpine Creek, a name that "belongs" and to which no one can possible have any objection.

Glimpse of Grass Lake, looking across and up Glen Alpine Canyon.

Angora Lake, Fallen Leaf Lake and Lake Tahoe.

Angora Lake, near Lake Tahoe.

CHAPTER XXIV

FALLEN LEAF LAKE AND ITS RESORTS

Fallen Leaf Lake is a noble body of water 3-1/2 miles long and about one mile across. Why it is called Fallen Leaf is fully explained in the chapter on Indian Legends. some people have thought it was named from its shape, but this cannot be, for, from the summit of Mt. Tallac, everyone instantly notices its resemblance to the imprint of a human foot. It is shaped more like a cork sole, as if cut out of the solid rock, filled up with a rich indigo blue fluid, and then made extra beautiful and secluded with a rich tree and plant growth on every slope that surrounds it.

The color of the water is as richly blue as is Tahoe itself, and there is the same suggestion of an emerald ring around it, as in the larger Lake, though this ring is neither so wide nor so highly colored.

In elevation it is some 80 feet above Lake Tahoe, thus giving it an altitude of 6300 feet.

At the upper end, near Fallen Leaf Lodge, under the cliffs it has a depth of over 380 feet, but it becomes much shallower at the northern or lower end near the outlet. Its surroundings are majestic and enthralling as well as picturesque and alluring. On the west Mt. Tallac towers its nearly 10,000 feet into the sea of the upper air, flanked on the south by the lesser noble and majestic Cathedral Peak. In the earlier part of the season when these are covered with snow, the pure white materially enhances the splendor of both mountain and lake by enriching their varied colorings with the marked contrast.

To the southwest rise the Angora Peaks, and these likewise catch, and hold the winter's snow, often, like Mt. Tallac, retaining beds of *névé* from year to year.

To the geological student, especially one interested in glacial phenomena, the lateral and terminal moraines of Fallen Leaf Lake are of marked and unusual interest. The moraine on the east is upwards of 1000 feet high, and is a majestic ridge, clothed from the lake shore to its summit with a rich growth of pines, firs and hemlocks.

Its great height and bulk will suggest to the thoughtful reader the questions as to how it was formed, and whence came all the material of its manufacture. It extends nearly the whole length of the lake, diminishing somewhat in size at the northern end. There is a corresponding moraine on the western side not less compelling in its interest though scarcely as large in size as its eastern counterpart.

The terminal moraine, which is the one that closed up the lake, separating and raising it above the level of Lake Tahoe, is a less noble mound, yet geologically it allures the mind and demands study as much as the others. In Chapter VIII, Dr. Joseph Le Conte's theories are given in full explaining the various glacial phenomena connected with this lake.

The fish of Fallen Leaf are practically the same as those of Tahoe, though rod and fly fishing is more indulged in here.

Boating, canoeing and the use of the motor boat are daily recreations, and swimming is regularly indulged in during the summer season.

FALLEN LEAF LODGE

The distinguishing characteristics of this resort are simplicity, home-likeness, unostentation. It makes its appeal especially to the thoughtful and the studious, the not luxuriously rich, those who love Nature rather than the elegance of a first class hotel, and who desire to climb trails, study trees, hunt, fish, and generally recreate out-of-doors rather than dress and fare sumptuously.

It is situated on the southwestern edge of Fallen Leaf Lake, five miles from Tallac, reached by a road that winds through the trees of the Baldwin estate, and then skirts the eastern and southern shores of the Lake. Stages — horse and automobile — run daily during the season and meet all the steamers at Tallac.

The "Lodge" consists of a number of detached buildings, conveniently and picturesquely scattered among the pines on the slopes and at the edge of the lake. There are dining hall, social hall, post office, store, electric power house, boat house, with stables far enough away to be sanitary, and cottages and tents located in every suitable nook that can be found. There are one, two or three-roomed cottages, tents, single and double, all in genuine camp style. There is no elegance or luxury, though most of the cottages have modern toilets, porcelain bathtubs with running hot and cold water. Electric lights are everywhere.

The camp has been in existence now (1915) for seven years and each year has seen considerable enlargement and improvement, until now Fallen Leaf Lodge in the heart of the summer season is an active, busy, happy and home-like community.

The table is wholesome, substantial and appetizing. There is no pretense at elaborateness. Home cooking, well served, of simple and healthful dishes, in reasonable variety, is all that is offered.

Needless to say there is no bar or saloon, though there is no attempt to compel a personal standpoint on the liquor question upon those who are accustomed to the use of alcoholic liquors at meals.

In its natural beauties and advantages Fallen Leaf Lodge claims — and with strong justification — one of the very best of locations. Fallen Leaf Lake is large enough to give scope to all the motor boats, row boats, canoes and launches that are likely to be brought to it for the next hundred years, and ten thousand fishermen could successfully angle upon its bosom or along its shores.

For millions of Tahoe trout, rainbow, Eastern brook, Loch Levin, Mackinac and German brown have been put into this and nearby lakes in the last few years. While some jerk line fishing is indulged in, this lake, unlike Lake Tahoe, affords constant recreation for the more sportsmanlike fly fishing.

Another of the special advantages of Fallen Leaf Lodge is its possession of a fine log house and camp on the shore of Lake of the Woods, five miles away, in Desolation Valley. To those who wish to fish in greater solitude, to climb the peaks of the Crystal Range, or boat over the many and various lakes of Desolation Valley, this is a great convenience.

Nothing can surpass the calm grandeur of the setting of this glorious, beautiful water. Lying at the lower edge of Desolation Valley and facing stupendous mountains, the picture it presents, with Pyramid Peak reflected in its gorgeously lit-up sunset waters, is one that will forever linger in the memory.

The close proximity of Fallen Leaf Lodge to Mt. Tallac, Cathedral Peak, the Angora Peaks, Mounts Jack, Dick, and Richardson, Ralston Peak, Keith's Dome, Maggie's Peaks, Tell's Peak, with the towering peaks of the Crystal Range — Pyramid and Agassiz — to the west, and Freel's, Job's and Job's Sister to the southeast, afford an abundance and variety of mountain climbing that are seldom found in any region, however favored.

But in addition to the peaks there are Sierran lakes galore, rich in unusual beauty and picturesqueness, and most of them stocked with trout that compel the exertion of the angler's skill, as much as tickle the palate of the uncorrupted epicure. Close by are Cascade, Cathedral, Floating Island, Echo, Heather, Lucile, Margery, Gilmore, Le Conte, Lily, Susie, Tamarack, Grouse, Lake of the Woods, Avalanche, Pit, Crystal, Pyramid, Half Moon, with the marvelous and alluring maze of lakes, bays, straits, channels, inlets and "blind alleys" of the Lake Olney of the ever-fascinating Desolation Valley.

Those I have named are all within comparatively easy walking distance to the ordinarily healthful and vigorous man or woman. For those who seek more strenuous exercise, or desire horseback or camping out trips another twenty, aye fifty, lakes within a radius of fifty miles may be found, with their connecting creeks, streams and rivers where gamey trout abound, and where flowers, shrubs and trees in never-ceasing variety and charm tempt the botanist and nature lover.

While to some it may not be an attraction, to others there may be both pleasure and interest in witnessing the operations of the Fallen Leaf sawmill. This is situated on the western side of the lake, and is a scene of activity and bustle when logging and lumbering are in progress. On the hills about the lake the "fellers" may be found, chopping their way into the hearts of the forest monarchs of pine, fir and cedar, and then inserting the saw, whose biting teeth soon cut from rim to rim and cause the crashing downfall of trees that have stood for centuries.

Denuded of their limbs these are then sawn into appropriate lengths, "snaked" by chains pulled by powerful horses to the "chute," down which they are shot into the lake, from whence they are easily towed to the mill. The chute consists of felled logs, laid side by side, evenly and regularly, so as to form a continuous trough. This is greased, so that when the heavy logs are placed therein they slide of their own weight, where there is a declivity, and are easily dragged or propelled on the level ground.

I use the word propelled to suggest the interesting method used in these chutes. Sometimes ten or a dozen logs will be placed, following each other, a few feet apart, on the trough (the chute). A chain is fastened to the rear end of the hindermost log. This chain is attached to a single tree fastened to a horse's harness.

the horse is started. This makes the hinder log strike the next one, this bumps into the third and gives it a start, in its turn it bumps the fourth, the fourth the fifth, and so on, until the whole dozen are in motion. Had the string of logs been fastened together, the horse would have found it impossible to move them, but "propelling" them in this fashion they are all set in motion, and their inertia once overcome there is no difficulty experienced in keeping them going.

the views from Fallen Leaf Lodge are varied and beautiful, one in particular being especially enchanting. Over the Terminal moraine, across the hidden face of Lake Tahoe, the eye falls upon the mountains in Nevada, on the faraway eastern side. In the soft light of evening they look like ;fairy mountains, not real rocky masses of gigantic, rugged substance, but something painted upon the horizon with delicate fingers, and in tints and shades to correspond, for they look tenderer and sweeter, gentler and lovelier than anything may could conceive or execute.

The owners of Fallen Leaf Lodge (1915) is Professor William W. Price, a graduate of Stanford University, who first came into this region to study and catch special Sierran birds and other fauna for the Smithsonian Institution, the American Museum of Natural History, and the British Museum. Later, when he founded the Agassiz school for boys, at Auburn, California, he established Camp Agassiz near Fallen Leaf Lake, in a grove of pines, firs and cedars.

Assisted by other university men, he made of this an ideal open air school and camp for boys. They were taught such practical things as to take care of themselves in the mountains, find a trail, or go to a given spot without a trail, fish, hunt, make camp, build fires in a rainstorm, find proper shelter during a lightning storm, carry a pack, pack a mule or burro, even to the throwing of the "diamond hitch," the "squaw hitch," and the "square" or other packer's especial "knots" and "ties."

They were induced to climb mountains, row, swim, "ski," and snow-slide, and all were taught to recognize at sight the common birds, smaller wild animals, trees, and flowers. Frequent camping out trips were arranged for, and the youngsters thus gained health, vigor and permanent strength while doing what they all enjoyed doing.

In due time the parents wished to share the fun,

joy, and out-of-door-experiences of their youngsters; then the friends, and those who heard about them, and out of the numerous requests for accommodations Fallen Leaf Lodge was born. For a time Mr. Price tried an ordinary hotel manager, but the peculiar and individualistic needs of his peculiar and individualistic camp at length led Mrs. Price and himself to take the complete control. From that time its success has been continuous.

Mr. Price is a scientific expert upon the flora (especially the trees), the birds and the four-footed fauna of the whole region, and his readiness and willingness to communicate his knowledge to his guests is a great advantage to the studious and inquiring.

Owing to the demands made upon his time by the management of Fallen Leaf Lodge Mr. Price has transferred his school into other hands, and has given up the Boys' Camp, though the lads are still welcome, with their parents, as regular guests at the Lodge.

It should be noted that Fallen Leaf Lodge is but two miles from Glen Alpine Springs and that all that is said of the close proximity of the most interesting features of the southern end of the Lake Tahoe region to Glen Alpine, applies with equal force (plus the two miles) to Fallen Leaf Lodge.

CATHEDRAL PARK ON FALLEN LEAF LAKE

One of the newest of the Tahoe region resorts is that of Cathedral Park, located on the western side of Fallen Leaf Lake. It was opened in the latter part of the season of 1912 by Carl Fluegge. Everything about it is new, from the flooring of the tents to the fine dining room, cottages and stables. A special road has been constructed on the west side of the lake, over which Cathedral Park stages run daily the three and a half miles, to meet every steamer during the season at Tallac.

Rising directly from the edge of the lake, surrounded by majestic trees, protected by the gigantic height of Mt. Tallac (9785 feet) from the western winds, a clear open view of Fallen Leaf Lake and the thousand-feet high lateral moraine on the eastern side is obtained; there could be no better location for such a resort.

The distinctive features of Cathedral Park are simplicity and home comforts, with special advantages for hunting, fishing and camping out. For ten years Mr. Fluegge has taken out some of the most distinguished patrons of the Tahoe region in his capacity as expert guide and huntsman. He knows every trail thoroughly and has scaled every mountain of the surrounding country. He knows the habits and haunts of bear, deer, and other game, and is a successful hunter of them, as well as of grouse and quail.

His office and social hall bear practical evidence of his prowess and skill in the mounted heads of deer, and the dressed skins of bear that he has shot. He is also an expert angler, and well acquainted with the best fishing in Granite, Eagle, the Rock-Bound, Gilmore and other lakes, as well as those closer at hand. There are twelve such lakes within easy reach of Cathedral Park.

Fishing and hunting are his hobbies and delights, hence he makes a thoroughly competent, because interested, and interesting guide. Nothing pleases him more than to get out with his guests and assist them in their angling and hunting. To aid in this he has established his own permanent camp at the beautiful Angora Lakes, four miles from Cathedral Park, which is placed freely at the disposal of his guests.

Especial arrangements are made for the perfect and satisfactory accommodation of guests who desire to sleep out of doors. Tents, sleeping porches and platforms are arranged with a view to the strictest privacy, and those who desire this healthful open-air mode of life can nowhere be better accommodated than here.

As Mark Twain has said, it is the "open air" sleeping in the Lake Tahoe region that is to beneficial. Again to quote him: "The air up there in the clouds is very pure and fine, bracing and delicious. And why shouldn't it be? — It is the same the angels breathe. I think that hardly any amount of fatigue can be gathered together that a man cannot sleep off in one night here. *Not under a roof, but under the sky.*" Therefore Cathedral Park says to those who wish to breathe the same air as the angels while they are yet on the earth: Come to us and we will meet your reasonable wishes in every possible way.

The presence of Mrs. Fluegge, who is associated with her husband in the management, guarantees to

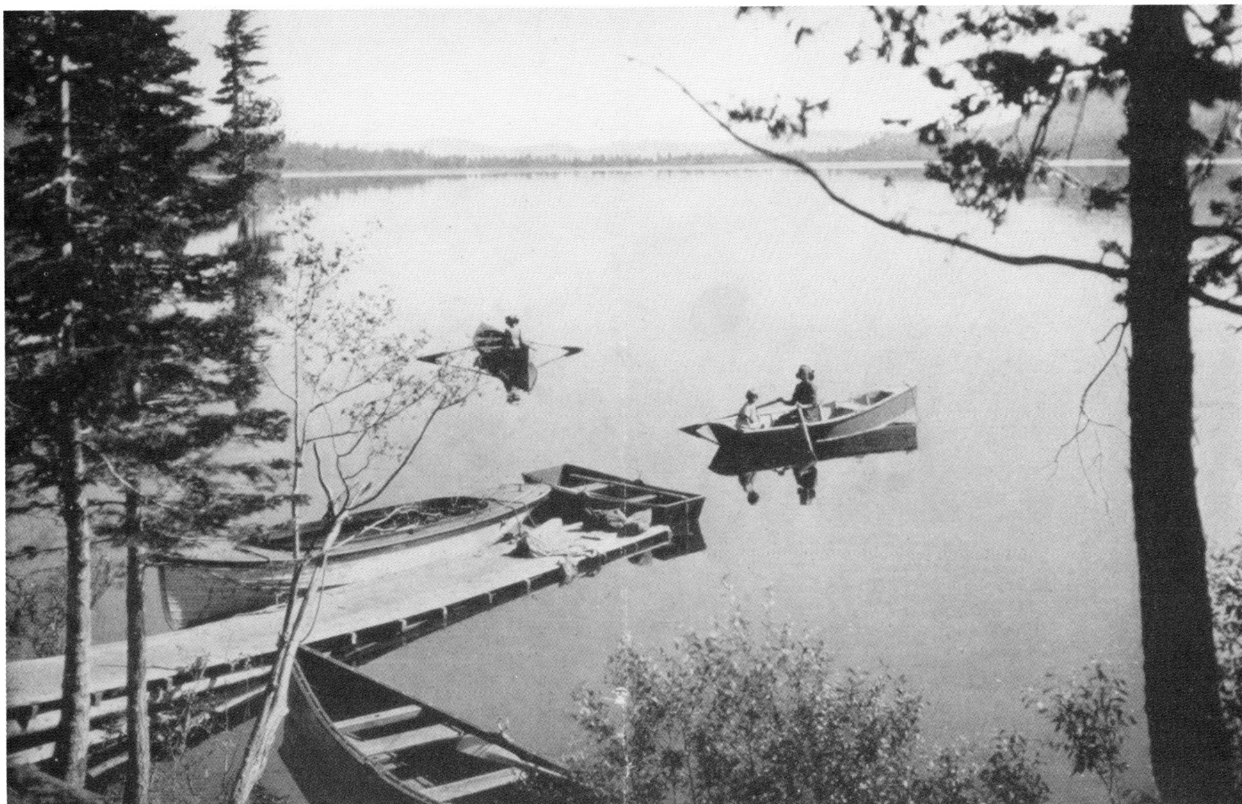

Fallen Leaf Lake, with boat landing at Fallen Leaf Lodge.

ladies, whether unaccompanied, or with their families, the best of care, and the former are especially invited to come and test the home-like qualities of the place.

The water supply of Cathedral Park is gained from its own springs, on the mountainside above the resort. It is piped down to every tent or cottage and the supply is super-abundant. Fish are caught almost daily on the landing in front of the hotel. Fallen Leaf is an ideal spot for rowing, canoeing, and launch rides, and the hotel owns its own launch in which parties are regularly taken around the lake. During the summer season bathing is as delightful here as in any of the seaside resorts of the Atlantic and Pacific, and almost everyone takes a plunge daily.

A campfire is built every night, where singing, story-telling, and open air amusements of an impromptu nature are indulged in to one's heart's content, though visitors are all expected to remember the rights of others and not keep too late hours.

Informal dances are indulged in occasionally and everything is done to promote the comfort, pleasure and enjoyment of the guests that earnest desire, constant watchfulness and long experience can suggest.

The table is simple and homelike, but abundant, well served and satisfactory. This department is entirely under the control of Mrs. Fluegge. Fresh fruit and vegetables, lake trout and game in season, fresh milk and cream, with everything of the best that the markets afford, are none too good for the guests at Cathedral Park.

Unlike most of the Lake Tahoe resorts, it keeps open throughout the whole year, and is managed with but one idea, viz., to give absolute and complete satisfaction to all its guests.

Its rates are reasonable, and especial prices are given to children under ten years of age and to families who wish to stay for any length of time.

The short trail to Mount Tallac rises directly from Cathedral Park, and all that has been said of the close proximity of Glen Alpine and Fallen Leaf Lodge to the most interesting peaks, lakes, etc., of the Tahoe region applies with equal force to Cathedral Park, plus the short additional distance, which is something less than a mile.

Picturesque Palo Alto Lodge at Lakeside Park, Lake Tahoe.

The long wharf at Lakeside Park.

CHAPTER XXV

LAKESIDE PARK

Situated on the shore of Lake Tahoe and at the same time on the great Lincoln Highway stretching from the Atlantic to the Pacific — a division of the State Automobile Highway reaching from Sacramento, California, to Carson City, Nevada, via Placerville, Lakeside Park is readily reached by travelers from every direction, whether they come by steamer, buggy, or automobile.

The Lakeside Park hotel was established in 1892 and has an enviable reputation. It consists of hotel, with adjacent cottages and tents, comfortably furnished and equipped with every healthful necessity. Here surrounded by beautiful trees, that sing sweet songs to the touch of the winds, drinking in health and vigor from their balsamic odors, enjoying the invigorating sunshine and the purifying breezes coming from mountain, forest and Lake, swimming in the Lake, rowing, canoeing, climbing mountain trails, exploring rocky and wooded canyons, fishing, hunting, botanizing, studying geology in one of the most wonderful volumes Nature has ever written, sleeping out-of-doors under the trees and the glowing stars after being lulled to rest by the soothing lappings of the gentle waves upon the beach — who can conceive a more ideal vacation time than this.

Unlike many parts of Lake Tahoe, Lakeside Park possesses the fine stretch of beautiful, clean, sandy beach. There are no rocks, deep holes, tide or undertow. Children can wade, bathe or swim in perfect safety as the shore gradually slopes into deeper water.

The whole settlement is abundantly supplied with purest spring water which is piped down from its source high on the mountain slopes to the south. The hotel is fully equipped with hot and cold water for baths and all other needed purposes, and there is a good store, well stocked livery stable, row boats, steam laundry and home dairy.

The store carries a very complete line of provisions and supplies, fresh fruits, vegetables, meats, dairy produce, ice, hay, grain, lumber, shingles, stove wood, paints, gasoline — in fact, everything that is likely to be in demand in such a community. Campfire wood is abundant and free to patrons. This is particularly advantageous for those who wish to tent and "board themselves." Housekeeping tents are provided, on platforms in the grove, at reasonable rates, and the hotel owns its pasture in which the horses of patrons are cared for free of charge.

The location of Lakeside Park in relation to Lake Tahoe is peculiarly advantageous in that it affords daily opportunity for driving, horseback riding or walking directly along the shore for miles. Indeed the twelve-mile drive to Glenbrook is one of the noted drives of the world, taking in the celebrated Cave Rock, and giving the widest possible outlooks of the whole expanse of the Lake.

Patrons of the hotel or camps are assured that there are no rattlesnakes, fleas, malaria, fogs, or poison oak. The character and tone of the place will also be recognized when it is known that saloons and gambling resorts are absolutely prohibited in the residential tract.

The most majestic of all the mountains of Lake Tahoe are closely adjacent to Lakeside Park. Mt. Sinclair, 9500 feet, rises immediately from the eastern boundary, whilst Monument Peak, Mounts Feel, Job, and Job's Sister, ranging from 10,000 to 11,200 feet above sea level are close by. Such near proximity to these mountains gives unequalled opportunities for tramping, riding and driving through and over marvelous diversity of hill, valley, woodland, canyon and mountain. Scores of miles of mountain trails remain to be thoroughly explored and to the hunter these highest mountains are the most alluring spots of the whole Tahoe region.

Yet while these mountains are close by, Lakeside Park is near enough to Fallen Leaf Lake, Glen Alpine Springs and Desolation Valley to give fullest opportunity for trips to these noted spots and their adjacent attractions.

In addition it allows ready incursions into Nevada, where the prehistoric footprints at Carson City, the marvelous Steamboat Springs, and the world-famed mines and Sutro Tunnel of Virginia City have been a lure for many thousands during the past decades.

It is also near to Hope Valley and the peak on which Frémont climbed when, in 1844, he discovered and first described Lake Tahoe, and is the natural stopping place for those who wish to go over the road the Pathfinder made, accompanied by Kit Carson, his guide and scout, whose name is retained in Carson City, Carson Tree, Carson Valley and Carson Canyon, all of which are within a day's easy ride.

PRIVATE RESIDENCES AT LAKESIDE PARK

To meet the ever-increasing demand for lots on which to build summer homes on Lake Tahoe the Lakeside Park Company has set aside a limited and desirable portion of its large property on the southeasterly shore of Lake Tahoe for cottages and log cabins, bungalows and lodges, or acre tracts for chalets and villas. Already quite a number have availed themselves of this privilege and a colony of beautiful homes is being established.

Mr. and Mrs. Hill, with a keen eye for the appropriate, and at the same time wishful to show how a most perfect bungalow can be constructed at a remarkably low price, have planned and erected several most attractive "specimens" or "models," at prices ranging from $450 to $1000 and over. The fact that the tract is so located in an *actual,* not merely a nominal, wooded park, where pines, firs, tamaracks and other Sierran trees abound, allow the proprietors to offer fine logs for cabins and rustic work in almost unlimited quantities, and in the granite-ribbed mountains close by is a quarry from which rock for foundations, chimneys and open fireplaces may be taken without stint. These are great advantages not to be ignored by those who desire to build, and those who are first on the scene naturally will be accorded the first choice both of lots and material.

There is but one Lake Tahoe in America, and as the men of California and Nevada cities find more time for leisure it will not be many years before every available spot will be purchased and summer residences abound, just as is the case in the noted eastern lakes, or those near to such cities as Minneapolis, etc., in the middle west.

In setting aside this residential section at Lakeside Park the owners have planned with far-sighted and generous liberality. The Lake frontage is reserved for general use of the hotel guests and cottage community, so there will be no conflict regarding privileges of boating, bathing, fishing, and "rest cure" on the beach.

Another wise provision is that a generous portion of the amounts received form early sales of lots is being devoted to general improvements that are for mutual benefit; such as the extension of roads, paths, trails and water pipes, a substantial breakwater for better protection of launches and boats, larger dancing pavilion or platform, automobile garage, more dressing rooms for bathers, etc.

CHAPTER XXVI

GLENBROOK AND MARLETTE LAKE

IN Chapter XVI the history of Glenbrook is given in some detail. It is now, however, converted into a pleasure resort especially popular with residents of Nevada, and largely used by automobiles crossing the Sierra and passing around Lake Tahoe.

The Inn, and its veranda overlooking the Lake, is built with an eye to comfort and convenience. Every need for pleasure and recreation is arranged for. For those who enjoy privacy, cosy cottages are provided, around which beautiful wild flowers grow in wonderful profusion. The guests here are especially favored in that the Inn has its own ranch, dairy, poultry farm, fruit orchard and vegetable garden. The table, therefore, is abundantly provided, and everything is of known quality and brought in fresh daily.

Glenbrook Inn makes no pretense to be a fashionable resort. It especially invites those individuals and families who wish to be free from the exhausting "frivolities of fashion," to come and enjoy to the full Nature's simple charms, regardless of the city's conventions as to dress and fashion. Rest and recreation, amusement and recuperation are the keynotes. Simplicity of life, abundance of sleep, sufficiency of good food, tastefully served, the chief hours of the day spent in the open air, fishing, boating, swimming, trail climbing, horseback riding, driving or automobiling — these bring health, renewed energy and the joy of life.

The specific pleasures provided at Glenbrook are varied. It is confessedly the best place for fishing on the Lake. During the season the fishermen from all the resorts at the south end of the Lake bring their patrons over in this direction. The Inn has its own fleet of gasoline launches and row boats, with experienced men to handle them, and it supplies fishing tackle free, but those who wish to use the rod must bring that with them. As is explained in the chapter on fishing, the trout of Lake Tahoe are taken both by rod and "jerk line" trolling. Near Glenbrook, however, the rod can be used to greater advantage than anywhere else, and catches of from one-half to thirty pounds are of daily occurrence.

While promiscuous fishing is not allowed now in the famous Marlette Lake, eight miles away, the patrons of Glenbrook Inn can always secure permits, without any vexatious inquiries or delays, and there an abundance of gamey trout of various species are caught.

The bathing facilities here are exceptionally good.

There is a long stretch of sandy beach, which extends far out into the water, thus ensuring both warmth and safety to children as well as adults.

In mountain and trail climbing Glenbrook has a field all its own. The ride or drive to Marlette Lake is a beautiful one, and the climb to Marlette Peak not arduous. The chief mountain peaks easily reached form Glenbrook are Dubliss, Edith, and Genoa Peaks, which not only afford the same wonderful and entrancing views of Lake Tahoe that one gains from Freel's, Mt. Tallac, Ellis and Watson's Peaks, but in addition lay before the entranced vision the wonderful Carson Valley, with Mt. Davidson and other historic peaks on the eastern horizon.

The drive along the shore by the famous Cave Rock to Lakeside Park or Tallac is one that can be enjoyed daily, and for those who like driving through and over tree-clad hills, surrounded by majestic mountains, the drive over the Carson road is enchanting.

It is at Glenbrook that the famous Shakespeare head is to be seen graphically described by John Vance Cheney, and quoted elsewhere (Chap. XVI).

TO MARLETTE LAKE FROM GLENBROOK

Marlette Lake and Peak are two of the attractive features to visitors at Glenbrook Inn. The trip can be made in a little over two hours, and as on the return it is downhill nearly all the way, the return trip takes a little less.

Leaving Glenbrook on the excellently kept macadamized road over which Hank Monk used to drive stage from Carson City, the eyes of the traveler are constantly observing new and charming features in the mountain landscape. The Lake with its peculiar attractions is left entirely behind, with not another glimpse of it until we stand on the flume at Lake Marlette. Hence it is a complete change of scenery, for now we are looking ahead to tree-clad summits where eagles soar and the sky shines blue.

About two and a half miles out we come to Spooner's, once an active, bustling, roadside hotel, where in the lumbering and mining days teams lined the road four, six and eight deep. Now, nothing but a ramshackle old building remains to tell of its former greatness. Here we made a sharp turn to the left, leaving the main road and taking the special Marlette Lake road.

We cross the grade of the abandoned railway — the rails, engines and equipment of which are now operating between Truckee and Tahoe — see in the distance the tunnel through which the trains used to take the lumber, and notice on the hillsides the lines of the old flumes which used to convey the water to the reservoir on the other side of the tunnel, or bring water and lumber ready to be sent on the further journey down to Carson City.

My driver was in a reflective mood, and as he pointed these things out to me, made some sage and pertinent remarks about the peculiar features of some industries which required large expenditures to operate, all of which were useless in a comparatively short time. Mainly uphill the road continues through groves of cottonwood, by logged-over mountain slopes and sheep-inhabited meadows until the divide is reached. Here a very rapid downhill speedily brings us to the south edge of Marlette Lake.

Skirting the southern end we follow the road to the caretaker's house, tie our horses, and walk down to the dam, and then on the flume or by its side to a point overlooking Lake Tahoe, from which a marvelously expansive view is to be obtained. We return now to Marlette and while drinking a cup of coffee prepared for us by the hospitable caretaker, glean the following facts in regard to the history and uses of Marlette Lake.

Marlette is an artificial lake, fifteen hundred feet above the level of Lake Tahoe, and about three miles form its easterly shore. Its waters are conveyed by tunnel, flume, etc., over the mountains, the Washoe Valley and up the mountain again to Virginia City. Originally the only supply of water available for Virginia City was from a few springs and mining tunnels. This supply soon became insufficient and many tunnels were run into hills both north and south from Virginia for the express purpose of tapping water.

These soon failed and it became necessary to look for a permanent supply to the main range of the Sierra Nevada twenty-five or more miles away. Accordingly the Virginia and Gold Hill Water Company called upon Hermann Schussler, the engineer under whose supervision the Spring Valley Water Works of San Francisco were constructed. After a careful survey of the ground he found water at Hobart Creek, in the mountains on the east side of Lake Tahoe, and in the spring of 1872, received orders to go ahead and install a water system. He ordered pipe made to fit every

Glenbrook Inn, on Nevada side, Lake Tahoe.

portion of the route. It had to pass across the deep depression of Washoe Valley with water at a perpendicular pressure of 1720 feet, equivalent to 800 pounds to the square inch.

The first operations were so successful that as needs grew the supply flume was extended eight and a half miles to Marlette Lake, thus making the total distance to Virginia City, 31-1/2 miles. This Lake was named after S.H. Marlette, formerly Surveyor General of Nevada, who was associated with W.S. Hobart, of San Francisco, the owner of the land and one of the original projectors of the Water Company.

The site was a natural basin, the dam of which had been broken down or eroded centuries ago. A dam was built in 1875, and later raised eleven feet higher so as to afford more storage capacity. The area of the lake is now about 600 acres (before the heightening of the dam it was 300 acres), and its storage capacity is about two billion gallons.

When the supply was enlarged a second pipe was laid alongside the first with an equal capacity, each being able to convey 2,200,000 gallons every twenty-four hours. A third pipe was installed later. The second and third pipes were laid by the late Captain J.B. Overton, who was Superintendent of the Company for over thirty-two years. Captain Overton also extended the flume lines, constructed the tunnel through the mountain ridge, built the Marlette Lake dam and made many other improvements and extensions.

On leaving Marlette Lake through an opening at the lower portion of the dam the water is conducted five miles in a covered flume and thence through a tunnel four thousand feet long through the summit of the dividing ridge or rim of the Tahoe basin to its easterly side.

From this point it is again conducted through covered flumes, together with water from Hobart Creek and other streams, to the intake of the pipes across Washoe Valley. These pipes are three in number, two twelve-inch and one ten-inch. The difference in elevation between the inlet and discharge from No. 1 and No. 2 pipes is 465 feet. The difference in elevation between the inlet and discharge of No. 3 pipe is 565 feet.

The pipes are laid across Washoe Valley in the form of inverted syphons. At the lowest point in the valley, the perpendicular pressure is 1720 feet on No. 1 and No. 2 pipes and 1820 feet on No. 3 pipe. The pipelines go up and down nine canyons in their course across the Valley. Each line is something over seven miles in length. The pressure gauges at Lake View, the point of heaviest pressure, register 820 lbs. on No. 1 and No. 2 pipes when filled, and 910 lbs. on No. 3 pipe when filled.

When this work was first contemplated, many hy-

Sunset at Glenbrook, looking west across Lake Tahoe.

draulic engineers condemned the project as impossible, as never before had water been carried so far under such pressure. But the fact that the first pipes laid by Engineer Schussler are still in active use demonstrates the scientific and practical knowledge and skill with which he attacked the problem.

It is an interesting fact to note that, prior to the building of the dam, part of the water was used for "fluming" lumber and wood to Lake View, and also for a short period of time after the dam was constructed. But for the past twenty years this practice has been discontinued, the water being solely for the supply of Virginia City.

The total cost of the work was about $3,500,000. The Company is now under the immediate and personal supervision of James M. Leonard. The flumes and pipelines have recently been rebuilt and repaired where necessary so that the entire system is in excellent condition and a high state of efficiency.

DUBLISS, EDITH AND GENOA PEAKS

The ride to these three peaks can easily be made in a day, and though they are all in reasonably close proximity, there are differences enough in their respective outlooks to make a visit to each of them enjoyable and profitable. With a good saddle horse from the Glenbrook stables, a guide, and a lunch tied to the saddle, one may start out confident that a most delightful scenic trip is before him. The first hour's riding is over the rocky and tree-clad slopes, far wilder and more rugged than one would imagine, rudely bordering the Lake southwards.

Then turning east, hills and vales, flowery meads and dainty native nurseries of pines, firs and hemlocks enchant the eye. Reaching the summit of any one of the peaks, a wide expanse of Lake is offered, extending to the surrounding mountains north, south and west, but on Genoa Peak an additional charm is found in the close proximity of the Nevada Valley, and mountains to the eastward. The contrast between the richly clad Sierra and the apparently unclothed, volcanic Nevada mountains is remarkable.

CHAPTER XXVII

CARNELIAN BAY AND TAHOE COUNTRY CLUB

ON making the circuit of the Lake, the last stopping place on the trip starting south, or the first when starting north and east, is Carnelian Bay. This is a new settlement rapidly coming into prominence because of the number of cottages and bungalows erected by their owners on their own lots. From early until late in the seasons of 1913 and 1914 the sounds of the saw and hammer were seldom still. The result is the growth of quite a summer settlement. Easy of access, either by train and steamer from Truckee, or by direct wagon or auto road via Truckee or the new boulevard from the south end of the Lake, Carnelian Bay attracts the real home seeker.

It has been the first section to fully realize what John Le Conte has so ably set forth in another chapter on Tahoe as a summer residence. With the completion of the state highway around Lake Tahoe and the automobile route from Reno and Carson City, Carnelian Bay will be adjacent to the main arteries of travel. The proposed link of the Lincoln Highway around the north shore of the Lake will put Carnelian Bay directly on the great international auto road.

The beauties of Lake Tahoe can hardly be magnified to the people of the West. Those who have once viewed its wonders and its magnificence, who have for a season breathed its invigorating and stimulating atmosphere, who have caught the wily trout which abound in its waters, who have sailed, or rowed, or motorboated over its indigo-blue surface, carry in memory pictures in comparison with which any word picture would be inadequate and incomplete.

Hence the projectors of Carnelian Bay struck a popular note when, out of their 81-acre tract, they put on sale convenient-sized lots. Of these 75 were purchased almost immediately, and by 1914 there were over 45 homes, large and small, already erected. Every lot was sold to a purchaser who expressed his definite intention of speedily erecting a house, cottage or bungalow for his own use. Hence the community is of a selected class into which one may come with confidence and assurance of congenial associations.

While there is no hotel at present, there are several cottages and bungalows especially erected for rent to transient guests, and a good store, together with its close proximity to Tahoe City and Tahoe Tavern, render a summer vacation here one of comfort, pleasure and perfect enjoyment.

Overview of Carnelian Bay, north shore, Lake Tahoe.

Cottage and tents made up the Carnelian Bay resort.

PROJECTED TAHOE COUNTRY CLUB AT CARNELIAN

The increasing need exists among those who are familiar with the beauties and advantages of Lake Tahoe as a summer residence resort for accommodations for families or transients where the usual comforts of home may be obtained at a cost not prohibitive to the family of ordinary means. Last year no less than 80,000 persons visited Lake Tahoe.

It is safe to say that this number will increase annually, particularly with added accommodations at the Lake and with better facilities for automobile travel. The proximity of Lake Tahoe to the coast cities and the cities of the Sierra and the Middle West makes it at once attractive to the businessman who desires to spend his summer vacation where the family is located for the summer months.

The Tahoe Country Club is designed to meet the need. The incorporators have taken over in fee simple a beautiful tract embracing about 1500 feet of the beach at Carnelian Bay, California, perhaps the most attractive site on Lake Tahoe. It commands a view of the entire length of the Lake, looking toward the south, and embracing a magnificent panoramic view of the mountains beyond. This site contains approximately nine acres, and includes a natural inland harbor, making off from a protected bay. The beach is shallow, of clean sand, sloping down from easy terraces beautified by shade trees and lawns.

The plan of organization of the Tahoe Country Club is cooperative. Its benefits are to be shared by its members, their families, and such of their friends as they may invite to be guests of the club. The properties taken over by the incorporation, including the 1500 feet of beach front, harbor, wharf, and a system of water works already installed, together with the perpetual title to the water rights, is conservatively appraised at $30,000. This is held in fee, free from encumbrance.

The charter or organizing members of the club will be the investors in the bonds issued and secured on the real estate taken over by the incorporation. This bond issue, the redemption of which will be guaranteed by first mortgage on the properties, will be for $20,000. These will be in denominations of $100 each, bearing six percent interest after two years from June 1, 1914, and will be redeemable, at the option of the mortgagor, at any regular annual interest period on or after five years from the date of issue. They will be payable in fifteen years.

Each original bond purchaser becomes a charter life member of the club, entitled, without the payment of annual dues or other assessments, to the privileges and benefits offered. These, briefly, aside from the natural advantages of location, scenery, etc., are an assured congenial environment, known associations (not always a possibility in a public summer hotel), the absence of every possible unpleasant influence, opportunities for fishing, boating, tennis, golf and other outdoor sports, and first class accommodations at a cost far below that charged at regular high class summer hotels.

CHAPTER XXVIII

FISHING IN THE LAKES OF THE TAHOE REGION

Fishing in Lake Tahoe and the other lakes of the region is a pleasure and a recreation as well as an art and a science. There are laymen, tyros, neophytes, proficients and artists. The real fraternity has passes, catchwords, grips and signals to which outsiders seek to "catch on" in vain.

The chief native trout of Lake Tahoe is locally known as the "cutthroat" because of a brilliant dash of red on either side of the throat. The name, however, gives no hint of the exquisite beauty of the markings of the fish, the skill required and excitement developed in catching it, and the dainty deliciousness of its flesh when properly cooked.

Owing to the wonderful adaptability of Lake Tahoe, and the lakes and brooks of the surrounding region, to fish life, several other well-known varieties have been introduced, all of which have thrived abundantly and now afford opportunity for the skill of the fisherman and delight the palate of the connoisseur. These are the Mackinac, rainbow, eastern brook, and Loch Levin.

There is also found a beautiful and dainty silver trout, along the shore where the cold waters of the various brooks or creeks flow into Lake Tahoe (and also in some of the smaller lakes), that is much prized. Some fishermen claim that it is the "prettiest, gamiest, sweetest and choicest" fish of the Lake, and it has been caught weighing as high as 12 pounds.

Another fish, native to Lake Tahoe, is found in vast numbers of the Indians in the fall. The ordinary summer visitor to Tahoe seldom sees or hears of these, as they rarely bite until the summer season is over, say in October. This is a white fish, varying in size from half a pound to four pounds in weight, with finely flavored flesh. It is found in shallow water and near the mouths of the creeks, and the Indians have a way of "snagging" them in.

Building a kind of half platform and half stone screen over the pools where they abound, the Indians take a long wire, the end of which they have sharpened and bent to form a rude hook. Then, without bait, or any attempt at sport, they lower the hook and as rapidly as the fish appear, "snag" them out, literally by the hundreds. Most of these are salted down for winter use. This is supposed to be a native fish, and the traditions of the Indians confirm the supposition.

The largest native Tahoe trout caught, of which there is any authentic record, was captured not far from Glenbrook and weighed 35 pounds; and, strange to say, its capturer was an amateur. This, the boatmen tell me, is generally the case — the amateurs almost invariably bringing in the largest fish. Although there are rumors of fish having been caught weighing as high as 45 pounds, it is impossible to trace these down to any accurate and reliable source. Hence, until there is positive assurance to the contrary, it may be regarded that this catch is the largest on record.

The common Tahoe method of "trolling" for trout is different from the eastern method. It is the result of years of experience and is practically as follows: A copper line, 100 to 200 feet long, which sinks of its own weight, on which a large copper spoon is placed above the hook, which is baited with a minnow and angleworm, is used.

Thrown into the water the line is gently pulled forward by the angler, then allowed to sink back. He takes care, however, always to keep it taut. This makes the spoon revolve and attracts the fish. The moment the angler feels a strike he gives his line a quick jerk and proceeds to pull in, landing the fish with the net. The local term for this method of fishing is "jerk-line."

The copper line used is generally a 6 oz. for 100 feet, and the length is adjusted to the places in which the fisherman wishes to operate.

Let us, for a short time, watch the would-be angler. Women are often far more eager than men. The hotels of Tahoe keep their own fishing boats. The larger ones have a fleet of twenty or more, and in the season this is found insufficient for the number who wish to try their hand and prove their luck.

Often great rivalry exists not only in securing the boatmen who have had extra good luck or displayed extraordinary skill, but also between the guests as to the extent of their various "catches." When a boatman has taken his "fare" into regions that have proven successful, and does this with frequency, it is natural that those who wish to run up a large score should try hard to secure him. This adds to the fun — especially to the onlookers.

The boat is all ready; the angler takes his (or her) seat in the cushioned stern, feet resting upon a double carpet — this is fishing *de luxe.* The oarsman pushes off and quietly rows away from the pier out into deep water which, at Tahoe, varies from 75 feet to the unknown depths of 1500 feet or more.

The color of the water suggests even to the tyro the depth, and as soon as the "Tahoe blue" is reached the boatman takes his large hand reel, unfastens the hook, baits it with minnow and worm and then hands it to the angler, with instructions to allow it to unreel when thrown out on the port side at the stern.

At the same time he prepares a second hook from a second reel which he throws out at the starboard side. At the end of each copper line a few yards of fish cord are attached in which a loop is adjusted for the fingers. This holds the line secure while the backward and forward pulls are being made, and affords a good hold for the hook-impaling "jerk" when a fish strike is felt. While the "angler" pulls on his line the boatman slowly rows along, and holding his line on the fingers of his "starboard" hand, he secures the proper motion as he rows.

Then, pulling over the ledges or ridges between shallow and deeper, or deeper and deep water, he exercises all his skill and acquired knowledge and experience to enable his "fare" to make a good catch. As soon as a strike is felt and duly hooked, he sees that the line is drawn in steadily so as not to afford the fish a chance to rid itself of the hook, and, as soon as it appears, he drops his oar, seizes the net, and lands the catch to the great delight of his less-experienced fare.

Many are the tales that a privileged listener may hear around the fisherman's night-haunts, telling of the antics of their many and various fares, when a strike has been made. Some become so excited that they tangle up their lines, and one boatman assures me that, on one occasion a lady was so "rattled" that she finally wrapped her line in such a fashion around both elbows that she sat helpless and he had to come to her rescue and release her.

On another occasion a pair of newly weds went out angling. When hubby caught a fish, the pair celebrated the catch by enthusiastically kissing, totally regardless of the surprise or envy that might be excited in the bosom of the poor boatman, and when "wifie" caught a fish the same procedure was repeated. "Of course," said the boatman, in telling me the story, "that pair caught more fish than anyone I had had for a month, simply to taunt me with their carryings on."

In the height of the season the guests become the most enthusiastic fishermen of all. They take a growing pride in their increasing scores and the fishing then resolves itself into an earnest, almost deadly, tournament in which each determines to outscore the others. This is what the boatmen enjoy — though it often means longer hours and more severe rowing — for it is far easier to work (so they say) for a fare who is really interested than for one who is half-hearted and indifferent.

As these rivals' boats pass each other, they call out in triumph their rising luck or listen gloweringly to the recital of others' good fortune, when they are compelled to silence because of their own failure.

Sometimes the boatmen find these rivalries rather embarrassing, for the excitement and nervousness of their fares become communicated to them. Then, perhaps, they lose a promising strike, or, in their hurry, fail to land the fish when it appears. Scolding and recriminations are not uncommon on such occasions, and thus is the gaiety of nations added to.

What is it that really constitutes fisherman's luck? Who can tell? The theories of Tahoe fishermen are as many as there are men. Some think one thing, some another. One will talk learnedly of the phases of the moon, another of the effect of warmer or colder weather upon the bugs upon which the fish feed.

Sometimes one will "jerk" half a day and never get a strike; other days the boat will scarcely have left the wharf before one pulls the fish in almost as fast as hooks can be baited and thrown out. When fishing is slow an amateur soon become tired out. The monotonous pull on the line soon makes the arm weary, and destroys all enthusiasm. But let the strikes begin and weariness disappears. Some days the fish will bite for an hour, say from eleven to twelve, and then quit and not give another strike all day. The very next day, in the same spot, one cannot get a bite until afternoon.

One of my fishermen friends once related the following: "Again and again I have heard old and experienced fishermen say that no fish can be caught in a thunderstorm. Yet in July 1913, four boats were towed by a launch out the the Nevada side, near to Glenbrook. It appeared stormy before the party left, but they refused to be daunted or discouraged by the doleful prognostications of the know-it-alls.

Before long the lightning began, the clouds hung heavy, and while they fished they were treated to alternate doses of thunder, lightning, cloud, sunshine, rain and hail. In less than an hour every member of the party — and there were several ladies — were soaked and drenched to the skin, but all were happy. For, contrary to the assertions of the experts, every angler was having glorious success. Each boat secured its full quota, 40 fish to each, and the catch averaged 70 pounds to a boat, scarcely a fish being pulled out that did not weigh over a pound. Talk about luck; these people surely had it."

Fishing in Grass Lake near Glen Alpine Springs.

Launch at right is towing boats to the fishing grounds.

Once again, I was out one day with Boat No. 14 (each boat has its own number) and the boatman told me the following story. I know him well and his truthfulness is beyond question. He had with him two well-known San Francisco gentlemen, whom I will name respectively, Rosenbaum and Rosenblatt. They were out for the day. For hours they "jerked" without success. At last one turned to the other and said: "Rosie, I've got a hunch that our luck's going to change. I'm going to count twenty, and before I'm through we'll each have a fish." Slowly he began to count, one — two — three. Just as he counted fourteen, both men felt a strike, gave the fateful jerk, and pulled in a large fish, and from that moment their luck changed.

This is not the whole of the story, however, Some days later the same boatman was out on the Nevada side with two gentlemen who could not get a bite. Merely to while away the time the boatman told the foregoing facts. To his surprise and somewhat to his disgust at his own indiscretion in telling the story, one of the gentlemen began to count, and, believe it or not, he assures me that at the fateful fourteen, he gained a first class strike, and continued to have success throughout the afternoon.

As he left the boat he turned to his companion and said, "Well, that fourteen's proved a lucky number. I'm going right over to the roulette wheel to see what luck it will give me over there."

My boatman friend added that as he heard nothing of any great winnings at the wheel that night, and Mr. X looked rather quiet and sober the next day, he is afraid the luck did not last. Needless to say that except to me, and then only in my capacity as a writer, the story has never been told.

Now, while the jerk-line method brings much joy to the heart of the successful and lucky amateur, the genuine disciple of Izaak Walton scorns this unsportsman-like method. He comes earlier in the season, April, May, or June, or later, in September, and brings his rod and line, when the fish keep nearer to the shore in the pot holes and rocky formations, and then angles with the fly. It is only at these times, however, that he is at all likely to have any success, as the Tahoe trout does not generally rise to the fly.

Yet, strange to say, in all the smaller trout-stocked lakes of the region, Fallen Leaf, Cascade, Heather, Lily, Susie, Lucile, Grass, Le Conte, Rock Bound, the Velmas, Angora, Echo, Tamarack, Lake of the Woods, Rainbow, Pit, Gilmore, Kalmia, Fontinalis, Eagle, Granite, and as many more, the trout are invariably caught with the fly, though the species most sought after is not the native Tahoe trout, but the eastern brook. This is essentially fish for the genuine angler, and many are the tales — true and otherwise — told of the sport the capture of this fish has afforded in the region.

There are several interesting peculiarities about the fish of Lake Tahoe and its region that it is well to note. In the large lake (Tahoe) the native cutthroat grows to much the largest size — the 35-lb. one referred to elsewhere being proof of its great growth.

The next in size is the Mackinac which is often caught as large as 10 lb., and now and again up to 15 lb.

In Fallen Leaf Lake, which was stocked with Mackinac some years ago, the native trout has become comparatively scarce, the former seemingly having driven it out, though in Lake Tahoe there is no such result. In Fallen Leaf not more than one or two in ten will be cutthroats, while Mackinacs abound, up to 6 lbs. and 7 lbs. in weight. Occasionally much larger fish are seen, though they are seldom brought to net. Not long ago a Loch Levin, weighing 12 lbs. was caught here.

While the catch of fish in the smaller lakes of the region is exceedingly large the fish themselves are smaller, the opportunities for hiding and fattening and growing older being comparatively greater in the larger body of water.

During the height of the season when there are a great many boats out it is common to hire a launch which will tow from four to a dozen boats over towards Emerald Bay on the California side, or towards Glenbrook on the Nevada side, where the fishing grounds are known to be of the best.

The boatmen especially enjoy these days out — although the fares may not always suspect it — as it gives them a change from their ordinary routine and table fare. They enjoy trout as well as do the visitors, and of course, they are all expert cooks as well as boatmen. When noon comes, if there has been any luck, a campfire is built and the fish are fried, or broiled on the coals, or by experts, made into an excellent chowder. And never does one enjoy a fish dinner so much as under these circumstances. The exercise, the fresh air, the motion over the water, the deliciousness and delicate flavor of the fish, all conspire to tempt the most capricious appetite.

Once in a while a black bass will be caught, though it is not believed that this is a native fish. It does not seem to thrive in Tahoe though the boatmen tell me they occasionally see a few, especially off the docks at Tallac and other points at the south end of the Lake.

Now and again small bull-heads will be seen, and a very small rock-bass. But these never bite on hook and line, and are seldom found more than two or three inches long.

On the other hand big schools of suckers and chubs are seen. The former naturally are scorned by all true fishermen as they are regarded as hogs, or scavengers, and are thrown back whenever caught, or are taken and

Chris Nelson, with his catch, a 23 pound Tahoe trout.

fed to the gulls or pelicans. The chubs occasionally are hooked and are from half a pound to a pound and a half in size. As a rule these are thrown back, though they make good eating to those who do not object to their excess of bones.

One of the most interesting of sights is to see one of the schools of minnows that fairly abound in Lake Tahoe. In the clear and pellucid water one can clearly see them swim along. As they pass a rocky place a trout will dart out and catch his prey. A flutter at once passes through the whole school. Yet, strange to say, the trout will sometimes swim around such a body and either stupify them with fear, or hypnotize them into forgetfulness of their presence, for they will float quietly in the center of the mass, catching the minnows one by one as they need them without exciting the least fear or attention.

The minnows generally remain in fairly shallow water, and keep so closely together that a line of demarcation is made between where they are and outside, as if it had been cut with a knife along a straight edge, and in some mysterious way the fish dare not cross it, though it constantly moves along with their movements.

It will be obvious that necessarily there is much market fishing in Lake Tahoe and its surrounding lakes. Indeed there are large numbers of fishermen — Indians and whites — who supply the various hotels both of the Lake region and in San Francisco, Oakland, Sacramento and adjacent cities, and even as far as Denver and Salt Lake City, eastwards, and Los Angeles to the south. These fishermen are very persistent in their work, keeping at it from early morning until late at night, though their catches are supposed to be officially regulated.

The amount of fish caught and shipped by these market fishermen is remarkable. In 1911 the report shows that over 22,000 pounds were sent out by express, over half of which were sent from Tallac alone. And this does not take any account of the amount caught and eaten by private residents around the Lake, by the visitors or by the hotels.

The fish that are to be shipped are not, as one might naturally suppose, packed in ice. Experience has demonstrated a better way which is now universally followed. At Tallac the hotel has a large place devoted to this process, which is practically as follows:

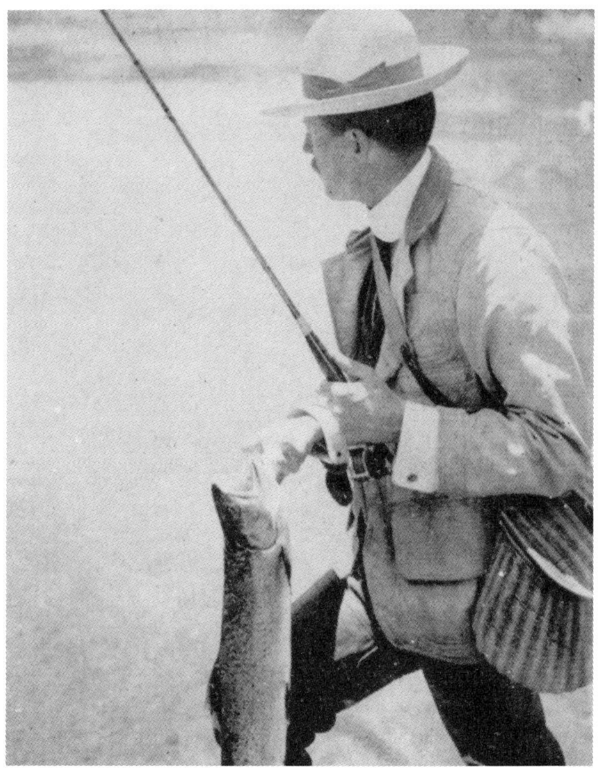

The triumphant angler at Lake Tahoe.

An early morning catch of Lake Tahoe trout.

Each boatman has a fishbox, numbered to correspond with his boat. These are kept in the water during the season, and if the catch of his fare for one day is not sufficient for a shipment it is placed in the box. When a sufficient number is on hand, they are taken out by the boatman, carefully cleaned and hung up to dry in fly-proof, open-air cages. When perfectly dry inside and out they are packed in sweet-smelling Tallac Meadow hay, and shipped by express.

Many visitors cannot understand why there are no fish in some of the lakes that, to their eyes, seem just as well adapted for fish as others that possess an abundance. Even old timers do not all know the reason. If a lake is shallow, when the deep snow falls it soon sinks below the surface in a heavy mushy mass that presses down upon the fish and prevents their breathing.

If a severe frost follows and the mass freezes, the ice squeezes the fish to the bottom. Over three years ago Watson took fish to Bessie Lake, putting in as many as 6000 fry of Lake Tahoe and other species. The next year, and the following years they were all right, having grown to eight or nine inches in length. Then came a severe winter and in the spring there was not a living fish left. The bottom was strewn with them, many of them with broken backs.

CHAPTER XXIX

HUNTING AT LAKE TAHOE

IN the chapter on the Birds and Animals of the Tahoe Region I have written of the game to be found. There are few places left in the Sierra where such good deer and bear hunting can be found as near Tahoe. During the dense snowfalls the deer descend the western slopes, approaching nearer and nearer to the settlements of the upper foothills, and there they do fairly well until the snow begins to recede in the spring.

They keep as near to the snow line as possible, and are then as tame and gentle almost as sheep. When the season opens, however, they soon flee to certain secret recesses and hidden lairs known to none but the old and experienced guides of the region. There are so many of these wooded retreats, however, and the Tahoe area is so vast, that it is seldom an expert goes out for deer (or bear) that he fails. Hence the sportsman is always assured of "something worthwhile."

As for bear I have told elsewhere of recent hunts on Mt. Freel from Tallac, and the two bears killed there in 1913, and of Carl Flugge's experiences. With Tallac hunters, Flugge, Bob Watson or any other experienced man, one can scarcely fail to have exciting and successful times.

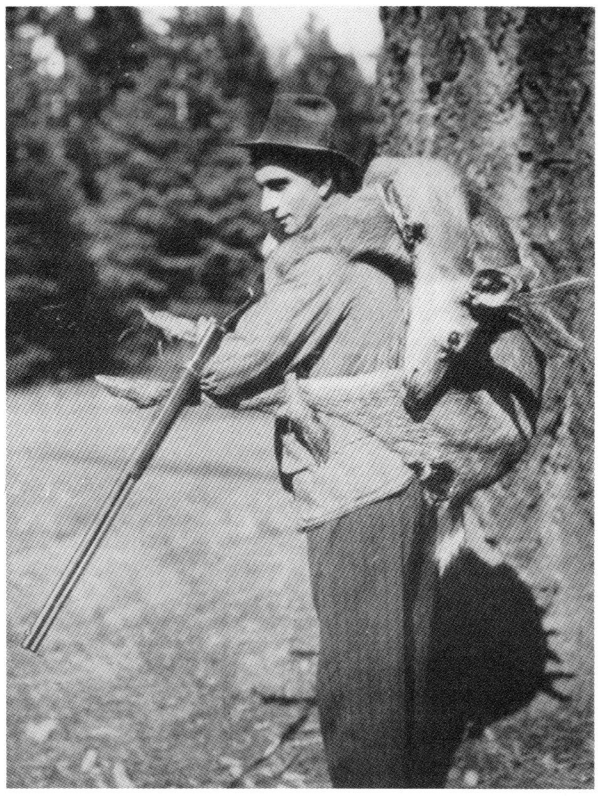

The successful deer hunter at Lake Tahoe.

CHAPTER XXX

THE FLOWERS OF THE TAHOE REGION

IT would be impossible in a space of a brief chapter to present even a list of all the flowers found and recorded in the Tahoe Region. Suffice it to say that 1300 different species already have been listed. This chapter will merely call attention to the most prominent or, on the other hand, the rarer and special flowering plants that the visitor should eagerly search for.

As fast as the snow retires from the sun-kissed slopes the flowers begin to come out. Indeed in April, were one at Tahoe, he could make a daily pilgrimage to the receding snow line and there enjoy new revelations of dainty beauty each morning. For the flowers, as the snow coating becomes thinner, respond to the "call of the sun," and thrust up their spears out of the softened and moistened earth, so that when the last touch of snow is gone they are often already in bud ready to burst forth into flower at the first kiss of sunshine.

In May they come trooping along in all their pristine glory, God's thoughts cast upon the mold of earth, so that even the men and women of downcast eyes and souls may know the ever fresh, ever present love of God.

Most interesting of all is the snow plant *(sarcodes sanguinea Torrey)*. The name is unfortunate. The plant doesn't look like snow, nor does it grow on or in the snow. It simply follows the snow line, as so many of the Sierran plants do, and as the snow melts and leaves the valley, one must climb to find it. It is of a rich red color, which glows in the sunlight like a living thing. It has no leaves but is supplied with overlapping scale-like bracts of a warm, flesh tint. At the lower part of the flower these are rigid and closely adherent to the stem, but higher up they become looser and curl gracefully about among the vivid red bells. In the spring of 1914 they were wonderfully plentiful at the Tavern and all around the Lake. I literally saw hundreds of them.

Next in interest comes the heather, both red and white. In Desolation Valley, as well as around most of the Sierran lakes of the Tahoe region, beds of heather are found that have won enthusiastic Scotchmen to declare that Tahoe heather beats that of Scotland.

The red heather is the more abundant, and its rich deep green leaves and crown of glowing red makes it to be desired, but the white heather is a flower fit for the delicate corsage bouquet of a queen, or the lapel of the noblest of men. Dainty and exquisite, perfect in shape and color, its tiny white bell is *par excellence* the emblem of passionate purity.

Blue gentians *(Gentina calycosa, Griseb)* abound, their deep blue blossoms rivaling the pure blue of our Sierra skies. These often come late in the season and cheer the hearts of those who come upon them with "a glad sweet surprise." There are also white gentians found aplenty.

The waterlilies of the Tahoe region are strikingly beautiful. In many of the Sierra lakes conditions seem to exist which make them flourish and they are found in plentiful quantities.

Wild marigolds abound in large patches, even on the mountain heights, where there is plenty of moisture and sunshine, and a species of marguerite, or mountain daisy, is not uncommon. The Indian paintbrush is found everywhere and is in full bloom in deepest red in September.

Wild sunflowers also abound except where the sheep have been. Then not a sign of once vast patches can be found. They are eaten clear to the ground.

The mullein attains especial dignity in this mountain region. Stately and proud it rises above the lesser though more beautiful flowers of the wild. It generally dies down in September, though an occasional flowering stalk may be seen as late as October.

Another very common but ever welcome plant, for its pungent and pleasing odor, is the pennyroyal. It abounds throughout the whole region and its hardiness keeps it flowering until late in the fall.

Beautiful and delicate at all times wherever seen, the wild snowdrop is especially welcome in the Tahoe region where, amid soaring pines and firs, it timidly though faithfully blooms and cheers the eye with its rare purity.

Now and again one will find the beautiful California fuschia *(zauschneria Californica,* Presl.), its delicate beauty delighting the eye and suggesting some of the rare orchids of a pale yellow tint.

The Sierra primrose *(Primula Suffrutescens)* is often found near to the snow line. Its tufts of evergreen leaves seem to revel in the cold water of the melting snow and the exquisite rose tints of the flowers are enhanced by the pure white of what snow is left to help bring them into being.

It is natural that, in a region so abounding in water, ferns of many kinds should also abound. The common brake flourishes on the eastern slopes, but I have never found the maiden hair. On the western slopes it is abundant, but rarely if ever found on the easterly exposures.

Mountain heather, in Desolation Valley.

Most striking and attractive among the shrubs are the mountain ash, the mountain mahogany *(cereocarpus parvifolius,* Nutt.), the California laurel *(umbellularia Californica,* Nutt.) and the California holly,or *toyon.* The rich berries, the green leaves, the exquisite and dainty flowers, the delicious and stimulating odors all combine to make these most welcome in every Sierran landscape, no matter at what season they appear.

While in the foregoing notes on the flowers of the Tahoe region I have hastily gone over the ground, one particular mountain to the north of Tahoe has been so thoroughly and scientifically studied that it seems appropriate to call more particular attention to it in order that botanists may realize how rich the region is in rare treasures.

One could almost write a "Botany" of Mt. Rose alone, so interesting are the floral specimens found there. This mountain stands unique in the Lake Tahoe region in that it is an intermediate between the high mountains of the Sierra Nevada and those of the interior of the Great Basin. Its flora are undoubtedly influenced by the dry atmospheric conditions that exist on the eastern side. A mere suggestion only can be given here of the full enjoyment afforded by a careful study of what it offers.

At from 10,000 feet up the following new species have been found. *Eriogonum rhodanthum,* a perennial which forms dense mats on hard rocky ground. The caudex is made up of many strands twisted together like rope, its numerous branches terminated by clusters of very small, new and old leaves, with flower clusters. Another similar species is the *E. rosensis.*

An interesting rockcress is found in the *Arabis Depauperata,* which here shows the results of its fierce struggles for existence. It bears minute purple flowers.

Flowering in the middle of August, but past flowering at the end of September the *Gilia montana* is found, with its numerous white and pink leaves.

Nearby is the *Phlox dejecta* in large quantities, resembling a desert moss, and covering the rocks with its tinted carpet.

An Indian paintbrush with a flower in an oblong cream-colored spike, with purple blotches, was named *Castilleia inconspicua,* possibly because it is so much less conspicuous and alluring to the eye than its well-known and striking brother of the California fields, *C. parviflora.*

This species has been of great interest to botanists, as when first observed it was placed in the genus *Orthocarpus.* Professor P. Beveridge Kennedy, of the University of Nevada, thinks it is undoubtedly a connecting link between the two genera. It has been found only on Mount Rose, where it is common at between 9000 and 10,000 feet elevation. It reaches, however, to the summit, though it is more sparingly found there.

Professor Kennedy describes *Hulsea Caespitosa,* or Alpine dandelion, a densely pubescent plant, emitting a disagreeable odor, whose large yellow flowers surprise one when seen glowing apparently out of the masses of loose volcanic rock. It is soon found, however, that they have roots deep down in good soil beneath. Another new species, *Chrysothamnus Monocephala,* or Alpine rabbit brush, is a very low, shrubby plant, with insignificant pale yellow flowers.

A beautiful little plant, well adapted to rockeries and suited for cultivation, is *Polemonium Montrosense.* Under good conditions it grows excellently. It was found on the summit of Mt. Rose, and at lower elevations.

Clusters of the Alpine Monkey flower *(Mimulus Implexus,* Greene), are also found on Mt. Rose, as well as on other Tahoe mountain summits. The rich yellow flowers bloom profusely, though their bed is often a moraine of wet rocks over which a turbulent cold stream has recently subsided.

Slightly below the summit the little elephant's head have been found *(Elephantella attolens* (Gray) Heller). Rydberg, in his *Flora of Montana,* showed that these were not properly the true *pendicularis,* as they had hitherto been regarded, hence the new name. The corolla strikingly resembles the head of an elephant, the beak of the galea forming the trunk, the lateral lobes of the lips the ears, and the stigma the finger-like appendage of the trunk.

In August, growing below the perpetual snow banks at about 10,000 feet elevation that supply an abundance of moisture, one will often find clumps of *Rhodiola Integrifolia,* which attract the eye with their deep reddish-purple flowers and fruits. The leaves also have a purple tinge.

Nearby, clambering over the granite boulders of the Alpine heath, *Cassiope Mertensianae,* with its multitude of rose-tinted flower bells, sometimes is found, though not in the profusion it displays in Desolation Valley.

Another very interesting plant is the alpine currant *(Ribes Inebrians,* Lindl.) which between the years 1832 and 1907 has received no less than eight different names accorded by European and American botanists. It is a remarkable shrub, in that it occurs higher on the mountain than any other form of vegetation except lichens. The roots penetrate deeply into the crevices of the lava rocks, enabling it to withstand the fierce winds.

The flowers, which appear in August, are white, shading to pink, and the red berries, which are not especially palatable on account of their insipid taste and numerous seeds, are abundant in September. Another new Mt. Rose *ribes* has been named *Churchii* in honor of Professor J.E. Church, Jr., whose original work at the Mt. Rose Observatory is described in the chapter devoted to that purpose.

Growing at elevations of from 6000 to 10,000 feet, displaying a profusion of white flowers sometimes delicately tinged with light purple is the *Phlox Douglasii,* Hook. It is low but with loose, much branched, prostrate stems and remarkably stout, almost woody roots.

A new Alpine willow *(Salix Caespitosa)* has also been discovered. Professor Kennedy thus writes of it:

> The melting snow, as it comes through and over the rocks in the nature of a spring, brings with it particles of sand and vegetation, which form a very shallow layer of soil on a flat area to one side of the main branch of the stream. On this the willow branches adhere like ivy, rooting at every joint and interlaced so as to form a dense mat. From these, erect leafy shoots, one or two inches high, appear, with the many flowered catkins extending above the foliage. The pistillate plants occupy separate but adjacent areas to the staminate ones.

CHAPTER XXXI

THE CHAPARRAL OF THE TAHOE REGION

The word *chaparral* is a Spanish word, transferred bodily into our language, without, however, retaining its strict and original significance. In Spanish it means a plantation of evergreen oaks, or, thick bramble bushes entangled with thorny shrubs in clumps. Hence, in the west, it has come to mean any low or scrub brush that thickly covers a hill or mountainside. As there is a varied chaparral in the Tahoe region, it is well for the visitor to know of what it is mainly composed.

Experience has demonstrated that where the larger lumber is cut off close on the Sierran slopes of the Tahoe region the low bushy chaparral at once takes full possession. It seems to prevent the tree seeds from growing and thus is an effectual preventive to reforestation.

This, however, is generally not so apparent east of the main range as it is on the western slopes. One of its chief elements is the manzanita *(Arctostaphylos patula)* easily distinguishable by the red wood of its stem and larger branches, glossy leaves, waxen blossoms (when in flower) and green or red berries in the early autumn.

The snowbush abounds. It is a low sage-green bush, very thorny, hence is locally called "bide-a-wee" from the name given by the English soldiers to a very thorny bush they had to encounter during the Boer War. In the late days of spring and even as late as July it is covered with a white blossom that makes it glorious and attractive.

Then there is the thimbleberry with its big, light yellow, sprawling leaves, and its attractively red, thimble-shaped, but rather tasteless, berries. The Indians, however, are very fond of them, and so are some of the birds and animals, likewise of the service berries, which look much like the blueberry, though their flavor is not so choice.

Here and there patches of the wild gooseberry add to the tangle of the chaparral. The gooseberries when ripe are very red, as are the currants, but they are armored with a tough skin completely covered with sharp, hairy thorns. In Southern California all the fruit of the wild *ribes* have the thorns, but they do not compare in penetrating power and strength with those of the Tahoe gooseberries.

One of the most charming features of the chaparral is the mountain ash, especially when the berries are ripe and red. The Scotch name *rowan* seems peculiarly appropriate. Even while the berries are yellow they are attractive to the eye, and alluring to the birds, but when they become red they give a splendid dash of rich color that sets off the whole mountainside.

The mountain mahogany is not uncommon (*Cereocarpus parvifolius*, Nutt.) and though its green flowers are inconspicuous, its long, solitary plumes at fruiting time attract the eye.

While the California laurel (*Umbellularia Californica*, Nutt.) often grows to great height, it is found in chaparral clumps on the mountainsides. It is commonly known as the bay tree, on account of the bay-like shape and odor of its leaves when crushed. It gives a spicy fragrance to the air and is always welcome to those who know it.

In many places throughout the mountains of the Tahoe region there are clumps or groves of wild cherry (*Prunus Demissa*, Walpers), the cherries generally ripening in September. But if one expects the ripe red *wild* cherries to have any of the delicious richness and sweetness of the ripe Queen Anne or other good variety, he is doomed to sad disappointment. For they are sour and bitter—bitter as quinine—and this is perhaps the reason their juice has been extracted and made into medicine supposed to have extraordinary tonic and healing virtue.

The elder is often found (*Sambucus Glauca*, Nutt.), sometimes quite tall and at other times broken down by the snow, but bravely covering its bent and gnarled trunks and branches with dense foliage and cream-white blossom clusters. The berries are always attractive to the eye in their purple tint, with the creamy blush on them, and happy is that traveler who has an expert make for him an elderberry pie, or distill the rich cordial the berries make.

Another feature of the chaparral often occupies the field entirely to itself, viz., the chamisal or greasewood (*Adenostoma fasciculatum*, Hook. and Arn.). Its small clustered and needle-like leaves, richly covered with large, feathery panicles of tiny blossoms, give it an appearance not unlike Scotch heather, and make a mountainside dainty and beautiful.

The California buckeye (*Aesculus Californica*, Nutt.) is also found, especially upon stream banks or on the moist slopes of the canyons. Its light gray limbs, broad leaves, and long, white flower spikes make it an attractive shrub or tree (for it often reaches 40 feet in height), and when the leaves drop, as they do early, the skeleton presents a beautiful and delicate network against the deep azure of the sky.

Another feature of the chaparral is the scrub oak. In 1913 the bushes were almost free from acorns. They generally appear only every other year, and when they do bear, the crop is a wonderfully numerous one.

A vast amount of wild lilac (*Ceanothus Velutinus*) is found on all the slopes. It generally blooms in June and then the hillsides are one fragrant and glowing mass of vivid white tinged with the creamy hue that adds so much charm to the flowers.

The year 1913, however, was a peculiar year, throughout, for plant life. In the middle of September in Page's Meadows a large patch of ceanothus was in full bloom, either revealing a remarkably late flowering, or a second effort at beautification.

Another ceanothus, commonly called mountain birch, is often found. When in abundance and in full flower it makes a mountainside appear as if covered with drifted snow.

Willows abound in the canyons and on the mountains of the Tahoe region, and they are an invariable sign of the near presence of water.

There is scarcely a canyon where alders, cottonwoods and quaking aspens may not be found. In 1913 either the lack of water, some adverse climatic condition, or some fungus blight caused the aspen leaves to blotch and fall from the trees as early as the beginning of September. As a rule they remain until late in October, changing to autumnal tints of every richness and hue and reminding one of the glorious hues of the eastern maples when touched by the first frosts of winter.

To one used to exploring dry and desert regions, such as the Colorado and Mohave Deserts of Southern California, the Grand Canyon region, the Navajo Reservation, etc., in Arizona and New Mexico, the constant presence of water in the Tahoe region is a perpetual delight. Daily in my trips here I have wondered at the absence of my canteen and sometimes in moments of forgetfulness I would reach for it, and be almost paralyzed with horror not to find it in its accustomed place. But the never-ending joy of feeling that one could start out for a day's trip, or a camping-out expedition of a week or a month and never give the subject of water a moment's thought, can only be appreciated by those who are direfully familiar with the dependence placed upon the canteen in less favored regions.

CHAPTER XXXII

DISTINGUISHING THE TREES OF THE TAHOE REGION

BY "trees" in this chapter I mean only the evergreen trees — the pines, firs, spruces, hemlocks, cedars, junipers and tamaracks. Many visitors like to know at least enough when they are looking at a tree, to tell which of the above species it belongs to. All I aim to do here is to seek to make clear the distinguishing features of the various trees, and to give some of the more readily discernible signs of the different varieties of the same species found in the region.

It must not be forgotten that tree growth is largely dependent upon soil conditions. The soil of the Tahoe region is chiefly glacial detritus.

John B. Leiberg, in *Forest Conditions in the Northern Sierra Nevada,* reports the following:

On the slopes and summits of the ridges it is sandy, gravelly, and liberally strewn with masses of drift boulders. The flats largely formed of silting while they still constituted beds of lakes, have a deep soil of fine sand and mold resting on coarse gravel and boulder drift. Ridges composed of brecciated lavas, which crumble easily under the influence of atmospheric agencies, are covered with soil two or three feet, or even more, in depth, where gentle slopes or broad saddles have favored deposition and prevented washing.

The granite areas of the main range and elsewhere have a very thin soil. The flats at the entrance of small streams into Lake Tahoe are covered with deep soil, owing to deposition of vegetable matter brought from the slopes adjacent to their channels. As a whole, the soil of the region is of sufficient fertility to support a heavy forest growth, its depth depends wholly on local circumstances favoring washing and removal of the soil elements as fast as formed, or holding them in place and compelling accumulations.

Coniferous species of trees constitute fully 95 percent of the arborescent growth in the region. The remaining five percent consists mostly of different species of oak, ash, maple, mountain mahogany, aspen, cottonwood, California buckeye, western red-bud, arborescent willows, alders, etc.

Of the conifers, the species are as follows: yellow pine, *pinus ponderosa;* Jeffrey pine, *pinus jeffreyi;* sugar pine, *pinus lambertiana;* lodge-pole pine, *pinus murrayana;* white pine, *pinus monticola;* digger pine, *pinus sabiniana;* white-bark pine, *pinus albicaulis;* red fir, *pseudotsuga taxifolia;* white fir, *abies concolor;* Shasta fir, *abies magnifica;* patton hemlock or alpine spruce, *tsuga pattoniana;* incense cedar, *libocedrus decurrens;* western juniper, *juniperus occidentalis;* yew, *taxus brevifolia.*

The range and chief characteristic of these trees, generally speaking, are as follows:

Digger Pine. This is seldom found in the Tahoe region, except in the lower reaches of the canyons on the west side of the range. It is sometimes known at the Nut Pine, for it bears a nut of which the natives are very fond. It has two cone forms, one in which the spurs point straight down, the other in which they are more or less curved at the tip. They grow to a height of 40 to 50 and occasionally 90 feet high; with open crown and thin gray foliage.

Western Juniper. This is a typical tree of the arid regions east of the Sierra, yet it is to be found scattered throughout the Tahoe country, generally at an elevation between 5000 and 8000 feet. It ranges in height from ten to 25 or even 65 feet. Its dull red bark, which shreds or flakes easily, its berries, which begin a green color, shade through to gray, and when ripe are a rich purple, make it readily discernible. It is a characteristic feature of the scenery at timber line in many Tahoe landscapes.

With the crowns beaten by storms into irregular shapes, often dead on one side but flourishing on the other, the tops usually dismantled and the trunks excessively thickened at base, such figures, whether erect, half overthrown or wholly crouching, are the most picturesque of mountain trees and are frequently of very great age. —*Jepson.*

Yew. This is not often found and then only in the west canyons above the main range. It is a small and insignificant tree, rarely exceeding 40 feet in height. It has a thin red-brown smooth bark which becomes shreddy as it flakes off in thin and rather small pieces. The seeds are borne on the underside of the sprays and when mature set in a fleshy scarlet cup, the whole looking like a brilliantly colored berry five or six inches long. They ripen in July or August.

Incense Cedar. This is commonly found all over the region at elevations below 7500 feet, though its chief habitat is at elevations of 3500 to 6000 feet. It grows to a height of 50 to 150 feet, with a strongly conical trunk, very thick at the base, and gradually diminishing in size upward. The bark is thick, red-brown, loose and fibrous, and when the tree is old, broken into prominent heavy longitudinal furrows. The cones are red-brown, oblong-ovate when closed, 3/4ths to an inch long.

An aged Juniper, the gnarled monarch of the Sierra, high above Lake Tahoe.

Shasta Fir. This is found on the summits, slopes and shores of Lake Tahoe, and to levels 6200 feet in elevation on the slopes and summits directly connected with the main range. It is found along the Mount Pluto ridge. It is essentially a tree of the mountains, where the annual precipitation ranges from 50 inches upward. In the Tahoe region it is locally known as the red fir. Sometimes it is called the red bark fir and golden fir.

It grows from 60 to even 175 feet high with trunk one to five feet in diameter and a narrowly cone-shaped crown composed of numerous horizontal strata of fan-shaped sprays. The bark on young trees is whitish or silvery, on old trunks dark red, very deeply and roughly fissured. The cones when young are of a beautiful dull purple, when mature becoming brown.

White Pine. This is found on northern slopes as low down as 6500 feet, though it generally ranges above 7000 feet, and is quite common. It sometimes is called the silver pine, and generally in the Tahoe region, the mountain pine. It grows to a height of from 50 to 175 feet, the branches slender and spreading or somewhat drooping, and mostly confined to the upper portion of the shaft.

The trunk is from one to six feet in diameter and clothed with a very smooth though slightly checked whitish or reddish bark. The needles are five (rarely four) in a place, very slender, one to 3-3/4th inches long, sheathed at the base by thinnish narrow deciduous scales, some of which are one inch long.

The cones come in clusters of one to seven, from six to eight or rarely ten inches long, very slender when closed and usually curved towards the tip, black-purple or green when young, buff-brown when ripe. It is best recognized by its light gray, smooth bark, broken into squarish plates, its pale blue-green foliage composed of short needles, and its pendulous cones so slender as to give rise to the name "Finger-Cone Pine."

Sugar Pine. This is found on the lower terraces of Tahoe, fringing the region with a sparse and scattering growth, but it is not found on the higher slopes of the Sierra. On the western side its range is nearly identical with that of the red fir. It grows from 80 to 150 feet high, the young and adult trees symmetrical, but the aged trees commonly with broken summits or characteristically flat-topped with one or two long arm-like branches exceeding shorter ones.

The trunk is from two to eight feet in diameter, and the bark brown or reddish, closely fissured into rough ridges. The needles are slender, five in a bundle, two to 3-1/2 inches long. The cones are pendulous, borne on stalks at the end of the branches, mostly in the very summit of the tree, very long-oblong, 13 to 18 inches long, four to six inches in diameter when opened.

> This pine gains its name from its sugary exudation, sought by the native tribes, which forms hard white crystallized nodules on the upper side of fire or ax wounds in the wood. This flow contains resin, is manna-like, has cathartic properties, and is as sweet as cane sugar. The seeds are edible.
>
> Although very small they are more valued by the native tribes than the large seeds of the Digger Pine on account of their better flavor. In former days, when it came October, the Indians went to the high mountains about their valleys to gather the cones. They camped on the ridges where the sugar pines grow and celebrated their sylvan journey by tree climbing contests among the men.
>
> In these latter days, being possessed of the white man's ax, they find it more convenient to cut the tree down. It is undoubtedly the most remarkable of all pines, viewed either from the standpoint of its economic value or sylvan interest. It is the largest of pine trees, considered whether as to weight or girth, and more than any other tree gives beauty and distinction to the Sierran forest. — *Jepson.*

The long cones found in abundance about Tahoe Tavern are those of the sugar pine.

Yellow Pine and Jeffrey Pine. These are practically one and the same, though the latter is generally regarded as a variety and the former the type. Leiberg says:

> The two forms differ chiefly in the size of the cones, in the tint and odor of the foliage, and in the color and thickness of the bark, differences which are insufficient to constitute specific characters. The most conspicuous of the above differences is that in the size of the cones, which may seemingly hold good if only a few hundred trees are examined. But when one comes to deal with thousands of individuals the distinction vanishes.
>
> It is common to find trees of the Jeffrey type as to foliage and bark that bear the big cones, and the characteristic smaller cones of the typical yellow pine, both at the same time and on the same individual, while old cones strewn about on the ground indicate that in some seasons trees of the Jeffrey type produce only small-sized cones.
>
> The odor and the color of leaves and bark are more or less dependent on soil conditions and the inherent vitality of the individual tree, and the same characters are found in specimens belonging to the yellow and Jeffrey pine. It is noticeable that the big-cone variety preferably grows at considerable elevation and on rocky sterile ground, while the typical form of the yellow pine prevails throughout the lower regions and on tracts with a more generous soil.
>
> The yellow pine has a wider range than any other of the Tahoe conifers, though on the high, rocky areas, south and west of Rubicon Springs it is lacking. It crosses from the western slopes to the eastern sides of the Sierra and down into the Tahoe basin over the heads of Miller and McKinney creeks, in both places as a thin line, or rather as scattering trees mixed with Shasta fir and white pine.

It grows from 60 to 225 feet high with trunk two to nine feet in diameter. The limbs in mature trees are horizontal or even drooping. The bark of typical trees is tawny yellow or yellow-brown, divided by fissures into large smoothish or scaly-surfaced plates which are often one to four feet long and 1/2 to 1-1/4 feet wide. The needles are in threes, five to ten inches long; the cones reddish brown.

It must be noted, too, that "the bark is exceedingly variable, black-barked or brown-barked trees, roughly or narrowly fissured, are very common and in their extreme forms very different in trunk appearance from the typical or most abundant 'turtle-back' form with broad, yellow or light brown plates." —*Jepson.*

Lodge Pole Pine. The range of this tree is almost identical with that of the Shasta fir, though there and there it is found at as low an altitude as 4500 feet. It loves the margins of creeks, glades and lakes situated at altitudes of 6000 feet and upward, where it usually forms a fringe of nearly pure growth in the wet and swampy portions of the ground. In the Tahoe region it is invariably called a tamarack or tamarack pine.

It is a symmetrical tree commonly reaching as high as 50 to 80 feet, but occasionally 125 feet. When stunted, however, it is only a few feet. The bark is remarkably thin, rarely more than 1/4 inch thick, light gray in color, very smooth but flaking into small thin scales. There are only two needles to a bunch, in a sheath, 1-1/2 to 2-3/4 inches long. The cones are chestnut brown, one to 1-3/4 inches long.

It is when sleeping under the lodge pole pines that you begin to appreciate their perfect charm and beauty. You unroll your blankets at the foot of a stately tree at night, unconscious and careless as to what tree it is. During the night, when the moon is at the full, you awaken and look up into a glory of shimmering light. The fine tapering shape, the delicate fairy-like beauty, instantly appeal to the sensitive soul and he feels he is in a veritable temple of beauty.

They are very sensitive trees. In many places a mere grass fire, quick and very fierce for a short time, has destroyed quite a number.

White Fir. This follows closely the range of the incense cedar, though in some places it is found as high as 8700 feet. It is one of the most perfect trees in the Sierra. Ranging from 60 to 150 and even 200 feet high, with a narrow crown composed of flat sprays and a trunk naked for 1/3 to 1/2 its height and from one to six feet in diameter, with a smooth bark, silvery or whitish in young trees, becoming thick and heavily fissured into rounded ridges on old trunks, and gray or drab-brown in color, it is readily distinguishable, with its companion, the red fir, by the regularity of construction of trunk, branch and branchlet. As Smeaton Chase expresses it, "The fine smooth arms, set in regular formation, divide and redivide again and again *ad infinitum,* weaving at last into a maze of exquisitely symmetrical twigs and branchlets."

Red Fir. The range of the red fir is irregular. It occurs on the Rubicon River and some of the headwaters of the west-flowing streams, reaching a general height of 6000 feet, though it is occasionally found as high as 7000 feet. In some parts of California this is known as Douglas Spruce, and Jepson, in his *Silva of California,* definitely states:

> The name "fir" as applied to the species is so well established among woodsmen that for the sake of intelligibility the combination Douglas Fir, which prevents confusion with the true firs and has been adopted by the Pacific Coast Lumberman's Association, is here accepted, notwithstanding that the name used by botanists, "Douglas Spruce", is actually more fitting on account of the greater number of spruce-like characteristics. It is neither the true spruce, fir, nor hemlock, but a marked type of a distinct genus, namely, *pseudotsuga.*

It must not be confounded with the red silver fir *(Abies Magnifica)* so eloquently described as the chief delight of the Yosemite region by Smeaton Chase. It grows from 70 to 250 or possibly 350 feet high, and is the most important lumber tree of the country, considering the quality of its timber, the size and length of its logs, and the great amount of heavy wood and freedom from knots, shakes or defects.

On young trees the bark is smooth, gray or mottled, sometimes alder-like; on old trunks one to 6-1/2 inches thick, soft or putty-like, dark drown, fissured into broad heavy furrows. The young rapid growth in the open woods produces "red fir," the older slower growth in denser woods is "yellow fit." Every tree to a greater or lesser extent exhibits successively these two phases, which are dependent upon situation and exposure.

The chief difference between the white and red fir is in the *spiculae* or leaves. Those of the red fir are shorter, stubbier, and stiffer than those of the white. The bark, however, is pretty nearly alike in young trees and shows a marked difference when they get to be 40 to 50 years old.

The Alpine Spruce. *(Hesperopeuce Pattoniana* Lemmon) is found only in the highest elevations. Common in Alaska, it is limited in the Tahoe region to the upper points of forests that creep up along glacier beds and volcanic ravines, close to perpetual ice. It disappears at 10,000 feet altitude on Mt. Whitney and is found nowhere south of this pint.

On Tallac, Mt. Rose and all the higher peaks of the Tahoe region it is common, giving constant delight with its slender shaft, 80 to 100 feet high, and with a diameter at its base of from six to 12 feet. It is only in the lower portions of the belt where it occurs. Higher it is reduced to low conical masses of foliage or prostrate creeping shrubs.

By many it is regarded as a hemlock, but it is not strictly so. It was first discovered in 1852 by John Jeffrey, who followed David Douglas in his explorations of the forests of the American Northwest.

> In favorable situations, the lower limbs are retained and become long, out-reaching, and spreading over the mountain slope for many feet; the upper limbs are irregularly disposed, not whorled; they strike downward from the start (so that it is almost impossible to climb one of the trees for want of foothold), then curving outward to the outline of the tree, they are terminated by short, hairy branchlets that decline gracefully, and are decorated with pendant cones which are glaucous purple until maturity, then leather brown, with reflexed scales.
>
> The main stem sends out strong ascending shoots, the leading one terminating so slenderly as to bend from side to side with its many purple pendants before the wind, and shimmering in the sunlight with rare beauty. — *Lemmon.*

On the slopes of Mt. Rose near timber line, which ranges from 9700 to 10,000 feet according to exposures, while still a tree of considerable size, it loses its symmetrical appearance. Professor Kennedy says:

> Buffeted by the fierce winter winds and snows, the branches on the west side of the tree are either entirely wanting or very short and gnarled, and the bark is commonly denuded. Unlike its associate, *Pinus Albicaulis,* which is abundant as a prostrate shrub far above timber line, the spruce is rarely encountered above timber line at this place, but here and there a hardy individual may be found lurking among the pines. The greatest elevation at which it was noticed is 10,500 feet.

To me this is one of the most beautiful of Sierran trees. Its delicate silvery hue, and the rarely exquisite shading from the old growth to the new, its gracefulness, the quaint and fascinating tilt of its tip which waveringly bends over in obedience to whichever breeze is blowing makes it the most alluringly feminine of all the trees of the Sierra Nevada.

It is interesting to note the differences in the cones, and in the way they grow; singly, in clusters, at the end of branches, on the stems, large, medium-sized, small, short and stubby, long and slender, conical, etc. Then, too, while the pines generally have cones every year, the firs seem to miss a year, and to bear only alternate years.

The gray squirrels are often great reapers of the cones, before they are ripe. They cut them down and then eat off the tips of the scales so that they present a pathetically stripped appearance.

CHAPTER XXXIII

THE BIRDS AND ANIMALS OF THE TAHOE REGION

BIRDS.

The bird life of the Tahoe region does not seem particularly interesting or impressive to the casual observer. At first sight there are not many birds, and those that do appear have neither so vivid plumage nor sweet song as their feathered relatives of the east, south and west. Nevertheless there are several interesting species, and while this chapter makes no pretense to completeness it suggests what one untrained observer without birds particularly on his mind has witnessed in the course of his several trips to the Tahoe region.

It soon becomes evident that altitude has much to do with bird life, some, as the meadowlark and blackbird never being found higher than the Lake shore, others at the intermediate elevations where the Alpine hemlock thrives, while still others, such as the rosy finch and the rock wren, are found only on the highest and most craggy peaks.

While water birds are not numerous in the summer, observant visitors at Lake Tahoe for the first time are generally surprised to find numbers of seagulls. They fly back and forth, however, to and from their native haunts by the sea. They never raise their young here, generally making their return flight to the shores of the Pacific in September, October and at latest November, to come back in March and April. While out on the mountain in these months, 50 or more miles west of Lake Tahoe I have seen them, high in the air, flying straight to the place they desired.

The blue heron in its solitary and stately watchfulness is occasionally seen, and again etches itself like a Japanese picture against the pure blue of the sky. The American bittern is also seen rarely.

Kingfishers are found, both on the lakes and streams. It is fascinating to watch them unobserved, perched on a twig, as motionless as if petrified, until, suddenly, their prey is within grasp, and with a sudden splash is seized.

On several of the lakes, occasionally on bays of Tahoe itself, and often in the marshy lands and sloughs of the Upper Truckee, near Tallac, ducks, mallard and teal are found. Mud chickens in abundance are also found pretty nearly everywhere all through the year.

The weird cry of the loon is not infrequently heard on some of the lakes, and one of these latter is named

Loon Lake from the fact that several were found there for a number of years.

Flocks of white pelicans are sometimes seen. Blackbirds of two or three kinds are found in the marshes, also killdeer, jacksnipe and the ever-active and interesting spotted sandpipers. A few meadowlarks now and again are heard singing their exquisite song, reminding one of Browning's wise thrush which "sings each song twice over, lest you should think he cannot recapture that first fine careless rapture."

Doves are not common, but now and again one may hear their sweet melancholy song, telling us in Joaquin Miller's poetic and exquisite interpretation: "There are many tomorrows, my love, my love, But only one today."

In the summer, robins are frequently seen. Especially do they revel on the lawns at Tahoe Tavern, their red breasts and their peculiar "smithing" or "cokeing" just as alluring and interesting as the plumage and voices of the richer feathered and finer songsters of the bird family.

Mountain quails are quite common, and one sometimes sees a dozen flocks in a day. Grouse are fairly plentiful. One day just on the other side of Granite Chief Peak a fine specimen sailed up and out from the trail at our very feet, soared for quite a distance, as straight as a bullet to its billet for a cluster of pine trees, and there hid in the branches. My guide walked down, gun in hand, ready to shoot, and as he came nearer, two others dashed up in disconcerting suddenness and flew, one to the right, the other to the left. We never got a sight of any of them again.

At another time I was coming over by Split Crag from the Lake of the Woods, with Mr. Price of Fallen Leaf Lodge, when two beautiful grouse arose from the trail and soared away in their characteristic style.

At one time sage hens were not infrequent on the Nevada side of the Lake, and as far west as Brockway. Indeed it used to be a common thing for hunters, in the early days, to come from Truckee, through Martis Valley, to the Hot Springs (as Brockway was then named) and shoot sage hens all along the way. A few miles north of Truckee, Sage Hen Creek still preserves, in the name, the fact that the sage hen was well known there.

Baldheaded and golden eagles are often seen in easy and circular flight above the highest peaks. In the fall and winter they pass over into the wild country near the almost inaccessible peaks above the American River and there raise their young. One year Mr. Price observed a pair of golden eagles which nested on Mt. Tallac. He and I were seated at lunch one day in September, 1913, on the very summit of Pyramid Peak, when, suddenly, as a bolt out of a clear sky, startling us with its wild rush, an eagle shot obliquely at us from the upper air.

The speed with which it fell made a noise as of a "rushing mighty wind." Down! down, it fell, and then with the utmost grace imaginable, swept up, still going at terrific speed, circled about, and was soon lost to sight.

Almost as fond of the wind-tossed pines high up on the slopes of the mountain as is the eagle of the most rugged peaks, is Clark's crow, a grayish white bird, with black wings, and a harsh, rasping call, somewhat between that of a crow and the jay.

Of an entirely different nature, seldom seen except on the topmost peaks, is the rosy-headed finch. While on the summit of Pyramid Peak, we saw two of them, and one of them favored us with his (or her) sweet, gentle song.

Hawks are quite common; among those generally seen are the long tailed grouse hawk, the sparrow hawk, and the sharp-shinned hawk. Nighthawks are quite conspicuous if one walks about after sunset. They are dusky with a white throat and band on the wing. They sail through the air without any effort, wings outspread and beak wide open, and thus glean their harvest of winged insects as they skim along. Oftentimes their sudden swoop will startle you as they rush by.

Woodpeckers are numerous, and two or three species may be seen almost anywhere in a day's walk through one of the wooded sections. Many are the trees which bear evidence of their industry, skill and providence. The huge crow-like pileolated woodpecker with its scarlet crest, the red-shafted flicker, the Sierra creeper, the red-breasted sapsucker, Williamson's sapsucker, the white-headed woodpecker, Cabanis's woodpecker with spotted wings and gray breast, the most common of woodpeckers, and Lewis's woodpecker, a large heavy bird, glossy black above, with a white collar and a rich red underpart, have all been seen for many years in succession.

The red-breasted sapsucker and Williamson's sapsucker are found most frequently among the aspens and willows along the lake sore, while the red-shafted flicker, Cabanis's woodpecker, and the white-head favor the woods. One observer says the slender-billed nuthatch is much more common than the red-breasted, and that his nasal laugh resounded at all times through the pines.

High up in the hemlock forests is the interesting Alpine three-toed woodpecker. It looks very much like Cabanis's, only it has three toes in place of four, and a yellow crown instead of a black and red one.

In importance after the woodpeckers come the members of the sparrow family that inhabit the Tahoe region. The little black-headed snowbird, Thurber's junco, is the most common of all the Tahoe birds. The thick-billed sparrow, a grayish bird with spotted breast and enormous bill, is found on all the brushy hillsides and is noted for its glorious bursts of rich song.

Now and again one will see a flock of English sparrows and the sweet-voiced song sparrow endeavors to make up for the vulgarity of its English cousin by the delicate softness of its peculiar song.

Others of the family are the two purple finches (reddish birds), the pine finch, very plain and streaked, the green-tailed towhee, with its cat-like call, and the white-crowned sparrow — its sweetly melancholy song, "Oh, dear me," in falling cadence, is heard in every Sierran meadow.

The mountain song sparrow, western lark, western chipping fox goldfinch, and house and cassin finches, are seen. The flycatchers are omnipresent in August, though their shy disposition makes them hard to identify. Hammond, olive-sided and western pewee are often seen, and at times the tall treetops are alive with kinglets.

Some visitors complain that they do not often see or hear the warblers, but in 1905, one bird lover reported seven common representatives. She says:

> The yellow bird was often heard and seen in the willows along the Lake. Late in August the shrubs on the shore were alive with the Audubon group, which is so abundant in the vicinity of Los Angeles all winter. Pileolated warblers, with rich yellow suits and black caps, hovered like hummers among the low shrubs in the woods. Now and then a Pacific yellow-throat sang his bewitching "witchity, witchity, witchity, wee."
>
> Hermit and black-throated gray warblers were also recorded. The third week in August there was an extensive immigration of Macgillivray warblers. Their delicate gray heads, yellow underparts, and the bobbing movement of the tail, distinguished them from the others.

The water ouzel finds congenial habitat in the canyons of the Tahoe region, and the careful observer may see scores of them as he walks along the streams and by the cascades and waterfalls during a summer's season. At one place they are so numerous as to have led to the naming of a beautiful waterfall, Ouzel Falls, after them.

Another bird is much sought after and can be seen and heard here, perhaps as often as any other place in the country. That is the hermit thrush, small, delicate, grayish, with spotted breast. The shyness of the bird is proverbial, and it frequents the deepest willow and aspen thickets. Once heard, its sweet song can never be forgotten, and happy is he who can get near enough to hear it undisturbed.

Far off, it is flute-like, pure and penetrating, though not loud. Gradually it softens until it sounds by as the faintest of tinkling bell-like notes, which die away leaving one with the assurance that he has been hearing the song of the chief bird of the fairies, or of birds which accompany the heavenly lullabies of the mother angels putting their baby angels to sleep.

Cliff swallows often nest on the high banks at Tahoe City, and a few have been seen nesting under the eaves of the store on the wharf. The nests of barn swallows also have been found under the eaves of the ice house.

Nor must the exquisite hummers be overlooked. In Truckee Canyon and near Tahoe Tavern they are quite numerous. They sit on the telephone wires and try to make you listen to their pathetic and scarcely discernible song, and as you sit on the seats at the Tavern, if you happen to have some bright-colored object about you, especially red, they will flit to and fro eagerly seeking for the honey-laden flower that red ought to betoken.

Several times down Truckee Canyon I have seen wild canaries. They are rather rare, as are also the Louisiana tanager, most gorgeous of all the Tahoe birds, and the black-headed grosbeak.

Of the wrens, both the rock wren and the canyon wren are occasionally seen, the peculiar song of the latter bringing a thrill of cheer to those who are familiar with its falling chromatic scale.

Then there is the merry chickadee, the busy creepers, and the nuthatches hunting for insects on the tree trunks.

The harsh note of the bluejay is heard from Tahoe Tavern, all around the Lake and in almost every wooded slope in the Sierra. He is a noisy, generally unlovable creature, and the terror of the small birds in the nesting season, because of his well-known habit of stealing eggs and young.

At Tahoe Tavern, however, I found several of them that were shamed into friendliness of behavior, and astonishing tameness, by the chipmunks. They would come and eat nuts from my fingers, and one of them several times came and perched upon my shoulder. There is also the grayish solitaire which looks very much like the mockingbird of less variable climes.

The foregoing account of the birds, which I submitted for revision to Professor Peter Frandsen, of the University of Nevada, called forth from him the following:

I have very little to add to this admirable bird account. Besides the gulls, their black relatives, the swallow-like terns, are occasionally seen. The black-crowned night heron is less common than the great blue heron. Clarke's crow is more properly called Clarke's nutcracker — a different genus. The road robin or chewink is fairly common in the thickets above the Lake. Nuttal's poor will, with its call of two syllables, is not infrequently heard at night.

The silent mountain bluebird, *sialia arctica*, is sometimes seen. So is the western warbling vireo. The solitary white-rumped shrike is occasionally met with in late summer. Owls are common but what species other than the western horned owl I do not know. Other rather rare birds are the beautiful lazuli bunting and the western warbling vireo. Among the woodpeckers I have also noted the bristle-bellied woodpecker, or Lewis's woodpecker, Harris's woodpecker, and the downy woodpecker.

ANIMALS.

These are even more numerous than the birds, though except to the experienced observer many of them are seldom noticed.

While raccoons are not found on the eastern slopes of the High Sierra, or in the near neighborhood of the Lake, they are not uncommon on the western slopes, near the Rubicon and the headwaters of the various forks of the American and other nearby rivers.

Watson assured me that every fall he sees tracks on the Rubicon and in the Hell Hole region of very large mountain lions. They hide, among other places, under and on the limbs of the wild grapevines, which here grow to unusual size. In the fall of 1912 he saw some strange markings, and following them was led to a cluster of wild raspberry vines, among which was a dead deer covered over with fir boughs. In telling me the story he said:

I can generally read most of the things I see in the woods, but this completely puzzled me. I determined to find out all there was to be found. Close by I discovered the fir from which the boughs had been stripped. It was as if someone of giant strength had reached up to a height of seven or eight feet and completely stripped the tree of all its lower limbs.

Then I asked myself the question: "Who's camping here?" I though he had used these limbs to make a bed of. But there was no water nearby, and no signs of camping, so I saw that was a wrong lead. Then I noticed that the limbs were too big to be torn off by a man's hands, and there were blood stains all about. Then I found the fragments of a deer. "Now," I said to myself, "I've got it. A bear has killed this deer and has eaten part of it and will come back for the rest." You know a bear does this sometimes. But when I hunted for bear tracks there wasn't a sign of a bear.

Then I assumed that some hunter had been along, killed a doe (contrary to law), had eaten what he could and hidden the rest, covering the hide with leaves and these branches. But then I knew a hunter would cut off those branches with a knife, and these were torn off. The blood spattered about, the torn-off boughs and the fact that there were no tracks puzzled me, and I felt there was a mystery and, probably, a tragedy.

But a day or two later I met a woodsman friend of mine, and I took him to the spot. He explained the whole thing clearly. As soon as he saw it, he said, "That's a mountain lion." "But," said I, "Where's his tracks?" "He didn't make any," he replied, "he surprised the doe by crawling along the vines. I've found calves and deer hidden like this before, and I've seen clear traces of the panthers, and once I watched one as he killed, ate and then hid his prey.

But as you know, he won't touch it after it begins to decompose, but a bear will. And that's the reason we generally think it is a bear that does the killing, when in reality it is a mountain lion who has had his fill and left the remains for other predatory animals, while he has gone off to hunt for a fresh kill.

Occasionally sheepherders report considerable devastations from mountain lions and bear to the forest rangers. James Bryden, who grazes his sheep on the Tahoe reserve near Downieville, lost sixteen sheep in one night in July, 1911.

There are three kinds each of chipmunks and ground squirrels. All of the former have striped backs and do more or less climbing of trees. Of their friendliness, greediness, and even sociability — where nuts are in evidence or anticipated — I have written fully in the chapter on Tahoe Tavern. Of the three ground squirrels, the largest is the common ground squirrel of the valleys of California. It is gray, somewhat spotted on the back, and has a whitish collar and bushy tail.

The next in size is the "picket pin," so called from his habit of sitting bolt upright on his haunches and remaining steadfast there, without the slightest movement, until danger threatens, when he whisks away so rapidly that it is quite impossible to follow his movements. In color he is of a grayish brown, with thick-set body, and short, slim tail. He has an exceeding sharp call, and makes his home in grassy meadows from the level of the Lake nearly to the summits of the highest peaks. The "copperhead" is the other ground squirrel, though by some he may be regarded as a chipmunk, for he has a striped back.

The flying squirrel is also found here. It comes out only at night and lives in holes in trees. On each side between the fore and hind legs it has a hairy flap, which when stretched out makes the body very broad, and together with its hairy tail it is enabled to sail from one tree to another, though always alighting at a lower level. A more correct name would be a "sailing" squirrel. The fur is very soft, of a mouse color and the animal makes a most beautiful pet. It has great lustrous eyes and is about a foot in length.

The tree squirrel about the Lake is the pine squirrel or "chickeree." The large tree squirrel is abundant on the west slope of the Sierra from about six thousand feet downward, but it is not in the Lake basin, so far as I am aware. The pine squirrel is everywhere, from the Lake side to the summits of the highest wooded peaks. It is dark above, whitish to yellow below, usually with a black line along the side. The tail is full, bushy, the hairs tipped with white forming a broad fringe. It feeds on the seeds of the pine cones.

The woodchuck or marmot is a huge, lumbering, squirrel-like animal in the rocky regions, wholly terrestrial and feeding chiefly on roots and grass. The young are fairly good eating and to shoot them with a rifle is some sport.

Of the fur-bearing and carnivorous animals, the otter, fisher, etc., all are uncommon, though some are trapped every year by residents of the Lake. The otter and mink live along the larger streams and on the Lake shore where they feed chiefly on fish. They may sometimes catch a wild fowl asleep. The martin and fisher live in pine trees usually in the deepest forests, and they probably prey on squirrels, mice and birds. They are usually nocturnal in their habits. The martin is the size of a large tree squirrel; the fisher is about twice that size. The foxes are not often seen, but the coyote is everywhere, a scourge to the few bands of sheep. Often at night his long-drawn, doleful howl may be heard, a fitting sound in some of the wild granite canyons.

One day while passing Eagle Crag, opposite Idlewild, the summer residence of C.F. Kohl of San Francisco, with Bob Watson, he informed me that, in 1877, he was following the tracks of a deer and they led him to a cave or grotto in the upper portion of the Crag. While he stood looking in at the entrance a snarling coyote dashed out, far more afraid of him than he was surprised at the sudden appearance of the creature.

A few bears are still found in the farther away recesses of the Sierra, and on one mountain range close to the Lake, viz., the one on which Freel's, Job's and Job's Sister are the chief peaks. These are brown or cinnamon, and black. There are no grizzlies found on the eastern slopes of the Sierra, nowadays, and it is possible they never crossed the divide from the richer-clad western slopes. In September, 1913, a hunting party, led by Mr. Comstock, of Tallac, and Lloyd Tevis, killed two black bears, one of them weighing fully 400 pounds, on Freel's Mountain, and in the same season Mr. Carl Flugge, of Cathedral Park, brought home a good-sized cinnamon from the Rubicon country, the skin of which now adorns my office floor.

The grizzly has long since been driven from the mountains, though there may be a few in southern Alpine County, but the evidence is not conclusive. The panther is migratory, preying on young colts and calves. They are not at all common, though some are heard of every year. The "ermine" is pure white in winter, except the tip of the tail, which is black. It is yellowish brown in summer.

A Tahoe meadow, with Mt. Tallac in the distance

There are two rabbits, one a huge jackrabbit of the great plains region, the other the "snowshoe" rabbit, so called because of its broad furry feet which keep it from sinking into the soft snow in winter. Both rabbits are very rare, and probably both turn white in winter. I have seen specimens of the snowshoe rabbit taken in winter that are pure white.

On the wildest and most desolate peaks and rock piles is found the cony or pika or "rock rabbit" as it is variously called. It is small, only six inches or so in length, tailless but with large round ears and soft grayish fur like a rabbit's.

The jumping mouse is interesting. It may be seen sometimes at evening in swampy areas and meadows. It is yellowish above, whitish below, with an extremely long tail. It travels by long leaps, takes readily to the water and is an expert swimmer. The meadow mice are bluish grey and are found in swampy places. The wood mice are pure white below, brown above and are found everywhere.

Quite a number of badgers are to be found in the Tahoe region, and they must find abundance of good food, for the specimens I have seen were rolling in fat, and as broad-backed as a fourteen inch board.

Several times, also, have I seen porcupines, one of them, weighing fully 25 pounds, on the slopes of Mt. Watson, waddling along as if he were a small bear. They live on the tender bark of the mountain and tamarack pines, sometimes girdling the trees and causing them to die. They are slow-gaited creatures, easily caught by dogs, but with their needle spines, and the sharp, quick-slapping action of their tails, by means of which they can thrust, insert, inject — which is the better word? — a score or more of these spines into a dog's face, they are antagonists whose prowess cannot be ignored.

Very few people would think of the porcupine as an animal destructive to forest trees, yet one of the Tahoe forest rangers reports that in the spring of 1913 fifty young trees, averaging 30 feet high, were killed or ruined by porcupines stripping them of their bark. Sometimes as many as 90 percent of the young trees growing on a burned-over area are thus destroyed. They travel and feed at night, hence the ordinary observer would never know their habits.

The bushy tailed woodrat proves itself a nuisance about the houses where it is as omnivorous an eater as is its far-removed cousin, the house rat.

The gopher is one of the mammals whose mark is more often seen than the creature itself. It lives like the mole in underground borrows, coming to the surface only to push up the dirt that it has been digging.

CHAPTER XXXIV

THE SQUAW VALLEY MINING EXCITEMENT

The Tahoe region was once thrilled through and through by a real mining excitement that be longed to itself alone. It had felt the wonderful activity that resulted from the discovery of the Comstock Lode in Virginia City. It had seen its southern border crowded with miners and prospectors hurrying to the new field, and later had heard the blasting and picking, the shoveling and dumping of rocks while the road from Placerville was being constructed.

It had seen another road built up from Carson over the Kings Canyon grade, and lumber mills established at Glenbrook in order to supply the mines with timbers for their tunnels and excavations, as the valuable ore and its attendant waste rocks were hauled to the surface.

But now it was to have an excitement and a stampede all its own. An energetic prospector from Georgetown, El Dorado County, named Knox, discovered a big ledge of quartz in Squaw Valley. It was similar rock to that in which the Comstock silver was found in large quantities. Though the assays of the floating rock did not yield a large amount of the precious metals, they showed a little—as high as $3.50 per ton. This was enough. There were bound to be higher grade ores deeper down. The finder filed his necessary locations,. and doubtless aided by copious draughts of "red-eye" saw, in swift imagination, his claim develop into a mine as rich as those that had made the millionaires of Virginia City. Anyhow the rumor spread like a prairie fire, and men came rushing in from Georgetown, Placerville, Last Chance, Kentucky Flat, Michigan Bluff, Hayden Hill, Dutch Flat, Baker Divide, Yankee Jim, Mayflower, Paradise, Yuba, Deadwood, Jackass Gulch and all the other camps whose locators and residents had not been as fortunate financially as they were linguistically.

Knox started a city which he named Knoxville, the remains of which are still to be seen in the shape of ruined log cabins, stone chimneys, foundations of hewed logs, a graveyard, etc., on the left hand side of the railway coming from Truckee, and about six miles from Tahoe.

One has but to let his imagination run riot for a few moments to see this now deserted camp a scene of the greatest activity. The many shafts and tunnels, dump piles and prospect holes show how busy a spot it must have been. The hills about teemed with men. At night the log store—still standing—and the saloons—tents, shacks and log houses — were crowded with those who sought in the flowing bowl some surcease from the burden of their arduous labors.

Now and again a shooting took place, a man actually died with his boots on, as in the case of one King, a bad man from Texas who had a record, and whose sudden end was little, if any, lamented. He had had a falling out with the storekeeper, Tracey, and had threatened to kill him on sight. The former bade him keep away from his store, but King laughed at the prohibition, and with the blind daring that often counts as courage with such men — for he assumed that the storekeeper would not dare to shoot — he came down the following day, intending himself to do all the shooting there was to be done. But he reckoned mistakenly. Tracey saw him coming, came to the door, bade him Halt! and on his sneering refusal, shot the bad man dead.

In September 1913, I paid a visit to Knoxville. Just above the town, on the eastern slope of the mountain, were several tunnels and great dump piles, clearly showing the vast amount of work that had been done. The quartz ledge that caused the excitement was distinctly in evidence. Indeed, when the Tahoe Railway roadbed was being graded, this quartz ledge was blasted into, and the director of operations sent a number of specimens for assay, the rock looked so favorable.

Here and there were the remains of old log cabins, with their outside stone chimneys. In some cases young tamaracks, 15 and 20 feet high, had grown up within the areas once confined by the walls. These ruins extended all the way down to Deer Creek, showing the large number of inhabitants the town once possessed.

I saw the graveyard by the side of the river, where King's body was the first to be buried, and I stood in the doorway of the store from which the shot that killed him was fired.

In imagination, I saw the whole life of the camp, as I have seen mining camps after a stampede in Nevada. The shacks, rows of tents, and the rudely scattered and varied dwellings that the ingenuity and skill of men hastily extemporized. Most of the log houses are now gone, their charred remnants telling of the indifferent carelessness of campers, prospectors or Indians.

The main street was in a pretty little meadowed vale, lined on either side with trees, and close to the Truckee, which here rushes and dashes and roars and sparkles among the boulders and rocks that bestrew its bed.

When it was found the ore did not "pan out," the excitement died down even more rapidly than it arose, and in 1863-4 the camp was practically dead.

It has been charged that the Squaw Valley claims were salted with ore brought from Virginia City. I am inclined to doubt this, and many of the old timers deny it. They assert that Knox was "on the square" and that he firmly believed he had paying ore. It is possible there may have been the salting of an individual claim or so after the cap started, but the originators of the camp started it in good faith, as they themselves were the greatest losers when the bottom of the excitement dropped out.

About a mile further up the river is still to be seen the site of the rival town of Claraville, founded at the same time as Knoxville. There is little left here, though the assay office, built up against a massive square rock, still stands. It is of hewed timbers rudely dovetailed together at the corners.

It would scarcely be worthwhile to recount even this short history of the long dead — almost stillborn — Squaw Valley camp were it not for the many men it brought to Lake Tahoe who have left their impress and their names upon its most salient canyons, streams, peaks and other landmarks. Many of these have been referred to elsewhere.

One of the first to arrive was William Pomin, the brother of the present captain of the steamer *Tahoe.* His wife gave birth to the first white child born on Lake Tahoe, and she was named after the Lake. She now lives in San Francisco. When she was no more than two or three months old, her mother took her on mule back, 60 miles over the trail to Forest Hill, *in one day.* Pomin removed to the north shore of the Lake when Squaw Valley busted, and was one of the founders of Tahoe City, building and conducting one of the first hotels there.

Another of these old timers was J.W. McKinney, from whom McKinney's was named. He came from the mining camp of Georgetown over the trail, and engaged himself in selling town lots at Knoxville. He and Knox had worked together in the El Dorado excitement.

He originally came over the plains in the gold alluring days of '49. When his party reached the land of the Indians, these aborigines were too wise to make open attacks. They hit upon the dastardly method of shooting arrows into the bellies of the oxen, so that the pioneers would be compelled to abandon them.

One night McKinney was on guard duty. He was required to patrol back and forth and meet another sentinel at a certain tree. There they would stop and chat for a few moments before resuming their solitary march. Just before daybreak, after a few words, they separated. On answering the breakfast call McKinney found he was alone, and on going back to investigate, found his companion lying dead with an arrow through his heart. The moccasin tracks of an Indian clearly revealed who was the murderer, and a little study showed that the Indian had swam the river, waited until the sentinel passed close by him, and had then sent the arrow true to its fatal mark.

The next night the Indians shot an arrow into an ox. In the morning it was unable to travel, but McKinney and his friends had determined to do something to put a stop to these attacks. Taking the ox in the shadow of a knoll, they shot it, and eight men then hid in the shelter of some brush where the carcass was clearly in view.

When the train pulled out it seemed as if they had abandoned the ox. The train was scarcely out of sight when the watchers saw eight Indians come sneaking up. Each man took the Indian allotted to him, but by some error two men shot at the same Indian, so that when the guns were fired and seven men fell dead, the other escaped. On one of them was found seven $20 gold pieces wrapped up in a dirty rag, which had doubtless cost some poor emigrant or miner his life. Some of the party wished to leave this gold with the dead Indian, but McKinney said his scruples would not allow him to do any such thing, and the gold found its way into his pocket.

Though a man of practically no education — it is even said by those who claim to have known him well that he could neither read nor write, but this seems improbable — he was a man of such keen powers of observation, retentive memory, ability in conversation and strong personality, that he was able to associate on an equality with men of most superior attainments. John Muir was a frequent visitor to his home, especially in the winter time when all tourists and resort guests had gone away. John McGee, another well known lover of the winter mountains, was also a welcome guest, who fully appreciated the manly vigor and sterling character of the transplanted Missourian.

John Ward, from whom Ward Creek and Ward Peak (8665 feet) are named, was another Squaw Valley mining excitement stampeder. He came in the early days of the rush, and as soon as the camp died down, located on the mouth of the creek that now bears his name.

The next creek to the south — Blackwood's — is named after still another Squaw Valley stampeder. For years he lived at the mouth of this creek and gained his livelihood as a fisherman. The same explanation accounts for Dick Madden Creek.

Barker, who has peak, pass and valley named after him, came from Georgetown to Knoxville, and like so many other of his unfortunate mining brethren from over the divide, started a dairy on the west side of the pass which bears his name. The valley, however, was so high and cold that more than half the year the cream would not rise, so he gave up dairying and went elsewhere.

These are but a few of many who might be mentioned; whose names are linked with the Tahoe re-gion, and who came to it in the hope of making their everlasting fortunes when Squaw Valley started up.

CHAPTER XXXV

THE FRÉMONT HOWITZER AND LAKE TAHOE

Hundreds of thousands of Americans doubtless have read "How a Woman's Wit Saved California to the Union," yet few indeed know how intimately that fascinating piece of history is linked with Lake Tahoe. Here is the story of the link.

When Frémont started out on his Second Exploration (dealt with in another chapter), he stopped at the Kansas frontier to equip. When he finally started, the party of 108 was armed generally with Hall's carbines, which, says Frémont, "with a brass 12-pound howitzer, had been furnished to me from the United States arsenal at St. Louis, agreeably to the command of Colonel S.W. Kearny, commanding the third military division. Three men were especially detailed for the management of this, under the charge of Louis Zindel, a native of Germany, who had been nineteen years a non-commissioned officer of the artillery in the Prussian army, and regularly instructed in the duties of his profession."

As soon as the news that he had added a cannon to his equipment reached Washington, the Secretary of War, James M. Porter, sent a message after him, post haste, countermanding the expedition on the ground that he had prepared himself with a military equipment, which the pacific nature of his journey did not require. It was specially charged a heinous offense that he had procured a small mountain howitzer from the arsenal at St. Louis, in addition to his other firearms.

But Frémont had already started. He was not far on his way, and the message could have reached him easily. It was not destined to do so, however, until after his return. The message came to the hands of his girl-wife, Jessie Benton Frémont, the daughter of Missouri's great senator, Thomas H. Benton, and she knew, as Charles A. Moody has well written, that "... this order, obeyed, would indefinitely postpone the expedition — probably wreck it entirely. She did not forward it.

"Consulting no one, since there was no one at hand to consult, she sent a swift messenger to her husband with word to break camp and move forward at one — 'he could not have the reason for haste, but there was reason enough.' And he, knowing well and well trusting the sanity and breadth of that girl-brain, hastened forward, unquestioning, while she promptly informed the officer whose order she had vetoed, what she had done, and why. So far as human wit may penetrate, obedience to that backward summons would have meant, three years later, the winning of California by another nation — and what *that* loss would have signified to the United States none can know fully, but any may partly guess who realizes a part of what California has meant for us."

In commenting later upon this countermand of the Expedition, Frémont remarks, "It is not probably that I would have been recalled from the Missouri frontier to Washington to explain why I had taken an arm that simply served to increase the means of defense for a small party very certain to encounter Indian hostility, and which involved very trifling expense. The administration in Washington was apparently afraid of the English situation in Oregon."

Unconscious, therefore, of his wife's action — which might easily have ruined his career — Frémont pushed on. The howitzer accompanied him into Oregon, back through into Nevada, and is clearly seen in the picture of Pyramid Lake drawn by Mr. Preuss (which appears in the original report), showing it after it had traveled in the neighborhood of 4000 miles.

The last time it was fired as far as the Frémont Expedition is concerned was on Christmas Eve, in 1843. The party was camped on Christmas Lake, now known as Warner Lake, Oregon, and the following morning the gun crew wakened Frémont with a salute, fired in honor of the day. A month later, 250 miles south, it was to be abandoned in the mountains near West Walker River, on account of the deep snow which made it impossible for the weary horses to drag it further.

On the 28th of January, Frémont thus writes, "Tonight we did not succeed in getting the howitzer into camp. This was the most laborious day we had yet passed through, the steep ascents and deep snows exhausting both men and animals."

Possibly now the thought began to take possession of him that the weapon must be left behind. For long weary days it had been a constant companion. It had been dragged over the plains, mountains and canyons. It was made to ford rivers, plunge through quicksands and wallow through bog, mire, mud, marsh and snow. Again and again it delayed them when coming over sandy roads, but tenaciously Frémont held on to it.

Now deep snow forbade its being dragged further. Haste over the high mountains of the Sierra Nevada was imperative, for such peaks and passes are no lady's playground when the forces of winter begin to linger there, yet one can well imagine the regret and distress felt by "the Pathfinder" at being compelled to abandon this cannon, to which he had so desperately clung on all the wearisome miles his company had hitherto marched.

On the 29th, he writes, "The principal stream still running through an impracticable canyon, we ascended a very steep hill, which proved afterwards the last and fatal obstacle to our little howitzer, which was finally abandoned at this place. [This place appears to be about eight or ten miles up the river from Coleville, and on the right or east side of the river.]

"We passed through a small meadow a few miles below, crossing the river, which depth, swift current, and rock, made it difficult to ford [this brings him to the west bank for the first time, but the cannon did not get this far, and therefore was left on the east side of the river. This is to be noted on account of the fact that it was found on the other side of the river in another canyon], and after a few more miles of very difficult trail, issued into a larger prairie bottom, at the farther end of which we camped, in a position rendered strong by rocks and trees."

The reader must not forget that the notes in brackets [ ] are interjections in Frémont's narrative by Mr. Smith (see the chapter on Frémont's discovery of Lake Tahoe.)

Frémont continues, "The other division of the party did not come in tonight, but camped in the upper meadow, and arrived the next morning. They had not succeeded in getting the howitzer beyond the place mentioned, and where it had been left by Mr. Preuss, in obedience to my orders; and, in anticipation of the snowbanks and snowfields ahead, foreseeing the inevitable detention to which it would subject us, I reluctantly determined to leave it there for a time. It was of the kind invented by the French for the mountain part of their war in Algiers; and the distance it had come with us proved how well it was adapted to its purpose.

"We left it, to the great sorrow of the whole party, who were grieved to part with a companion which had made the whole distance from St. Louis, and commanded respect for us on some critical occasions, and which might be needed for the same purpose again.

[It is the impression of those of the old settlers on Walker River, of whom we have inquired regarding the subject, that the cannon was found early in the '60's near the head of Lost Canyon. This canyon comes into Little Antelope Valley — a branch of Antelope Valley — from the south. This impression evidently was accepted by the government geological surveyors, for they twisted the name of the creek coming down this canyon to "Lost Cannon Creek," and called a peak, which looks down into this canyon, Lost Cannon Peak.

[The origin of the name of this canyon lies in the fact that an emigrant party, on its way to the Sonora Pass, and in an endeavor probably to avoid the rough river canyon down which Frémont came, essayed this pass instead of the meadows above. It is a canyon which, at first, promises an easy pass but finally becomes almost impassable. The party in question found it necessary to abandon several of their wagons before they could get over. They, or another party, buried one of their men there, also some blacksmith tools. My endeavors to ascertain what party this was have thus far not been successful. Mr. Timothy B. Smith, who went to Walker River in 1859, says that the wagons were there at that time.

[The cannon is supposed to have been found with or near these wagons. Mr. Richard Watkins, of Coleville, who went into that section in 1861, or soon after, informs me that wagons were also found in one of the canyons leading to the Sonora Pass from Pickle Meadow. The cannon, according to Mr. Watkins, was found with these wagons. At any rate, it seems likely that the cannon was not found at the place where Frémont left it, but had been picked up by some emigrant party, who, in turn, were compelled to abandon it with several of their wagons.]

For several years the cannon remained where its emigrant finders removed it, then at the breaking out of the Civil War, "Dan de Quille," William Wright, the author of *The Big Bonanza*, the fellow reporter of Mark Twain on one of the Virginia City newspapers, called the attention of certain belligerent adherents of the south to it, and they determined to secure it. But the loyal sons of the Union were also alert and Captain A.W. Pray, who was then in the Nevada mining metropolis, succeeded in getting and maintaining possession of it.

As he moved to Glenbrook, on Lake Tahoe, that year, he took the cannon with him. Being mounted on a carriage with fairly high wheels, these latter were taken and converted into a hay wagon, with which, for several years, he hauled hay from the Glenbrook meadows to his barn in town. The cannon itself was mounted on a heavy wooden block to which it was affixed with iron bands, securely held in place by bolts and nuts.

For years it was used at Glenbrook on all patriotic

and special occasions. Frémont never came back to claim it. The government made no claim upon it. So while Captain Pray regarded it as his own it was commonly understood and generally accepted that it was town property, to be used by all alike on occasions of public rejoicing.

After Captain Pray's death, however, the cannon was sold by his widow to the Native Sons of Nevada, and the news of the sale soon spread abroad and caused no little commotion. To say that the people were astonished is to put it mildly. They were in a state of consternation. Frémont's cannon sold and going to be removed? Impossible! No! it was so! The purchasers were coming to remove it the next day.

Were they? That remained to be seen!

That night in the darkness, three or four determined men quietly and stealthily removed the nuts from the bolts, and, leaving the block of wood, quietly carried the cannon and hid it in a car of scrap iron that was to be transported the next day from Glenbrook to Tahoe City.

When the day dawned and the purchasers arrived, the cannon was not to be found, and no one, apparently, knew what had become of it. Solicitations, arguments, threats had no effect. The cannon was gone. That was all there was to it, and Mrs. Pray and the Nevada purchasers had to accept that — to them — disagreeable fact.

But the cannon was not lost. It was only gone on before. For several years it remained hidden under the blacksmith shop at Tahoe City, its presence known only to the few conspirators — one of whom was my informant. About five years ago it was resurrected and ever since then its brazen throat has bellowed the salutation of the Fourth of July to the loyal inhabitants of Tahoe. It now stands on the slight hill overlooking the Lake at Tahoe City, a short distance east of the hotel.

CHAPTER XXXVI

THE MOUNT ROSE OBSERVATORY

While Californians rightly and justly claim Tahoe as their own, it must not be forgotten that Nevadans have an equal claim. In the Nevada State University, situated at Reno, there is a magnificent band of young men, working and teaching as professors, who regard all opportunities as sacred trusts, and who are making for their university a wonderful record of scientific achievement for universal benefit.

Located on the Nevada side of the Tahoe region line, at the northeast end of the Lake, is Mount Rose. It is one of the most salient and important of the peaks that surround Tahoe, its elevation being 10,800 feet. The professor of Latin in the Nevada University, James E. Church, Jr., a strenuous nature lover, a mountain-climber, gifted with robust physical and mental health, making the ascent of Mt. Whitney in March, 1905, was suddenly seized with the idea that a meteorological observatory could be established on Mt. Rose, and records of temperature, wind, snow or rainfall taken throughout the winter months.

The summit of Mt. Rose by road is approximately twenty miles in a southwesterly direction from Reno, and Professor Church and his associates deemed it near enough for weekend visits. The courage, energy and robust manliness required to carry the work along can be appreciated only by those who have gone over the ground in winter, and forms another chapter of quiet and unknown heroism in the interest of science written by so many of our younger western professors who are not content with mere academic attainment and distinction.

The idea of obtaining winter temperatures on the mountains of the Pacific Coast was first suggested by Professor McAdie, head of the Weather Bureau in San Francisco. He responded to the request for instruments, and through his recommendation, thermometers, rain gauge, etc., were speedily forthcoming from the Weather Bureau. On June 24, 1905, with "Billy" and "Randy," family ponies, loaded with a newly designed thermometer shelter, constructed so as to withstand winter gales and yet allow the easy exit of snow, the first advance on Mt. Rose was made.

From that day the work has been carried on with a vigor and enthusiasm that are thrilling in their inspiration. An improved instrument was added that recorded temperatures on a self-registering roll, all fluctuations, and the highest and lowest temperatures,

Refuge hut and headquarters for snow studies on Mt. Rose at 9000 feet.

The meteorograph on Mt. Rose Summit, wrecked by hanging snow "feathers" up to six feet long.

wind pressures, all variations in humidity, temperature, and air pressure as well as the directions and the velocity of the wind for periods of 70 days and more. This instrument was the achievement of Professor S.P. Fergusson, for many years a pioneer worker in mountain meteorology at Blue Hill Observatory and an associate of Professor Church at the Mount Rose Observatory, which has now become a part of the University of Nevada.

After two winters' work it was discovered, on making comparisons with the records at the Central Weather Station at Reno, 6268 feet below, that frost forecast could probably be made on Mt. Rose from 24 to 48 hours in advance of the appearance of the frost in the lower levels, provided the weather current was traveling in its normal course eastward from the coast.

Second only in importance was the discovery and photographic recording of evidence of the value of timber high up on mountains, and especially on the lips of canyons, for holding the snow until late in the season.

This latter phase of the Observatory's work has developed into a most novel and valuable contribution to practical forestry and conservation of water, under Dr. Church's clear and logical direction. At Contact Pass, 9000 feet elevation, and at the base of the mountain, supplementary stations have been established, where measurements of snow depth and density, the evaporation of snow, and temperatures within the snow have been taken. Lake Tahoe, with its 70 miles of coast line, also affords ready access throughout the winter, by means of motor boat, snowshoes and explorer's camp, to forests of various types and densities where snow measurements of the highest importance have been made.

Delicate instruments of measurement and weight, etc., have been invented by Dr. Church and his associates to meet the needs as they have arisen, and continuous observations for several years seem to justify the following general conclusions. These are quoted from a bulletin by Dr. Church, issued by the International Irrigation Congress.

> The conservation of snow is dependent on mountains and forests and is most complete where these two factors are combined. The mountain range is not only the recipient of more snow than the plain or the valley at its base, but in consequence of the lower temperature prevailing on its slopes the snow there melts more slowly.
>
> However, the mountains, because of their elevation, are exposed to the sweep of violent winds which not only blow the snow in considerable quantities to lower levels, where the temperature is higher, but also dissipate and evaporate the snow to a wasteful degree. The southern slopes, also, are so tilted as to be more completely exposed to the direct rays of the sun, and in the Sierra Nevada and probably elsewhere are subjected to the persistent action of the prevailing southwest wind.
>
> On the other hand, the mountain mass, by breaking the force of the wind, causes much of the drifting snow to pile up on its lee slope and at the base of its cliffs, where it finds comparative shelter from the wind and sun.
>
> Forests, also, conserve the snow. In windswept regions,

Snow surveyor at the meteorograph at Mt. Rose observatory, 10,090 feet.

An alpine whiter pine, defying the storms on the north slope of Mt. Rose, 9,500 ft.

they break the force of the wind, catching the snow and holding it in position even on the windward slopes of the mountains. On the lower slopes, where the wind is less violent, the forests catch the falling snow directly in proportion to their openness, but conserve it after it has fallen directly in proportion to their density. This phenomenon is due to the crowns of the trees, which catch the falling snow and expose it to rapid evaporation in the open air but likewise shut out the sun and wind from the snow that has succeeded in passing through the forest crowns to the ground.

Both mountains and forests, therefore, are to a certain extent wasters of snow — the mountains because they are partially exposed to sun and wind; the trees, because they catch a portion of the falling snow on their branches and expose it to rapid disintegration. However, the mountains by their mass and elevation conserve immeasurably more snow than they waste, and forested areas conserve far more snow than unforested. If the unforested mountain slopes can be covered with timber, much of the waste now occurring on them can be prevented, and by thinning the denser forests the source of waste in them also can be checked.

The experiences met with by the voluntary band of observers to secure the data needed in their work are romantic in the extreme. An average winter trip requires from a day and a half to two days and a half from Reno. From the base of the mountain the ascent must be made on snowshoes. When work first began there was no building on the summit, and no shelter station on the way.

Imagine these brave fellows, daring the storms and blizzards and fierce temperatures of winter, calmly ascending these rugged and steep slopes in the face of every kind of winter threat, merely to make scientific observations. In March 1906, Professor Johnson and Dr. Rudolph spent the night at timber line in a pit dug in the snow to obtain protection from a gale, at the temperature of 5° Fahr. *below* zero, and fought their way to the summit. But so withering was the gale at that altitude even at midday, that a precipitate retreat was made to

Snow surveyor on the mountains above Glen alpine in winter.

avoid freezing.

The faces of the climbers showed plainly the punishment received. Three days later Dr. Church attempted to rescue the record just as the storm was passing. He made his way in an impenetrable fog to 10,000 feet, when the snow and ice crystals deposited by the storm in a state of unstable equilibrium on crust and trees were hurled by a sudden gale high into the air in a blinding blizzard. During his retreat he wandered into the wildest part of the mountain before he escaped from the skirts of the storm.

Other experiences read like chapters from Peary's or Nansen's records in the frozen North, and they are just as heroic and thrilling. Yet in face of all these physical difficulties, which only the most superb courage and enthusiasm could overcome, Dr. Church writes that, to the spirit, the mountain reveals itself, at midnight and at noon, at twilight and at dawn, in storm and in calm, in frost plume and in verdure, as a wonderland so remote from the ordinary experiences of life that the traveler unconsciously deems that he is entering another world.

In the last days of October, 1913, I was privileged to make the trip from Reno in the company of Dr. Church, and two others. We were just ahead of winter's storms, however, though "Old Boreas" raved somewhat wildly on the summit and covered it with snow a few hours after our descent. The experience was one long to be remembered, and the personal touch of the heroic spirit afforded by the trip will be a permanent inspiration.

CHAPTER XXXVII

LAKE TAHOE IN WINTER

by Dr. J.E. Church, Jr., of the University of Nevada

Lake Tahoe is an ideal winter resort for the red-blooded. For the Viking and the near Viking; for the man and the woman who, for the very exhilaration of it, seek the bracing air and the snow-clad forests, Lake Tahoe is as charming in winter as in summer, and far grander. There is the same water — in morning placid, in afternoon foam-flecked, on days of storm tempestuous.

The Lake never freezes; not even a film of ice fringes its edge. Sunny skies and warm noons and the Lake's own restlessness prevent. Emerald Bay alone is sometimes closed with ice, but more often it is as open as the outer Lake. Even the pebbles glisten on the beach as far back as the wash of the waves extends.

But beyond the reach of the waves a deep mantle of white clads the forests and caps the distant peaks. The refuse of the forests, the dusty roads, and the inequalities of the ground are all buried deep. A smooth, gently undulating surface of dazzling white has taken their place.

The forest trees are laden with snow — each frond bears its pyramid and each needle its plume of white. The fresh green of the foliage and the ruddy brown of the bark are accentuated rather than subdued by their white setting. But as the eye travels the long vista of ascending and retreating forest, the green and the brown of the nearby trees fade gradually away until the forest becomes a fluffy mantle of white upon the distant mountainside. Above and beyond the forests' utmost reaches rise the mountain crags and peaks, every angle rounded into gentle contours beneath its burden of snow.

Along the margin of the Lake appear the habitations and works of men deeply buried and snow-hooded until they recall the scenes in Whittier's *Snow Bound.*

The lover of the Lake and its bird life will miss the gulls but will find compensation in the presence of the wild fowl — the ducks and the geese — that have returned to their winter haunts.

Lake Tahoe is remarkably adapted as a winter resort for three prime reasons: first, it is accessible; second, no place in the Sierra Nevada, excepting not even Yosemite, offers so many attractions; third, it is the natural and easy gateway in winter to the remote fastnesses of the northern Sierra.

Among the attractions prëeminently associated with Lake Tahoe in winter are boating and cruising, snowshoeing and exploring, camping for those whose souls are of sterner stuff, hunting, mountain climbing, photography, and the enjoyment of winter landscape. Fishing during the winter months is prohibited by law.

If one asks where to go, a bewildering group of trips and pleasures appears. But there come forth speedily from out the number a few of unsurpassed allurement. These are a ski trip from Tallac to Fallen Leaf Lake to see the breakers and the spray driven by a rising gale against the rock-bound shore, and, when the lake has grown quieter, a boat ride to Fallen Leaf Lodge beneath the frowning parapets of Mount Tallac. Next a ski trip up the Glen to the buried hostelry at Glen Alpine, where one enters by way of a dormer window but is received to a cheerful fire and with royal hospitality.

Then under the skillful guidance of the keeper, a day's climb up the southern face of Mount Tallac for an unrivalled panoramic view from its summit and a speedy but safe glissade back to the hostelry far, far below.

And if the legs be not too stiff from the glissade, a climb over the southern wall of the Glen to Desolation Valley and Pyramid Peak, whence can be seen the long gorge of the Rubicon. The thousand lakes that dot this region present no barrier to one's progress, for they are frozen over and lie buried deep beneath the snow that falls here in an abundance hardly exceeded elsewhere in the Tahoe region.

A close rival of these is the climb from Rubicon Park up the stately range in its rear to visit the mountain hemlock, the graceful queen of the high mountain, and to gaze across the chasm at the twin crags beyond.

And peer of them all, though requiring but little exertion, is a trip to Brockway to enjoy the unrivalled view of the "Land's End" of the Lake and catch the colors of the pansies that are still in bloom in a niche of the old sea wall. If one possess the artist's mood, he will add thereto a boat ride round State Line Pint in the lazy swell of the evening sea beneath the silent pine-clad cliffs, while the moon, as beautiful as any summer moon, rides overhead. Only the carpet of snow and the film of ice that gathers from the spray upon the boat keeps one alive to the reality that the season is winter.

Finally a rowing trip along the western shore of the Lake with stops at pleasure en *route.* One can have weather to suit his taste, for the waters on this shore are safe in storm, and the barometer and the sky will give full warning long before the weather attains the danger point. The man who loves the breath of the storm and the glow of excitement will loose his boat from Tallac when the clouds swing down the canyon and speed forth borne, as it were, on the wings of the waves toward the distant foot of the Lake — past the black water wall where the waves of Emerald Bay sweep into Tahoe, through the frothy waters where the wind shifts and whips around Rubicon Point, over the white caps of Meek's Bay until by skillful maneuvering the jutting cape is weathered and quieter water is found in McKinney Bay. Full time there is, with the wind astern, to reach the river's mouth at Tahoe City, but the voyager who loves the woodland will tarry for a night in the dense fir forest of Blackwood, while his boat rides safely moored to the limb of a prostrate tree.

Regarding the eastern side of the Lake, the bald shore and jutting headlands, the fewness of the landing places, and the sweep of the waves make cruising in these waters a matter of supreme skill and farsightedness. Let the Viking learn with broad-beamed boat the mastery of the western shore before he turns his boat's prow to the east.

For the man of milder tastes the motorboat will suffice or the mail steamer, which plies the waters of Lake Tahoe twice a week.

In tobogganing, the hills and open meadows at Tahoe City and at Glenbrook will furnish royal sport for the devotee. Skating and ice yachting must be sought in regions where the show is less deep and the cold more intense.

Skiing is the chief method of locomotion in winter at the Lake and the novice soon becomes expert in the milder forms of the sport. Ski trails thread the forests at Tahoe City and radiate from every resort.

The open inns at Tahoe City and Glenbrook, and The Grove near Tallac and the resorts on Fallen Leaf Lake insure the traveler's comfort, while the hospitality of the caretakers at all of the resorts is proverbial.

The question of when and how to go is naturally a leading one. During the months of November to April, two sledging services are furnished each thrice a week — one from Carson City to Glenbrook, the other from Truckee to Tahoe City. (The narrow gauge railway has also established a semi-weekly winter schedule.) The mail boat connects with the incoming sledges and train on Tuesday and Saturday. The route from Carson City, which crosses the heights of the Carson Range, affords a superb view of the Lake at sunset. The route from Truckee traverses the wooded canyon of the Truckee River, when scenically at its best.

The traveler who approaches the Lake by way of Glenbrook and leaves by way of the canyon of the Truckee will have an experience in winter travel both unique and replete with beautiful landscapes.

The journey from Truckee to the Lake can also be made on ski in one short day. It is an exhilarating trip, if one travels light. If one desires to tarry *en route,* he may carry his blankets and food on his back or haul them on a toboggan, and spend the night at the halfway station, known as Uncle Billy's.

The best time to visit the Lake is after the heaviest of the winter snows have fallen. The period of steady and heavy precipitation occurs in January. After this month is past, there are long periods of settled weather broken only occasionally by storms, which add to rather than detract from one's pleasure.

The special equipment requisite for winter trips to Tahoe is slight. The list includes goggles (preferably amber), German socks and rubbers, woolen shirt, sweater, short heavy coat, and mittens. For mountain climbing a pair of Canadian snowshoes should be added to the equipment; for traveling on the level, a pair of skis can be rented at Truckee or the Lake. If one desires to camp instead of stopping at the resorts around the Lake, a tent and waterproof sleeping bag should be procured.

The cost of transportation in winter is scarcely more than in summer. The sledge trip from either Truckee or Carson City to the Lake is $2.50, an amount only $1.00 in excess of the regular fare b y rail. Board will cost no more than in summer.

TRUCKEE

Closely associated with Lake Tahoe as a center for winter sports is Truckee, the natural point of departure for the Lake. Here a winter carnival is held annually for the entertainment of outsiders. Among the chief sports are ski racing and jumping and tobogganing. The toboggan course is 2000 feet long and has a fall of 150 feet. A device is employed for drawing the toboggans back to the starting point. The hotel facilities are ample. Toboggans and skis can be rented for use here or at the Lake. Clothing and other winter outfits can be procured. Canadian snowshoes, however, must be obtained in San Francisco.

CHAPTER XXXVIII

LAKE TAHOE AS A SUMMER RESIDENCE

One of the most marked differences that the traveler observes between the noted lakes of Europe and Lake Tahoe is the comparative dearth of homes, summer villas, bungalows, residences, on the latter. This is natural. California and Nevada are new countries. They have scarcely had time to "find themselves" fully as yet. It took a thousand years to people the shores of the European lakes as we find them today, and in due time Tahoe will assuredly come to its own in this regard.

Indeed, as John Le Conte well wrote a number of years ago:

The Shores of Lake Tahoe afford the most beautiful sites for summer residences. When the states of California and Nevada become more populous, the delicious summer climate of this elevated region, the exquisite beauty of the surrounding scenery, and the admirable facilities afforded for fishing and other aquatic sports, will dot the shores of this mountain Lake with the cottages of those who are able to combine health with pleasure.

But it must be remembered that the prolonged severity of the winter climate, and especially the great depth of snowfall, render these elevated situations unfit for permanent residences. According to the observations of Dr. G.M. Bourne, during the winter of 1873-74, the aggregate snowfall near the shores of the Lake amounted to more than 34 feet. In fact, frequently there are not more than four months in the year in which the ground of the margin of the Lake is entirely free from snow. And the vast gorges which furrow the sides of the surrounding amphitheater of lofty mountain peaks are perpetually snow-clad.

Hence it is unreasonable to assume that many persons besides the wealthy will be able to enjoy the luxury of private residences here, which can be occupied only during the summer months of the year. Nevertheless, when the refinement and taste incident to the development of an older civilization shall have permeated the minds of the wealthy classes of citizens, this charming lake region will not only continue to be the favorite resort of tourists and artists, but will become, during the summer season, the abode of families whose abundant means enable them to enjoy the healthful climate, the gorgeous scenery, and the invigorating sports which lend an inexpressive charm to the sojourn on its shores.

Amidst the magnificent nature that surrounds this region, there should be an inspiration corresponding

Tahoe guide at his summer home.

more or less with the grandeur of the aspect of the material world. The modifications impressed upon the moral and intellectual character of man by the physical aspects of nature, is a theme more properly belonging to those who have cultivated the aesthetic side of humanity. The poet and the artist can alone appreciate, in the fullness of their humanizing influence, the potent effects of these aesthetic inspirations. The lake districts in all Alpine countries seem to impress peculiar characteristics upon their inhabitants.

When quietly floating upon the placid surface of Lake Tahoe, the largest of the Gems of the Sierra — nestled, as it is, amidst a huge amphitheater of mountain peaks — it is difficult to say whether we are more powerfully impressed with the genuine childlike awe and wonder inspired by the contemplation of the noble grandeur of nature, or with the calmer and more gentle sense of the beautiful produced by the less imposing aspects of the surrounding scenery.

On the one hand, crag and beetling cliff sweeping in rugged and colossal massiveness above dark waves of pine and fir, far into the keen and clear blue air; the huge mantle of snow, so cumulus-like in its brightness, thrown in many a solid fold over ice-sculptured crest and shoulders; the dark cathedral-like spires and splintered pinnacles, half snow, half stone, rising into the sky like the very pillars of heaven.

On the other hand, the waving verdure of the valleys below, the dash of waterfalls, the plenteous gush of springs, the laugh and dance of brook and rivulet as they hurry down the plains. Add to this picture the deep repose of the azure water, in which are mirrored snow-clad peaks, as well as marginal fringes of waving forests and green meadows, and it is difficult to decide whether the sense of grandeur or of beauty has obtained the mastery of the soul.

CHAPTER XXXIX

THE TAHOE NATIONAL FOREST

The Tahoe National Forest was first set apart by proclamation, September 17, 1906. Previous to this there had been the Tahoe and Yuba Forest Reserves which were established by proclamation under the acts of March 3, 1891 and June 4, 1897. The original Tahoe Forest Reserve consisted of six townships along the west side of Lake Tahoe. Part of this territory is now in the Tahoe and part in the El Dorado National Forest. Changes and additions were later made by proclamations of March 2, 1909 and July 28, 1910.

Although Lake Tahoe does not lie within any National Forest it is almost surrounded by the Tahoe and El Dorado Forests. There are a few miles of shore line on the Nevada side in the vicinity of Glenbrook which are not within the National Forest Boundary.

The gross area of the Tahoe National Forest is 1,272,470 acres. Of this amount, however, 692,677 acres are privately owned. The El Dorado National Forest has a gross area of 836,200 acres with 284,798 of them in private hands. These privately owned lands are technically spoken of as "alienated lands."

The towns of Truckee, Emigrant Gap, Cisco, Donner, Fulda, Downieville, Sierra City, Alleghany, Forest, Graniteville, Goodyear's Bar, and Last Chance, as well as Tahoe City, are all within the Tahoe National Forest.

It is estimated that there are probably 350 people living on the Forest outside of the towns. These are principally miners or small ranch owners living along the rivers in the lower altitudes.

Slowly but surely the people are awakening to the great value of the natural resources that are being conserved in the National Forests. In the Tahoe Reserve the preservation of the forest cover is essential to the holding of snow and rainfall, preventing rapid run-off, thereby conserving much of what would be waste and destructive flood water, until it can be used for irrigation and other beneficial purposes.

Many streams of great power possibilities rise and flow through the Tahoe Forest Reserve, such as the Truckee, Little Truckee, Yuba and American rivers. Working in conjunction with the U.S. Reclamation Service, the Truckee General Electric Company uses the water that flows out of Lake Tahoe down the Truckee River for the development of power. The Pacific Gas and Electric Company, of San Francisco, controls the waters of the South Yuba river, and its Colgate plant is on the main Yuba, though it obtains some of its water supply from the North Yuba. Lake Spaulding, one of the largest artificial lakes in the world, is a creation of this same company. It is situated near Emigrant Gap and is used for the development of power.

The Northern Water and Power Company controls the Bowman reservoir and a string of lakes on the headwaters of Canyon Creek, a branch of the South Yuba river. As yet its power possibilities are not developed.

Through the activities of these companies, electricity and water for irrigation are supplied to towns and country regions contiguous to their lines, and they have materially aided in the development of the Sacramento Valley.

Only about five percent of the Reserve is barren land, and this is mostly situated at a high elevation above timber line. The tree growth is excellent and, under proper direction, reproduction *could* be made all that anyone could desire.

Fully 20 percent, however, of the present Reserve is covered with chaparral. Practically all of this originally was timbered. The chaparral has grown up because nothing was done at the proper time to foster reproduction over acres that had been cut.

Systematic and scientific efforts are now being made to remedy this condition, the rangers being encouraged to study the trees, gather seeds from the best of their type, plant and cultivate them. Tree cutting is now so regular as to obtain by natural reproduction a second crop on the logged-over areas.

Where natural reproduction fails, planting is resorted to. Thus it is hoped, in time, to replant all the logged-over areas now owned by the government, serving the double purpose of conserving the water supply and providing timber for the needs of the future. Much of the timber land, however, of the Tahoe region is patented to private owners. Little, if anything, is being done towards reforestation on these private tracts. Legal enactments, ultimately, may produce effective action along this needed line.

As has elsewhere been shown, the world owes a debt of gratitude to the Tahoe region. Had it not been for the timber secured so readily from the Tahoe slopes, the mining operations of Virginia City, Gold Hill, Silver City and Dayton would have been seriously retarded and crippled. As it was, the Tahoe trees were transferred as mining timbers for propping up the immense and continuous excavations of that vast series of honeycombings underground, the products of which revivified the gold supply of the world.

White Cloud Falls, Cascade Lake.

Tahoe timber also has contributed much to the upbuilding of the towns and country farms on the whole upper Pacific Coast and interior regions of Northern California, and today much of its timber finds it way to San Francisco and other Pacific Coast markets.

At Floriston, on the Truckee River, a mill is in successful operation, using Tahoe fir for the making of paper. Red and white fir, which are practically useless for lumber, are found to make excellent wrapping and tissue papers, and thus, from being unremunerative products of our forests, become sources of income. After planing off the bark, the wood is made into small chips, about a half inch square, and an eighth of an inch thick. These chips are then "digested" by a process of mixing with acids and cooking, through which it becomes "wood pulp."

Different processes produce different pulps, two of

Upper Eagle Falls above Emerald Bay.

which are mixed together, allowed to flow out on a very fine wire screen nine feet wide, revolving at a rate of 300 feet a minute, with a "jigging" movement from side to side. This makes all the fibers lie flat. They are then sent through steel rollers, the water squeezed out, and finally carried over and around 25 revolving steam-heated cylinders which completely dry the paper and put the needed gloss or finish on it.

The rainfall on the Tahoe Reserve averages about 50 inches annually, the most frequent rains occurring between October and May. Necessarily there is much snowfall on the higher regions. Further down, the snow disappears in the early spring, say March, but in the upper altitudes it remains until late June, with perpetual snow in the sheltered portions of the topmost peaks.

Agriculture, owing to the average high altitude, is a negligible industry in the Reserve, little more being done than to raise a little fruit, grain and vegetables, mainly for home consumption. Naturally there is a fair amount of grazing, almost the whole area of the Reserve being used for this purpose during the summer months. Many portions of meadow land are used for dairy herds, most of the hotels and resorts on and near Lake Tahoe having their own herds and meadows.

Bands of beef cattle are also pastured, together with large bands of sheep, the two kinds of stock often grazing in common, the cattle using the meadows and the sheep the ridges and timber lands. In taking the trail rides described in other chapters, I invariably came across both cattle and sheep, and all the nearby meadows are occupied by the dairy herds belonging to the hotels. Patented lands of private ownership within the bounds of the Forest are often also leased to cattlemen and sheepmen.

Last year it was estimated that there were 47,000 head of sheep and about 6000 head of cattle on the Reserve. Under the protection of the rangers, grazing conditions are rapidly improving, the cattlemen and sheepmen being held strictly to certain rules laid down by the Supervisor. Systematic efforts are made to rid the Forest, as far as possible, of predatory animals that kill the sheep, also of poisonous plants which render grazing dangerous.

There are far less cattle on the Sierra ranges in the Tahoe region that there are sheep. During the summer, most of the mountain valleys have their great sheep bands. Many are brought over from Nevada, and far more from the Sacramento Valley and other regions near the Pacific. The feed, as a rule, is good and abundant from the time the snow leaves until the end of September or even later.

But well may John Muir dislike sheep in his beloved Sierra, and term them in his near-to-hatred "the locusts of the mountains." When the most fertile valley has been fed off by sheep, or they have bedded down night after night upon it, it takes some time before the young growth comes up again.

It is the custom when the lambing season is over, and the lambs are strong enough to travel and old enough to ship, to move to some convenient point on the railway, where there is an abundance of feed and water on the way, and there ship either to Reno, Carson and Virginia City, or to some market on the Pacific Coast. Hence overland travelers on the Southern Pacific trains are often surprised to see vast flocks of sheep and hear the bleating of the lambs at un-looked-for stations at the highest points of the Sierra Nevada, as at Soda Springs,

Cisco, Emigrant Gap, Blue Canyon, or sidings on the way.

There is a large mining industry within the Reserve. Since 1849 the western part of the Forest has been most active, one county, Sierra, having produced since then upwards of $200,000,000. The present output is much smaller than formerly, still it is large enough to render mining an important factor in the productive wealth of the state. In 1853 hydraulic mining was inaugurated near Nevada City. This gave renewed interest to placer mining.

Four of the old emigrant roads cross the Tahoe and El Dorado Reserves. The most famous of these is the one across Donner Pass and through Emigrant Gap. This was the general course taken by the unfortunate Donner Party, as recorded in another chapter.

Another road was the Heuness Pass road, on a branch of which was Nigger Tent, a rendezvous of robbers and cut-throats in the early days. Prospectors and miners were often robbed and murdered at this place. The Heuness Pass Road and the Donner Road branch in Sardine Valley, the former going through by Webber Lake, and the latter through the present site of Truckee. On the latter road, in the vicinity of You Bet, is a large tree which bears the name "Frémont's Flag-pole," though it is doubtful whether it was ever used by Frémont for this purpose.

The third important road is the present Placerville Road — a portion of the State Highway and the great transcontinental Lincoln Highway, elsewhere described.

The fourth is the Amador Grade Road, on which stood the tree whereupon Kit Carson carved his name.

The Georgetown Road is an important and historic feature of the Tahoe Region, for it connects Georgetown with Virginia City, and it was from the former place so many Tahoe pioneers came. I have already referred to the trail built in the early 1860s. Then when the Georgetown miners constructed a ditch to convey water for mining purposes from Loon Lake, they soon thereafter, about 1872 or '73, built a road about 40 miles long, to enable them to reach the Lake, which was their main reservoir. Loon, Pleasant and Bixby's Lakes were all dammed and located upon for the water company.

When the Hunsakers built the road from McKinney's to their Springs in 1883 there was a stretch of only about seven miles from Loon Lake to the Springs to complete a road between Lake Tahoe and Georgetown. The matter was laid before the Supervisors of Placer and El Dorado counties, and they jointly built the road in 1884, following as nearly as possible the old Georgetown trail, which was practically the boundary between the two counties.

While automobiles have gone over it, it is scarcely good enough for that form of travel, but cattle, sheep and horses are driven over it constantly, campers make good use of it in the summer, and though it has not the activity of the days when it was first built, it has fully justified its existence by the comfort and convenience it gives to the sparsely settled population of the region for which the waters of the Reserve were flumed in every direction.

When legal enactment practically abolished placer mining, owing to its ruining the agricultural lands lower down by the carrying of the mud and silt upon them, the water systems were utilized for domestic and irrigation purposes, thus laying the foundation of the great systems now being used for power purposes.

One of the greatest excitements known in the Tahoe region occurred when the first notice of the discovery of the Comstock Lode in Virginia City appeared in the *Nevada City Journal*, July 1, 1859. Immediately the whole country was aroused, fully one-third of all the male population setting forth for the mines. This was also one of the great urgencies in the building of a railway which soon ultimated in the Central Pacific.

There are several mineral springs of note on the Forest, chief of which are Deer Park Springs, Glen Alpine Spring, and Brockway's.

The most northern grove of Big Trees, *Sequoia Gigantea,* in existence is found in the Tahoe Forest, on the Forest Hill Divide, near the southern boundary of Placer County, on a tributary of the Middle Fork of the American River. There are six of these trees as well as several which have fallen.

Dotted over the Reserve are cabins of the rangers. These men live a most interesting, and sometimes adventurous and daring life. Primarily their days and nights are largely those of solitude, and it is interesting to throw a little light upon the way they spend their time.

Necessarily their chief thought and care is that of protecting the Forest from fire. To accomplish this end fire-brakes — wide passages, trails, or roads — are cut through the trees and brush, so that it is possible to halt a fire when it reaches one of the constant patrols and watches that are maintained. Lookout stations are placed on elevated points.

In the fall of 1911 a Lookout Tower was erected in Banner Mountain, four miles southeast of Nevada City, in which a watchman with a revolving telescope is on duty day and night. This mountain is at 3900 feet elevation and affords an unobstructed view of about one-third of the whole area of the Tahoe Forest.

By a system of maps, sights and signals, the location of fires can be determined with reasonable accuracy, and the telephone enables warnings to be sent to all concerned.

Telephone lines bisect the Reserve in several directions, and firefighting appliances are cached in accessible places ready for immediate use. When a Forest officer is notified of the approximate location of a fire he goes immediately with what help he thinks he needs. If he finds that the fire is larger than he can handle with the available force at his command, he notifies the Supervisor, who secures men from the most practical point and dispatches them to the fire as soon as possible, by automobile or train.

To give further fire protection a gasoline launch — the *Ranger* — 26 feet long and with a carrying capacity of fifteen men, and a speed of about nine miles an hour, was placed on Lake Tahoe in 1910, at the Ken Ranger Station, located a mile below the Tavern. The guard who is in charge of this boat is on the Lake about eight hours each day, going up the Lake in the morning towards Tallac and taking the northern end of the Lake in the afternoon. The launch is put in service each year about the 15th of June and kept there until the fire danger is over in the fall. Normal years this is about the 15th of September, but in 1913 the launch remained and the patrolman was on duty much later.

If the guard sights a fire anywhere within the watershed of Lake Tahoe, he immediately obtains men at the nearest point and proceeds to the fire. Since the launch has been on the Lake there have been no serious fires. Every fire has been caught in its infancy and put out before any damage has been done. There has been only one fire of any size on the Lake since the launch was installed. This burned about 20 acres just east of Brockway. Numerous small fires of an acre or less have been put out each year.

The Forest Guard in charge of the launch for the years of 1912—13 was Mark W. Edmonds. Mr. Edmonds is the son of Dr. H.W. Edmonds, who is now in the Arctic doing scientific work for the Carnegie Institute.

The force of men at work on the Reserve varies in number according to the season of the year. When the fire season is on, many more men are on duty than in the winter season. The year-long force consists of the Supervisor, Deputy Supervisor, Forest Clerk, Stenographer, thirteen Rangers and two Forest Examiners who are Forest School men engaged chiefly on timber sale and investigative work.

The force in 1913 during the season of greatest danger was 56. Some of the temporary employees are engaged for six months, some for three months and others for shorter periods. The longer-termed men are generally Assistant Rangers who cannot be employed the year around, but who are considered first for permanent jobs that occur on the statutory roll on account of their Civil Service standing.

Forest fires are caused in a variety of ways, but chiefly through inexcusable carelessness. Now and then lightning produces fire, but the throwing down of lighted matches by smokers, the butt ends of cigars and cigarettes that are still alight, leaving campfires unextinguished, or building them too large, allowing fires for burning wasteland or brush to get from under control — these are the chief sources of forest fires. Accordingly the local and federal authorities constantly keep posted on Forest Reserves notices calling attention to the dangers and urging care upon all who use the forests for any purpose whatever.

In addition to firefighting the rangers are required to give constant oversight to the sheep and cattle ranges, and to the animals that are brought there, so that the feed is not eaten out, or too many head pastured upon a given area. Seeds of forest trees must be gathered at the proper season and experiments in reforestation conducted, besides a certain amount of actual planting out performed. The habits of seed-eating birds and animals are studied, especially in relation to reforestation. A very small number of squirrels or mice can get away with a vast number of seeds in a season. Methods of protecting the seeds without destroying too many of the wild animals must be devised.

Available areas of timber are sought for and offered for sale. Certain men are detailed to measure the trees and determine the value of the timber; they must mark the trees included in the sale, leaving out enough seed trees for satisfactory reproduction. If it be a second sale over a cut-over area, the problems

Island Park, Lake Tahoe.

are somewhat altered. Will the trees that are left suffer from windfall? If partially suppressed trees are left, can they be depended upon to recover and make a good growth?

Then, too, the questions of natural versus artificial reforestation have to be scientifically studied and exhaustive tests made. Shall seeds be sown, or shall young trees be planted? Which trees are best suited for certain localities, and which are the more profitable when grown?

To many people it is not known that dwellers in or near National Forests can obtain free-of-charge timber for their domestic needs. The rangers determine where this free area shall be located, exactly what trees, whether dead or alive, shall be taken, and endeavor to lay down rules that shall give equal chances for all comers.

As one of the mottos of the Forest Service is "the greatest good to the greatest number," small sales are encouraged to those who wish to make their own lumber or shakes. Settlers in remote localities are often helped in this manner.

Cases of trespass have to be guarded against, and now and again suits have had to be brought against loggers for encroaching upon the territory of the Reserve, and removing timber which they had not purchased.

In 1911 every District Ranger was appointed a Deputy Fish and Game Commissioner and thus was duly authorized to enforce the law in regard to fish and game.

Another subject of interest and importance to the ranger is the study of insect infestation. Many trees are killed annually by certain insects, and these must be discovered and their devastation prevented.

Then, too, there are diseases and parasites that affect the trees, and this branch of study demands constant attention.

Hence it will be seen that the office of the Forest Ranger is by no means a sinecure. He works hard and he works long and alone, and our kindly thoughts should go out to him in his solitary patrols and vigils.

CHAPTER XL

PUBLIC USE OF THE WATERS OF LAKE TAHOE

There has always been considerable discussion and dissention among conflicting interests as to the use of the waters of Lake Tahoe for private or semi-public uses, and finally, in 1903, the U.S. Reclamation Service entered into the field. At my request D.W. Cole, engineer-in-charge of the Truckee-Carson project, kindly furnishes the following data:

Along in the '60's of the last century the region around the Lake acquired great importance on account of the fine growth of timber on the surrounding mountain slopes. It is said that a great many million feet of lumber were harvested in this region. For many years the entire lumber supply for the old Comstock mines was derived from this source.

Virginia City, Carson City, and the neighboring mining communities were built from the timber of the Lake Tahoe basin, and it might be said that the foundation of the fortunes of the California gold kinds, who developed the Comstock mines, was made of the pine wood which grew upon the shores of Lake Tahoe, without which that wonderful output of $700,000,000 of gold from the Comstock Lode would have been impossible.

Supplementing the timber supply the water from Marlette Lake, a tributary to Lake Tahoe, was diverted by a remarkable engineering achievement for supplying Virginia City and the deep mines. Marlette Lake lies several hundred feet above Lake Tahoe on the Nevada side, and half a century ago its waters were taken through flume, tunnel and pipeline across the dividing mountain range and out into the desert valley of the Carson River for sustaining gold seekers of Virginia City. This work of the pioneer engineers was scarcely less bold in its conception and wonderful in its execution than the famous Sutro tunnel which drains the underground waters from the Comstock mines.

About 1870 the first use of Lake Tahoe for other than navigation purposes was made by building a log crib dam at the outlet for the purpose of storing floodwaters to be used in log driving in the Truckee River below the Lake.

The outlet of the Lake was in a land grant section belonging to the Central Pacific Railway Company, and one of the earlier lumber companies procured a charter from the State of California and proceeded to build a dam and operate it for log driving purposes.

In the course of time the development of water power in the Truckee River below the Lake became of considerable importance, both for sawmill and other manufacturing purposes. The dam at the Lake's outlet was passed from the possession of the Donner Boom & Lumber Company into the hands of other interests who were making a larger use of power.

Eventually, in the last decade of the century, the water power plants were converted into hydro-electric plants and began to furnish electric current for power and lighting in the city of Reno and as far south as Virginia City.

About the year 1908 the ownership of the several hydro-electric plants was passed to the Truckee River General Electric Company, under the management of the Stone & Webster Engineering Corporation, of Boston, one of the very large public utilities corporations of the country.

This company has enlarged and improved the plants and is now furnishing a large amount of electric current for all purposes in Reno, Virginia City, Carson City, Yerington, Minden and various other towns and mining camps in the State of Nevada, forming a group of communities which are wholly dependent upon this power for their various purposes.

In 1903 the United States Reclamation Service filed an appropriation of all surplus waters which had theretofore gone to waste from Lake Tahoe, and under this appropriation, with others covering waters in the Carson River, the Truckee-Carson Reclamation Project in Nevada was commenced.

By this irrigation project it is proposed to cover an area of about 206,000 acres, of which 35,000 acres are now being irrigated and about 500 families have their homes upon productive lands, which were formerly a part of the great desert which was traversed with much suffering by the pioneer gold seekers.

In 1908 the Reclamation Service entered into negotiations for the purchase of the real estate and dam controlling the outlet of Lake Tahoe, but before the purchase was concluded the reorganized power company secured possession of the property. A condemnation suit was then brought by the United States to acquire possession and control of the Lake's outlet. A contract was entered into with the power company for the joint building of a new dam with gates for controlling the outlet from the Lake.

This dam was partly built in 1909, replacing a portion of the old timber structure. Owing to various complications this new cement dam has stood in an incomplete condition until the fall of 1913 when arrangements were made for its completion, and now the structure is entirely done and is well adapted to control the outlet from the Lake so as to hold the waters at satisfactory levels according to the various uses for which the water is required.

There have been confusing statements made in the public press and otherwise concerning the intentions and actions of the Reclamation Service and of the power company. The gist of the whole matter is that both the Reclamation Service and the power company have proposed by means of the new dam to regulate the Lake within a range of six feet vertically, this being well within the limits of fluctuations which have occurred during the past 40 years when the Lake has been partially controlled by means of the old logging dam, and during which period the navigation and resort interests have taken the place of the lumber business in the commercial aspects of the Lake.

The records show that during these 40 years the Lake has fluctuated to the extent of a little more than eight feet between low and high water marks.

The landowners around the Lake are principally interested in its esthetic qualities as a basis for the commercial interests involved in the tourist traffic and summer resort business. These interests would naturally desire the Lake to be held at a fixed level.

Likewise the navigation interests which operate a large number of boats of various sizes would be best pleased with a stationary level of the Lake, in order that their wharves and boat routes might be built and maintained for a single level of the water.

On the other hand the natural conditions and the use of water for power and irrigation, which are among the older vested rights, require the Lake to be used to some extent as a storage reservoir, which implies a fluctuating level.

The whole problem is to reconcile these various interests so as to derive the greatest possible economic advantages while maintaining the great beauties of the Lake for those whose interests lie mainly in that direction.

There has been suspicion on the part of some of the riparian owners that either the power company of the government, or both, have been entertaining ulterior motives with the purpose of drawing down the Lake to unprecedented levels and of extracting from the Lake an amount of water greater than the average annual inflow. It may be stated once for all that there has never been such a purpose and that all calculations of the available water in the Lake have been based upon a long record of seasonable fluctuations which prove that the average annual outflow from the Lake is about 300,000 acre feet.

All plans have contemplated the use of *only* this average amount of water annually.

The Lake has an area of 193 square miles. The elevation of its high water mark has been at 6231.3, whereas its low water mark is recorded at elevation 6223.1 above sea level.

Should the government be successful in acquiring the outlet property from the power company by the condemnation suit now in court, it is proposed to operate the gates of the dam at all times so as to maintain the Lake at the highest level consistent with the maintenance of a desirable shoreline and the conservation of water for the public utilities. It is proposed never to draw the Lake below the previous low water mark or to allow it to rise as high as the previous high water mark, at which low and high limits damage in some degree was done to one or another's interests at the Lake.

The regulation proposed by the government provides for recognition and protection of all rights in and to the waters and shores of Lake Tahoe, including the rights of the general public and of the lovers of natural beauty everywhere, and it is believed that the charms, as well as the utilities, of this paragon of lakes can more safely be entrusted to a permanent government agency than to any single private interest.

A few additions to Mr. Cole's lucid statement will help the general reader to a fuller comprehension of the difficulty between the states of Nevada and California. It will be recalled that Lake Tahoe has an area of about 193 square miles, of which 78 square miles are in the counties of Washoe, Ormsby and Douglas, Nevada, the remaining 115 square miles being in Placer and El Dorado counties, California.

Because of this fact, that nearly two-thirds of the superficial area of the Lake is in California, the people of California claim that they have the natural and inherent right to control, even to determining of its disposal, at least nearly two-thirds of the water of the Lake.

The situation, however, is further complicated by the fact that the only outlet to the Lake is in California near Tahoe City, in Placer County, into the Truckee River, which meanders for some miles in a northeasterly course until it leaves California, enters Nevada, passes through the important city of Reno, and finally empties into Pyramid Lake, which practically has no outlet.

In response to the claim of California, the people of Nevada, in which it appears they are backed up by the U.S. Reclamation Service, contend that Nature has already determined whither the overflow waters of Lake Tahoe shall go. That, while they do not wish in the slightest to restrict the proper use of the waters of the Truckee River by the dwellers upon that river, they insist that no one else is entitled to their use, and that every drop of superfluous water, legally and morally, belongs to them, to be used as they deem proper.

In accordance with this conception of their rights, the Nevada legislature passed the following act, which was approved, March 6, 1913:

> That for the purpose of aiding the Truckee-Carson reclamation project now being carried out by the Reclamation Service of the United States of America, under the Act of Congress approved June 17, 1902 (32 Stat. p. 384) known as the Reclamation Act, and acts amendatory thereof or supplementary thereto, consent is hereby given to the use by the United States of America of Lake Tahoe, situated partly in the State of California dn partly in the State of Nevada, and the waters, bed, shores and capability of use for reservoir purposes thereof, in such manner and to such extent as the United States of America through its lawful agencies shall think proper for such purpose, and as fully as the State of Nevada could use the same, provided, however, that the consent hereby given is without prejudice to any existing rights that persons or corporations may have in Lake Tahoe or the Truckee River.

At the present time (winter of 1914-15) the matter is in the courts awaiting adjudication, which it is to be hoped, while being satisfactory to all parties to the suit, will fully conserve for the scenic enjoyment of the world all the charms for which Tahoe has been so long and so justly famous.

APPENDIX A

MARK TWAIN AT LAKE TAHOE

Early in the 1860s the immortal Mark made his mark at Lake Tahoe. In his Roughing It, *he devotes Chapters XXII and XXIII to the subject. Later, when in Italy, he described Lake Como and compared it with Tahoe in* Innocents Abroad, *and while his prejudices against the Indians led him to belittle the Indian name — Tahoe — and in so doing to make several errors of statement, the descriptions are excellent and the interested reader is referred to them as being well worthy of his attention.*

CHAPTER XXII, *ROUGHING IT.*

We had heard a world of talk about the marvelous beauty of Lake Tahoe, and finally curiosity drove us thither to see it. Three or four members of the Brigade [A company of 14 camp-followers of the Governor of Nevada, who boarded at the same house as Twain. They were popularly known as the 'Irish Brigade,' though there were only a few Irish among them.] had been there and located some timber lands on its shores and stored up a quantity of provisions in their camp. We strapped a couple of blankets on our shoulders and took an ax apiece and started — for we intended to take up a wood ranch or so ourselves and become wealthy. We were on foot. The reader will find it advantageous to go on horseback. We were told that the distance was eleven miles.

We tramped a long time on level ground, and then toiled laboriously up a mountain about a thousand miles high and looked over. No lake there. We descended on the other side, crossed the valley and toiled up another mountain three or four thousand miles high, apparently, and looked over again. No lake yet. We sat down tired and perspiring, and hired a couple of Chinamen to curse those people who had beguiled us. Thus refreshed, we presently resumed the march with renewed vigor and determination.

We plodded on, two or three hours longer, and at last the Lake burst upon us — a noble sheet of blue water lifted six thousand three hundred feet above the level of the sea, and walled in by a rim of snow-clad mountain peaks that towered aloft full three thousand feet higher still! It was a vast oval, and one would have to use up eighty or a hundred good miles in traveling around it. As it lay there with the shadows of the mountains brilliantly photographed upon its still surface I though it must surely be the fairest picture the whole earth affords.

... After supper as the darkness closed down and the stars came out and spangled the great mirror with jewels, we smoked meditatively in the solemn hush and forgot our troubles and our pains. In due time we spread our blankets in the warm sand between two large boulders and soon fell asleep .... The wind rose just as we were losing consciousness, and we were lulled to sleep by the beating of the surf upon the shore.

It is always very cold on that Lake shore in the night, but we had plenty of blankets and were warm enough. We never moved a muscle all night, but waked at early dawn in the original positions, and got up at once thoroughly refreshed, free from soreness, and brim full of fris-kiness. There is no end of wholesome medicine in such an experience. That morning we could have whipped ten such people as we were the day before — sick ones at any rate.

But the world is slow, and people will go to "water cures" and "movement cures" and to foreign lands for health. Three months of camp life on Lake Tahoe would restore an Egyptian mummy to his pristine vigor, and give him an appetite like an alligator. I do not mean the oldest and driest mummies, of course, but the fresher ones.

The air up there in the clouds is very pure and fine, bracing and delicious. And why shouldn't it be? — It is the same the angels breathe. I think that hardly any amount of fatigue can be gathered together that a man cannot sleep off in one night on the sand by its side. Not under a roof, but under the sky; it seldom or never rains there in the summer time.

... Next morning while smoking the pipe of peace after breakfast we watched the sentinel peaks put on the glory of the sun, and followed the conquering light as it swept down among the shadows, and set the captive crags and forests free. We watched the tinted pictures grow and brighten upon the water till every little detail of forest, precipice, and pinnacle was wrought in and finished, and the miracle of the enchanter complete. Then to "business."

that is, drifting around in the boat. We were on the north shore. There, the rocks on the bottom are sometimes gray, sometimes white. This gives the marvelous transparency of the water a fuller advantage than it has elsewhere on the Lake. We usually pushed out a hundred yards or so from the shore, and then lay down on the thwarts in the sun, and let the boat drift by the hour whither it would.

We seldom talked. It interrupted the Sabbath stillness, and marred the dreams the luxurious rest and indolence brought. The shore all along was indented with deep, curved bays and coves, bordered by narrow sand beaches; and where the sand ended, the steep mountainsides rose right up aloft into space — rose up like a vast wall a little out of the perpendicular, and thickly wooded with tall pines.

So singularly clear was the water, that there it was only twenty or thirty feet deep the bottom was so perfectly distinct that the boat seemed floating in the air! Yes, where it was even eighty feet deep. Every little pebble was distinct, every speckled trout, every hand's breadth of sand. Often, as we lay on our faces, a granite boulder, as large as a village church, would start out of the bottom apparently, and seem climbing up rapidly to the surface, till presently it threatened to touch our faces, and we could not resist the impulse to seize an oar and avert the danger.

But the boat would float on, and the boulder descend again, and then we could see that when we had been exactly above it, it must have been twenty or thirty feet below the surface. Down through the transparency of these great depths, the water was not merely transparent, but dazzlingly, brilliantly so.

All objects seen through it had a bright, strong vividness, not only of outline, but of every minute detail, which they would not have had when seen simply through the same depth of atmosphere. So empty and airy did all spaces seem below us, and so strong was the sense of floating high aloft in mid-nothingness, that we called these boat excursions "balloon voyages."

We fished a good deal, but we did not average one fish a week. We could see trout by the thousand winging about in the emptiness under us, or sleeping in shoals on the bottom, but they would not bite — they could see the line too plainly, perhaps. We frequently selected the trout we wanted, and rested the bait patiently and persistently on the end of his nose at a depth of eighty feet, but he would only shake it off with an annoyed manner, and shift his position.

MARK TWAIN AND THE FOREST RANGERS

In a quarterly magazine published solely for the Rangers of the Tahoe Reserve, one of the Rangers thus "newspaperizes" Mark's experiences in two different sketches, one as it was in 1861 "before" the establishment of the Reserve, and the other as it would be "now."

This wood engraving depicting the fire at Lake Tahoe started by Mark Twain appeared as a frontispiece in early editions of his famous book *Roughing It.*

As It Was in 1861

Extract from January Harper's. *Mark Twain heard that the timber around Lake Bigler (Tahoe) promised vast wealth which could be had for the asking. He decided to locate a timber claim on its shores. He went to the Lake with a young Ohio lad, staked out a timber claim, and made a semblance of fencing it and of building a habitation, to comply with the law. They did not sleep in the house, of which Mark Twain says: "It never occurred to us for one thing, and besides, it was built to hold the ground, and that we enough. We did not wish to strain it."*

They lived by their campfire on the borders of the Lake and one day—it was just at nightfall—it got away from them, fired the Forest, and destroyed their fence and habitation. His picture of the superb night spectacle—the mighty mountain conflagration—is splendidly vivid.

"The level ranks of flame were relieved at intervals by the standard-bearers, as we called the tall dead trees, wrapped in fire, and waving their blazing banners a hundred feet in the air. Then we could turn from the scene to the Lake and see every branch and leaf, and cataract of flame upon its banks perfectly reflected, as in a gleaming, fiery mirror. The mighty roaring of the conflagration, together with our solitary and somewhat unsafe position (for there was no one within six miles of us), rendered the scene very impressive."

As It Would Be Now

Press Dispatch — August 15, 1912.

Mark Twain Fires Forest!!!

Noted Humorist Charged by Forest Officers

with Criminal Carelessness

Mark Twain and a friend from Ohio, who have been camping on Lake Tahoe, are responsible for a Forest fire which burned over about 200 acres before it was checked by Forest officers. The fire was sighted at 6 o'clock P.M. by one of the cooperative patrolmen of the Crown Columbia Paper Company, who at once telephoned to the tender of the Launch 'Ranger' for help. Within an hour the launch was on the scene with a dozen men picked up at Tahoe City, and by 10 o'clock the fire was practically under control.

Twain and his friend were found spell-bound by the Rangers, at the impressiveness of the fire. After fighting it for several hours, however, its grandeur palled upon them, and at the present time they are considerably exercised in as much as it was ascertained that the fire was a result of their carelessness in leaving a campfire to burn unattended. It is extremely likely that the well-known humorist will find the penalty attendant to his carelessness, no "joking" matter.

To which I take the liberty of adding the following:

Subsequent Proceedings

From the *Nevada City Bulletin,* Sept. , 1912

Samuel L. Clemens (popularly known as Mark Twain), together with Silas Snozzlebottom, of Columbus, Ohio, was today arraigned before Justice Brown, of the Superior Court, charged with having caused a destructive fire by leaving his campfire unattended. The eminent humorist and author was evidently unaware of the seriousness of his offense for he positively refused to engage an attorney to defend him.

When called upon to plead he began to explain that while he confessed to lighting the fire, and leaving it unattended, he wished the Judge to realize that it was the act of God in sending the wind that spread the flames that caused the destructive fire which ensued. The Judge agreed with him, and then grimly said it was a similar act of God which impelled him to levy a fine of $500.00 and one month in jail for leaving his campfire subject to the influence of the wind.

The humorist began to smile "on the left," and expressed an earnest desire to argue the matter out with the Judge, but with a curt "Next Case!" Mark was dismissed in charge of an officer and retired "smiling a sickly smile," and though he did not "curl up on the floor," it is evident that the subsequent proceedings interested him no more.

APPENDIX B

JOSEPH LE CONTE AT LAKE TAHOE

Joseph Le Conte, from whom Le Conte Lake is named, the best-beloved professor of the University of California, and its most noted geologist, in the year 1870 started out with a group of students of his geology classes, and made a series of *Ramblings in the High Sierra.* These were privately printed in 1875, and from a copy given to me many years ago by the distinguished author, I make the following extracts on Lake Tahoe:

August 20, (1870). I am cook today. I therefore got up at daybreak and prepared breakfast while the rest enjoyed their morning snooze. After breakfast we hired a sail boat, partly to fish, but mainly to enjoy a sail on this beautiful Lake.

Oh! the exquisite beauty of the Lake — its clear waters, emerald-green, and the deepest ultramarine blue; its pure shores, rocky or cleanest gravel, so clean that the chafing of the waves does not stain in the least the bright clearness of the waters; the high granite mountains, with serried peaks, which stand close around its very shore to guard its crystal purity — this Lake, not *among*, but *on*, the mountains, lifted six thousand feet towards the deep-blue overarching sky, whose image it reflects!

We tried to fish for trout, but partly because the speed of the sail boat could not be controlled, and partly because we enjoyed the scene far more than the fishing, we were unsuccessful, and soon gave it up. We sailed some six or eight miles, and landed in a beautiful cove on the Nevada side. Shall we go in swimming?

Newspapers in San Francisco say there is something peculiar in the waters of this high mountain Lake. It is so light, they say, that logs of timber sink immediately, and bodies of drowned animals never rise; that it is impossible to swim in it; that, essaying to do so, many good swimmers have been drowned. These facts are well attested by newspaper scientists, and therefore not doubted by newspaper readers. Since leaving Oakland, I have been often asked by the young men the scientific explanation of so singular a fact. I have uniformly answered, "We will try scientific experiments when we arrive there."

That time had come. "Now the, boys," I cried, "for the scientific experiment I promised you!" I immediately plunged in head-foremost, and struck out boldly. I then threw myself on my back, and lay on the surface with my limbs extended and motionless for ten minutes, breathing quietly the while. All the good swimmers quickly followed. It is as easy to swim and float in this as in any other water. Lightness from diminished atmospheric pressure? Nonsense! In an almost incompressible liquid like water, the diminished density produced by diminished pressure would be more than counterbalanced by increased density produced by cold.

After our swim, we again launched our boat, and sailed out into the very middle of the Lake. The wind had become very high, and the waves quite formidable. We shipped wave after wave, so that those of us who were sitting in the bows got drenched. It was very exciting. The wind became still higher; several of the party got very sick, and two of them *cascaded.* I was not in the least affected, but, on the contrary, enjoyed the sail very much. about 2 p.m. we concluded it was time to return, and therefore tacked about for camp.

The wind was now dead ahead, and blowing very hard. The boat was a very bad sailer, and so were *we.* We beat up against the wind a long time, and made but little headway. Finally, having concluded we would save time and patience by doing so, we ran ashore on the beach about a mile from camp and towed the boat home. The owner of the boat told us that *he* would not have risked the boat or his life in the middle of the Lake on such a day. "Where ignorance is bliss," etc.

After a hearty supper we gathered around the fire, and the young men sang in chorus until bedtime. "Now then, boys," cried I, "for a huge campfire, for it will be cold tonight!" We all scattered in the woods, and every man returned with a log, and soon the leaping blaze seemed to overtop the pines. We all lay around, with our feet to the fire, and soon sank into deep sleep.

August 21. Sunday at Tahoe! I wish I could spend it in perfect quiet. But my underclothes must be changed. Cleanliness is a Sunday duty. Some washing is necessary. Some of the party went fishing today. The rest of us remained in camp and mended or washed clothes.

At 12 M. I went out alone, and sat on the shore of the Lake, with the waves breaking at my feet. How brightly emerald-green the waters near the shore, and how deeply and purely blue in the distance! The line of demarcation is very distinct, showing that the bottom drops off suddenly. How distinct the mountains and cliffs all around the Lake; only lightly tinged with blue on the farther side, though more than twenty miles distant!

How greatly is one's sense of beauty affected by association! Lake Mono is surrounded by much grander and more varied mountain scenery than this; its waters are also very clear, and it has the advantage of several very picturesque islands; but the dead volcanoes, the wastes of volcanic sand and ashes covered only by interminable sagebrush, the bitter, alkaline, dead, slimy waters, in which nothing but worms live; the insects and flies which swarm on its surface, and which are thrown upon its shore in such quantities as to infect the air — all these produce a sense of desolation and death which is painful; it destroys entirely the beauty of the lake itself; it unconsciously mingles with and alloys the pure enjoyment of the incomparable mountain scenery in its vicinity.

On the contrary, the deep-blue, pure waters of Lake Tahoe, rivaling in purity and blueness the sky itself; its clear, bright emerald shore waters, breaking snow-white on its clean rock and gravel shores; the Lake basin, not on a plain, with mountain scenery in the distance, but counter-sunk in the mountain's top itself — these produce a never-ceasing and ever-increasing sense of joy, which naturally grows into love. There would seem to be no beauty except as associated with human life and connected with a sense of fitness for human happiness. Natural beauty is but the type of spiritual beauty.

Enjoyed a very refreshing swim in the Lake this afternoon. The water is much less cold that that of Lake Tenaya or the Tuolumne River, or even the Nevada River.

The party which went out fishing returned with a very large trout. It was delicious.

I observe on the Lake ducks, gulls, terns, etc., and about it many sandhill cranes — the white species, the clanging cry of these sounds pleasant to me by early association.

August 22. Nothing to do today. Would be glad to sail on the Lake or fish, but too expensive hiring boats. Our funds are nearly exhausted. Would be glad to start for home, but one of our party — Pomroy — has gone to Carson City, and we must wait for him.

I went down alone to the Lake, sat down on the shore and enjoyed the scene. Nothing to do, my thoughts today naturally went to the dear ones at home. Oh! how I wish they could be here and enjoy with me this lovely Lake! I could dream away my life here with those I love. How delicious a dream! Of all the places I have yet seen, this is the one I could longest enjoy and love the most. Reclining thus in the shade, on the clean white sand, the waves rippling at my feet, with thoughts of Lake Tahoe and of my loved ones mingling in my mind, I fell into a delicious doze. After my doze I returned to camp, to dinner.

About 5 p.m. took another and last swim in the Lake.

Pomroy, who went to Carson, returned 7 p.m. After supper, again singing in chorus, and then the glorious campfire.

LeCONTE'S GLACIAL HISTORY OF LAKE TAHOE

a. Evidences of the Existence of the Great Lake Valley Glacier.

On the south shore of Lake Tahoe, and especially at the northern or lower end of Fallen Leaf Lake, I found many pebbles and some large boulders of a beautiful striped agate-like slate. The stripes consisted of alternate b ands of black and translucent white, the latter weathering into milk white, or yellowish, or reddish.

It was perfectly evident that these fragments were brought down from the canyon above Fallen Leaf Lake. On ascending this canyon I easily found the parent rock of these pebbles and boulders. It is a powerful outcropping ledge of beautifully striped siliceous slate, full of fissures and joints, and easily broken into blocks of all sizes, crossing the canyon about a half mile above the lake. This rock is so peculiar and so easily identified that its fragments become an admirable index of the extent of the glacial transportation.

I have traced these pebbles only a little way along the western shores of the great Lake, as my observations were principally confined to this part; but I learn from my brother, Professor John Le Conte, and from Mr. John Muir, both of whom have examined the pebbles I have brought home, that precisely similar fragments are found in great abundance all along the western shore from Sugar Pine Pint northward, and especially on the extreme northwestern shore nearly thirty miles from their source.

I have visited the eastern shore of the Lake somewhat more extensively than the western, and nowhere did I see similar pebbles. Mr. Muir, who has walked around the Lake, tells me that they do not occur on the eastern shore. We have, then, in the distribution of these pebbles, demonstrative evidence of the fact that Fallen Leaf Lake glacier was once a tributary of a much greater glacier which filled Lake Tahoe.

The only other agency to which we could attribute this transportation is that of shore ice and icebergs, which probably did once exist on Lake Tahoe; but the limitation of the pebbles to the western, and especially the northwestern shores, is in exact accordance with the laws of glacial transportation, but contrary to those of floating ice transportation — for lake ice is carried only by winds, and would, therefore, deposit equally on all shores.

Again: I think I find additional evidence of a Lake Tahoe "mer de glace" in the contrasted character of the northern and southern shores of this Lake.

All the little glacial lakes described above are deep at the upper end and shallow at the lower end. Further, all of them have a sand beach and a sand flat at the upper end, and great boulders thickly scattered in the shallow water, and along the shore at the lower end. These facts are easily explained, if we remember that while the glacial *scooping* was principally at the upper end, the glacial *droppings* were principally at the lower end. And further: that while the *glacial* deposit was principally at the lower end, the *river* deposit, since the glacial epoch, has been wholly at the upper end.

Now the great Lake, also, has a similar structure. It also has a beautiful sand and gravel beach all along its upper shore, and a sand flat extending above it; while at its lower, or northern end, thickly strewed in the shallow water, and along the shore line, and some distance above the shore line, are found in great abundance *boulders of enormous size.*

May we not conclude that similar effects have been produced by similar causes — that these huge boulders were dropped by the great glacier at its lower end? Similar boulders are also found along the northern portion of the eastern shore, because the principal flow of the ice current was from the southwest, and in the fullness of glacial times the principal exit was over the northeastern lip of the basin.

b. Origin of Lake Tahoe.

That Lake Tahoe was once wholly occupied by ice, I think, is certain; but that it was scooped out by the Lake Valley glacier is perhaps more doubtful. All other Sierra lakes which I have seen certainly owe their origin to glacial agency. Neither do I think we should be staggered by the size or enormous depth of this Lake.

Yet, from its position, it may be a plication hollow, or a trough produced by the formation of two parallel mountain ridges, and afterward modified by glacial agency, instead of a pure glacial-scooped rock basin. In other words, Lake Valley, with its two summit ridges, *may be regarded as a phenomenon belonging to the order of mountain formation and not to the order of mountain sculpture.* I believe an examination of the rocks of the two summit ridges would probably settle this. In the absence of more light than I now have, I will not hazard an opinion.

c. Passage of slate into granite.

From the commencement of the rocky canyon at the head of Fallen Leaf Lake, and up for about two miles, the canyon walls and bed are composed of *slate.* The slate, however, becomes more and more metamorphic as we go up, until it passes into what much resembles *trap.* In some places it looks like *diorite* and in others like *porphyry.* I saw no evidence, however, of any outburst.

This latter rock passes somewhat more rapidly into *granite* at Glen Alpine Springs. From this point the canyon bed and lower walls are granite, but the highest peaks are still a dark, splintery, metamorphic slate. The glacial erosion has here cut through the slate and bitten deep into the underlying granite. The passage from slate through prophyritic diorite into granite may, I think, be best explained by the increasing degree of metamorphism, and at the same time a change of the original sediments at this point; granite being the last term of metamorphism of pure clays, or clayey sandstones, while bedded diorites are similarly formed from ferruginous and calcareous slates.

Just at the junction of the harder and tougher granite with the softer and more jointed slates, occur, as might be expected, cascades in the river. It is probable that the cascades at the head of Cascade Lake and Emerald Bay mark, also, the junction of the granite with the slate — only the junction here is covered with débris. Just at the same junction, in Fallen Leaf Lake Canyon (Glen Alpine Basin), burst out the waters of Glen Alpine Springs, highly charged with bicarbonates of iron and soda.

d. Glacial Deltas.

I have stated that the moraines of Cascade Lake and Emerald Bay glaciers run down to the margin of Lake Tahoe. An examination of this portion of the Lake shore shows that *they run far into the Lake* — that the Lake has been filled in, two or three miles, by glacial débris.

On the eastern margin of Lake Tahoe, the water, close along the shore, is comparatively shallow, the shore rocky, and along the shore line, above and below the water, are scattered great boulders, probably dropped by the main glacier. But on the west margin of the Lake the shore line is composed wholly of moraine matter, the water very deep close to shore, and the bottom composed of precisely similar moraine matter.

In rowing along the shore, I found that the exquisite ultramarine blue of the deep water extends to within 100 to 150 feet of the shore line. At this distance, the bottom could barely be seen. Judging from the experiments of my brother, Professor John Le Conte, according to which a white object could be seen at a depth of 115 feet, I suppose the depth along the line of junction of the ultramarine blue and the emerald green water is at least 100 feet.

The slope of the bottom is, therefore, nearly, or quite, 45 degrees. It seems, in fact, a direct continuation beneath the water of the moraine slope. The materials, also, which may be examined with ease through the wonderfully transparent water, are exactly the same as that composing the moraine, viz: earth, pebbles, and boulders of all sizes, some of them of enormous dimensions.

It seems almost certain that *the margin of the great Lake Valley glacier, and of the Lake itself when this glacier had melted and the tributaries first began to run into the Lake, was the series of rocky points at the head of the three little lakes, about three or four miles back from the present margin of the main Lake; and that all lakeward from these points has been filled in and made land by the action of the three glaciers described.*

At that time Rubicon Point was a rocky promontory, projecting far into the Lake, beyond which was another wide bay, which has been similarly filled in by débris brought down by glaciers north of this point. The long moraines of these glaciers are plainly visible from the Lake surface; but I have not examined them. Thus, all the land, for three or four miles back from the Lake-margin, both north and south of Rubicon Point, is composed of *confluent glacial deltas,* and on these deltas the moraine ridges are the *natural levees* of these ice streams.

e. Parallel Moraines.

The moraines described above are peculiar and almost unique. Nowhere, except about Lake Tahoe and near Lake Mono, have I seen moraines in the form of *parallel ridges* lying on a level plain the terminating abruptly *without any signs of transverse connection (terminal moraine) at the lower end.* Nor have I been able to find any description of similar moraines in other countries.

They are not terminal moraines, for the glacial pathway is open below. They are not lateral moraines, for these are borne on the glacier itself, or else stranded on the deep canyon sides. Neither do I think moraines of this kind would be formed by a glacier emerging from a steep narrow canyon and running out on a level plain; for in such cases, as soon as the confinement of the bounding walls is removed, the ice stream spreads out into an *ice lake.*

It does so as naturally and necessarily as does water under similar circumstances. The deposit would be nearly transverse to the direction of the motion, and, therefore, more or less crescentic. There must be something peculiar in the conditions under which these parallel ridges were formed. I believe the conditions were as described below.

We have already given reason to think that the original margin of the Lake, in glacial times, was three or four miles back from the present margin, along the series of rocky points against which the ridges abut; and that all the flat plain thence to the present margin is made land. If so, then it is evident that at that time the three glaciers described ran far out into the Lake, until reaching deep water, where they formed icebergs.

Under these conditions, it is plain that the pressure on this, the subaqueous portion of the glacial bed, would be small, and become less and less until it becomes nothing at the point where the icebergs float away. The pressure on the bed being small, not enough to overcome the cohesion of ice, there would be no spreading.

A glacier running down a steep narrow canyon and out into the deep water, and forming icebergs at its point, would maintain its slender, tongue-like form, and drop its débris on each side, forming parallel ridges, and would not form a terminal moraine because the materials not dropped previously would be carried off by icebergs.

In the subsequent retreat of such a glacier, imperfect terminal moraines might be formed higher up, where the water is not deep enough to form icebergs. It is probable, too, that since the melting of the great "mer de glace" and the formation of the Lake, the level of the water has gone down considerably, by the deepening of the Truckee Canyon outlet by means of erosion. Thus not only did the glaciers retreat from the Lake, but also the Lake from the glaciers.

As already stated, similar parallel moraine ridges are formed by the glaciers which ran down the steep eastern slope of the Sierras, and out on the level plains of Mono. By far the most remarkable are those formed by Bloody Canyon Glacier, described by me in a former paper. These moraines are six or seven miles long, 300 to 400 feet high, and the parallel crests not more than a mile asunder. There, also, as at Lake Tahoe, we find them terminating abruptly in the plain without any sign of terminal moraine.

But higher up there are small, imperfect, transverse moraines, made during the subsequent retreat, behind which water has collected, forming lakes and marshes. But observe: these moraines are also *in the vicinity of a great lake;* and we have abundant evidence, in very distinct terraces described by Whitney (*Geological Survey of California, Vol. I, 451*), and observed by myself, that in glacial times the *water stood at least six hundred feet above the present level.*

In fact, there can be no doubt that at that time the waters of Mono Lake (or a much greater body of water of which Mono is the remnant) washed against the bold rocky points from which the débris ridges start. *The glaciers in this vicinity, therefore, must have* run out into the water six or seven miles, and doubtless formed icebergs at their point, and, therefore, formed there no terminal moraine.

That the glaciers described about Lake Tahoe and Lake Mono ran out far into the water and formed icebergs I think is quite certain, and that parallel moraines open below are characteristic signs of such conditions I also think nearly certain.

f. Glacial Erosion.

My observations on glacial pathways in the High Sierra, and especially about Lake Tahoe, have greatly modified my views as to the nature of glacial erosion. Writers on this subject seem to regard glacial erosion as mostly, if not wholly, a *grinding* and *scoring;* the débris of this erosion as rock meal; the great boulders which are found in such immense quantities in the terminal deposit, as derived wholly from the crumbling cliffs above the glacial surface; the *rounded* boulders, which are often the most numerous, as derived in precisely the same way, only they have been engulfed by crevasses, or between the sides of the glacier and the bounding wall, and thus carried between the moving ice and its rocky bed, as between the upper and nether millstone. In a word, all boulders, whether angular or rounded, are supposed to owe their *origin* or *separation* and *shaping* to glacial agency.

Now, if such be the true view of glacial erosion, evidently its effect in mountain sculpture must be small indeed. *Roches moutonnées* are recognized by all as the most universal and characteristic sign of a glacial bed. Sometimes these beds are only imperfect *moutonnées,* i.e., they are composed of *broken angular surface with only the points and edges planed off.*

Now, *moutonnées* surfaces always, and especially angular surfaces with only points and edges beveled, show that the erosion by grinding has been only very superficial. They show that if the usual view of glacial erosion be correct, the great canyons, so far from being *formed,* were only very *slightly modified* by glacial agency.

But I am quite satisfied from my own observations, that this is not the only *nor the principal* mode of glacial erosion. I am convinced that a glacier, by its enormous pressure and resistless onward movement, is *constantly breaking off large blocks* from its bed and bounding walls. Its erosion is not only a grinding and scoring, but also a *crushing and breaking.* It makes by its erosion not only rock meal, but also large *rock chips.*

Thus, a glacier is constantly breaking off blocks and making angular surfaces, and then grinding off the angles both of the fragments and the bed, and thus forming rounded boulders and *moutonnées* surfaces. Its erosion is a constant process of alternate *rough hewing and planing.* If the rock be full of fissures, and the glacier deep and heavy, the rough hewing so predominated that the plane has only time to touch the corners a little before the rock is again broken and new angles formed. This is the case high upon the *canyon walls,* at the head of Cascade Lake and Emerald Bay, but also in the *canyon beds wherever the slate is approached.*

If, on the other hand, the rock is very hard and solid, and the glacier be not very deep and heavy, the planing will predominate over the rough hewing, and a smooth, gentle billowy surface is the result. This is the case in the hard granite forming the beds of all the canyons high up, but especially high up the canyon of Fallen Leaf Lake (Glen Alpine Basin), there the canyon spreads out and extensive but comparatively thin snow sheets have been at work.

In some cases *on the cliffs,* subsequent disintegration of a glacier-polished surface may have given the appearance of angular surfaces with beveled corners; but, in other cases, in the *bed of the canyon,* and on elevated level places, where large loosened blocks could not be removed by water nor by gravity, I observed the same appearances, under conditions which forbid this explanation. Mr. Muir, also in his *Studies in the Sierra,* gives many examples of undoubted rock-breaking by ancient glaciers.

Angular blocks are mostly, therefore, the ruins of crumbling cliffs, borne on the surface of the glacier and deposited at its foot. Many *rounded* boulders also have a similar origin, having found their way to the bed of the glacier through crevasses, or along the sides of the glacier. But *most of the rounded boulders* in the terminal deposit of *great glaciers* are fragments *torn off by the glacier itself.*

The proportion of rounded boulders — of upper or air-formed — to nether or glacier—formed fragments, depends on the depth and extent of the ice current. In the case of the universal ice sheet (ice flood) there are, of course, no upper formed or angular blocks at all — there is nothing borne on the surface. The moraine, therefore, consists wholly of nether-formed and nether-borne severely triturated materials *(moraine profunde).*

The boulders are, of course, all rounded. This is one extreme. In the case of the thin, moving ice fields, the *glacierets* which still linger among the highest peaks and the shadiest hollows of the Sierra, on the other hand, the moraines are composed *wholly of angular blocks.* This is the character of the terminal moraine of Mount Lyell glacier. These glacierets are too thin and feeble and torpid to break off fragments — they can only *bear* away what falls on them. This is the other extreme.

But in the case of ordinary glaciers — ice streams — the boulders of the terminal deposit are mixed; the angular or upper-formed predominating in the small existing glaciers of temperate climates, but the rounded or nether-formed greatly predominating in the grand old glaciers of which we have been speaking. In the terminal deposits of these, especially in the materials pushed into the Lake, it is somewhat difficult to find a boulder which has not been subjected to severe attrition.

APPENDIX C

THOMAS STARR KING AT LAKE TAHOE

IN 1863 Thomas Starr King, perhaps the most noted and broadly honored divine ever known on the Pacific Coast, visited Lake Tahoe, and on his return to San Francisco preached a sermon, entitled: "Living Water from Lake Tahoe." Its descriptions are so felicitous that I am gratified to be able to quote them from Dr. King's volume of Sermons *Christianity and Humanity,* with the kind permission of the publishers, Houghton, Mifflin Company, Boston, Mass.

LIVING WATER FROM LAKE TAHOE

When one is climbing from the west, by the smooth and excellent road, the last slope of the Sierra ridge, he expects, from the summit of the pass, which is more than seven thousand feet above the sea, higher than the famous pass of the Splugen, or the little St. Bernard, to look off and down upon an immense expanse. He expects, or, if he had not learned beforehand, he would anticipate with eagerness, that he should be able to see mountain summits beneath him, and beyond these, valleys and ridges alternating till the hills subside into the eastern plains.

How different the facts that await the eye from the western summit, and what a surprise! We find, on gaining what seems to be the ridge, that the Sierra range for more than a hundred miles has a double line of jagged pinnacles, twelve or fifteen miles apart, with a trench or trough between, along a portion of the way, that is nearly fifteen hundred feet deep if we measure from the pass which the stages traverse, which is nearly three thousand feet deep if the plummet is dropped from the highest points of the snowy spires.

Down into this trench we look, and opposite upon the eastern wall and crests, as we ride out to the eastern edge of the western summit. In a stretch of forty miles the chasm of it bursts into view at once, half of which is a plain sprinkled with groves of pine, and the other half an expanse of level blue that mocks the azure into which its guardian towers soar. This is Lake Tahoe, an Indian name which signifies "High Water." We descend steadily by the winding mountain road, more than three miles to the plain, by which we drive to the shore of the Lake; but it si truly Tahoe, "High Water."

For we stand more than a mile, I believe more than six thousand feet above the sea, when we have gone down from the pass to its sparkling beach. It has about the same altitude as the Lake of Mount Cenis (6280 feet) in Switzerland, and there is only one sheet of water in Europe that can claim a greater elevation (Lake Po de Vanasque, 7271 feet).

There are several, however, that surpass it in the great mountain chains of the Andes and of Hindustan. The Andes support a lake at 12,000 feet above the sea, and one of the slopes of the Himalaya, in Thibet, encloses the upholds a cup of crystal water 15,600 feet above the level of the Indian Ocean, covering an area, too, of 250 square miles. I had supposed, however, that within the immense limits of the American Republic, or north of us on the continent, there is no sheet of water that competes with Tahoe in altitude and interest. But in Mariposa County of our State there are two lakes, both small — one 8300 feet, and the other 11,000 feet — on the Sierra above the line of the sea.

To a wearied frame and tired mind what refreshment there is in the neighborhood of this lake! The air is singularly searching and strengthening. The noble pines, not obstructed by underbrush, enrich the slightest breeze with aroma and music. Grand peaks rise around, on which the eye can admire the sternness of everlasting crags and the equal permanence of delicate and feathery snow. Then there is the sense of seclusion from the haunts and cares of men, of being upheld on the immense billow of the Sierra, at an elevation near the line of perpetual snow, yet finding the air genial, and the loneliness clothed with the charm of feeling the sense of the mystery of the mountain heights, part of a chain that link the two polar seas, and of the mystery of the water poured into the granite bowl, whose rim is chased with the splendor of perpetual frost, and whose bounty, flowing into the Truckee stream, finds no outlet into the ocean, but sinks again into the land.

Everything is charming in the surroundings of the mountain Lake; but as soon as one walks to the beach of it, and surveys its expanse, it is the color, or rather the colors, spread out before the eye, which holds it with greatest fascination. I was able to stay eight days in all, amidst that calm and cheer, yet the hues of the water seemed to become more surprising with each hour.

The Lake, according to recent measurement, is about twenty-one miles in length, by twelve or thirteen in breadth. There is no island visible to break its sweep, which seems to be much larger than the figures indicate. And the whole of the vast surface, the boundaries of which are taken in easily at once by the range of the eye, is a mass of pure splendor. When the day is calm, there is a ring of the Lake, extending more than a mile from shore, which is brilliantly green.

Within this ring the vast center of the expanse is of a deep, yet soft and singularly tinted blue. Hues cannot be more sharply contrasted than are these permanent colors. They do not shade into each other; they lie as clearly defined as the course of glowing gems in the wall of the New Jerusalem. It is precisely as if we were looking upon an immense floor of lapis lazuli set within a ring of flaming emerald.

The cause of this contrast is the sudden change in the depth of the water at a certain distance from shore. For a mile or so the basin shelves gradually, and then suddenly plunges off into unknown depths. The center of the Lake must be a tremendous pit. A very short distance from where the water is green and so transparent that the clean stones can be seen on the bottom a hundred feet below, the blue water has been found to be fourteen hundred feet deep; and in other portions soundings cannot be obtained with a greater extent of line.

What a savage chasm the lake bed must be! Empty the water from it and it is pure and unrelieved desolation. And the sovereign loveliness of the water that fills it is its color. The very savageness of the rent and fissure is made the condition of the purest charm. The Lake does not feed a permanent river. We cannot trace any issue of it to the ocean. It is not, that we know, a well-spring to supply any large district with water for ordinary use. It seems to exist for beauty. And its peculiar beauty has its root in the peculiar harshness and wildness of the deeps it hides.

Brethren, this question of color in nature, broadly studied, leads us quickly to contemplate and adore the love of God. If God were the Almighty chiefly — if he desired to impress us most with his omnipotence and infinitude, and make us bow with dread before him, how easily the world could have been made more somber, how easily our senses could have been created to receive impressions of the bleak vastness of space, how easily the mountains might have been made to breathe terror from their cliffs and walls, how easily the general effect of extended landscapes might have been monotonous and gloomy!

If religion is, as it has so often been conceived to be, hostile to the natural good and joy which the heart seeks instinctively — if sadness, if melancholy, be the soul of its inspiration, the misery for myriads the burden of its prophecy — I do not believe that the vast deeps of space above us would have been tinted with tender azure, hiding their awfulness; I do not believe that storms would break away into rainbows, and that the clouds of sunset would display the whole gamut of sensuous splendor; I do not believe that the ocean would wear such joy for the eye over its awful abysses; I do not believe that the mountains would crown the complete, the general loveliness of the globe.

The eloquent preacher then continues to draw other lessons from the Lake, but, unfortunately, our space is too limited to allow quotation in full. The following, however, are short excerpts which suggest the richness of the fuller expression:

The color of the Lake is a word from this natural Gospel. It covers the chasms and wounds of the earth with splendor. It is what the name of the lovely New Hampshire lake, Winnepesaukee, indicates, "The Smile of the Great Spirit."

And this color is connected with purity. The green ring of the Lake is so brilliant, the blue enclosed by it is so deep and tender, because there is no foulness in the water. The edge of the waves along all the beach is clean. The granite sand, too, often dotted with smooth-washed jaspers and garnets and opaline quartz, is especially bright and spotless.

In fact, the Lake seems to be conscious, and to have an instinct against contamination. Several streams pour their burden from the mountains into it; but the impurities which they bring down seem to be thrown back from the lip of the larger bowl, and form bars of sediment just before they can reach its sacred hem. Dip from its white-edged ripples, or from its calm heart, or from the foam that breaks over its blue when the wind rouses it to frolic, and you dip what is fit for a baptismal font — you dip purity itself.

• • •

The purity of nature is the expression of joy, and it is a revelation to us that the Creator's holiness is not repellent and severe. God tries to win you by His Spirit, which clothes the world with beauty, to trust Him, to give up your evil that you may find deeper communion with Him, and to recognize the charm of goodness which alone is harmony with the cheer and the purity of the outward world.

I must speak of another lesson, connected with religion, that was suggested to me on the borders of Lake Tahoe. It is bordered by groves of noble pines. Two of the days that I was permitted to enjoy there were Sundays. On one of them I passed several hours of the afternoon in listening, alone, to the murmur of the pines, while the waves were gently beating the shore with their restlessness. If the beauty and purity of the Lake were in harmony with the deepest religion of the Bible, certainly the voice of the pines was also in chord with it.

• • •

I read under the pines of Lake Tahoe, on that Sunday afternoon, some pages from the recent English work that raises the question of inspiration. Is the Bible the word of God, or the words of men? It is neither. It is the word of God breathed through the words of men, inextricably intertwined with them as the tone of the wind with the quality of the tree. We must go to the Bible as to a grove of evergreens, not asking for cold, clear truth, but for sacred influence, for revival to the devout sentiment, for the breath of the Holy Ghost, not as it wanders in pure space, but as it sweeps through cedars and pines.

• • •

In my Sunday musing by the shore of our Lake, I raised the question — Who were looking upon the waters of Tahoe when Jesus walked by the beach of Gennesareth? Did men look upon it then? And if so were they above the savage level, and could they appreciate its beauty? And before the time of Christ, before the date of Adam, however far back we may be obliged to place our ancestor, for what purpose was this luxuriance of color, this pomp of garniture? How few human eyes have yet rested upon it in calmness, to drink in its loveliness!

There are spots near the point of the shore where the hotel stands, to which not more than a few score intelligent visitors have yet been introduced. Such a nook I was taken to by a cultivated friend. We sailed ten miles on the water to the mouth of a mountain stream that pours foaming into its green expanse.

We left the boat, followed this stream by its downward leaps through uninvaded nature for more than a mile, and found that it flows from a smaller lake, not more than three miles in circuit, which lies directly at the base of two

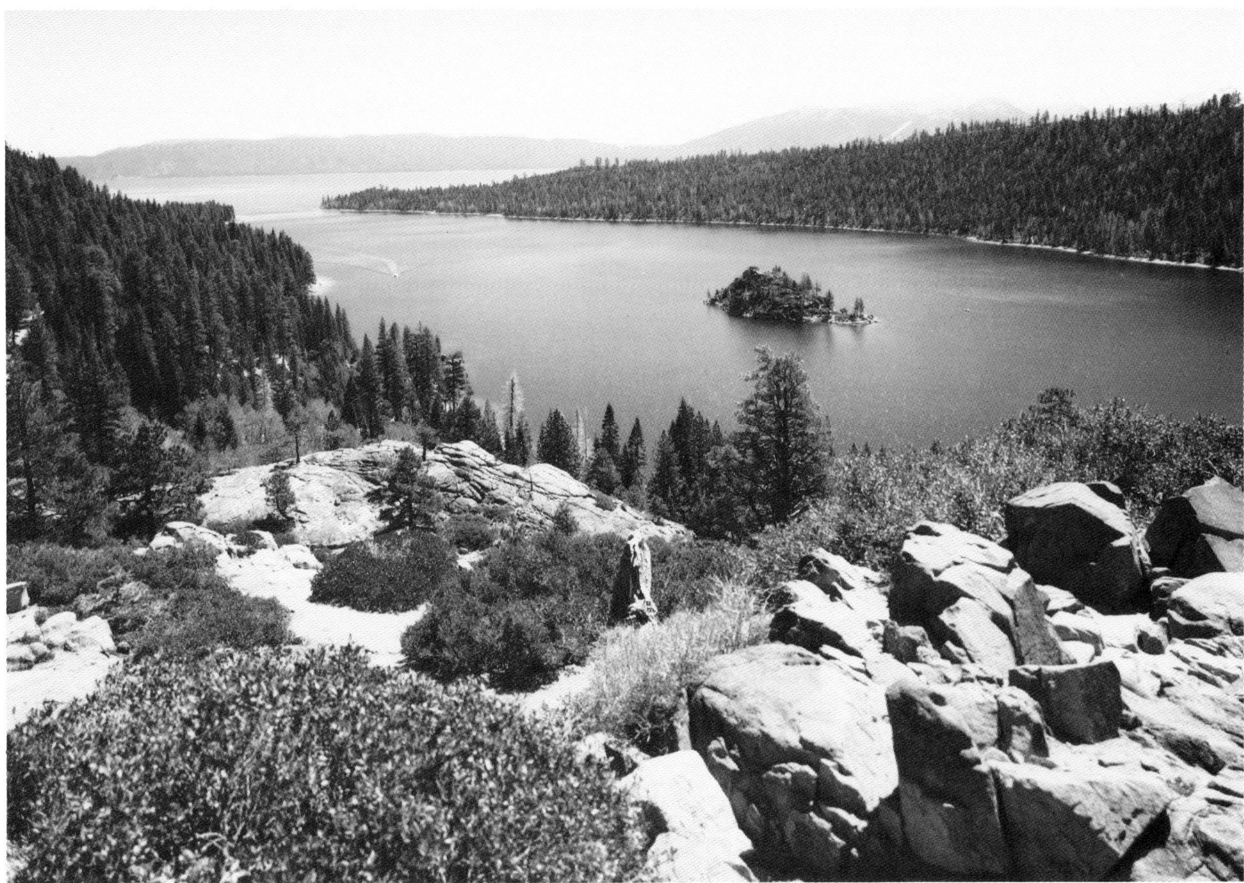

Emerald Bay, looking southeast.

tremendous peaks of the Sierra, white with immense and perpetual snowfields. The same ring of vivid green, the same center of soft deep blue, was visible in this smaller mountain bowl, and it is fed by a glorious cataract, supported by those snowfields, which pours down in thundering foam, at one point, in a leap of a hundred feet to die in that brilliant color, guarded by those cold, dumb crags.

Never since the creation has a particle of that water turned a wheel, or fed a fountain for human thirst, or served any form of mortal use. Perhaps the eyes of not a hundred intelligent spirits on the earth have yet looked upon that scene. Has there been any waste of its wild and lonely beauty? Has Tahoe been wasted because so few appreciative souls have studied and enjoyed it? If not a human glance had yet fallen upon it, would its charms of color and surroundings be wasted charms?

• • •

Where we discern beauty and yet seclusion, loveliness and yet no human use, we can follow up the created charm to the mind of the Creator, and think of it as realizing a conception or a dream by him. He delights in His works. To the bounds of space their glory is present as one vision to His eye. And it is our sovereign privilege that we are called to the possibility of sympathy with His joy.

The universe is the home of God. He has lined its walls with beauty. He has invited us into His palace. He offers to us the glory of sympathy with His mind. By love of nature, by joy in the communion with its beauty, by growing insight into the wonders of color, form, and purpose, we enter into fellowship with the Creative art. We go into harmony with God.

By dullness of eye and deadness of heart to natural beauty, we keep away from sympathy with God, who is the fountain of loveliness as well as the fountain of love. But the inmost harmony with the Infinite we find only through love, and the reception of his love. Then we are prepared to see the world aright, to find the deepest joy in its pure beauty, and to wait for the hour of translation to the glories of the interior and deeper world.

APPENDIX D

JOHN VANCE CHENEY AT LAKE TAHOE

One of America's poets who long lived in California, and then, after an honorable and useful sojourn as Director of one of the important libraries of the East, returned to spend the remainder of his days— John Vance Cheney — in 1882, made the trip to Lake Tahoe by stage from Truckee, and, among other fine pieces of description, wrote the following which appeared in *Lippincott's* for August, 1883:

One more ascent has been made, one more turn rounded, and behold, from an open elevation, close upon its shore, Lake Tahoe in all its calm beauty bursts suddenly upon the sight. Nestled among the snowy summit-peaks of the Sierra Nevada, more than six thousand feet above sea-level, it lies in placid transparency. The surrounding heights are all the more pleasing to the eye because of their lingering winter cover; and as we gaze upon the Lake, unruffled by the gentlest breeze, we marvel at the quiet — almost supernatural — radiancy of the scene.

Lakes in other lands may present greater beauty of artificial setting — beauty dependent largely upon picturesqueness, where vineyards and ivied ruins heighten the effect of natural environment — but for nature pure and simple, for chaste beauty and native grandeur, one will hesitate before naming the rival of Lake Tahoe. This singularly impressive sheet of water, one of the highest in the world, gains an indescribably but easily perceived charm by its remoteness, its high, serene, crystal isolation. Its lights and shades, its moods and passions, are changing, rapid, and free as the way of the wind.

A true child of nature, it varies ever, from hour to hour enchanting with new and strange fascination. The thousand voices of the lofty Sierra call to it, and it answers; all the colors of the rainbow gather upon it, receiving in their turn affectionate recognition. Man has meddled with it little more than with the sky; the primeval spell is upon it, the hush, the solitude of the old gods.

The breath of powers invisible, awful, rouse it to the sublimity of untamable energy; again, hush it into deepest slumber. Night and day it is guarded, seemingly, by wonder-working forces known to man only through the uncertain medium of the imagination. The traveler who looks upon Lake Tahoe for a few hours only learns little of its rich variety. Like all things wild and shy, it must be approached slowly and with patience.

But our sketch must not include more than the hasty

Steamer on north end of Lake Tahoe

glimpses of a day. The stage conveyed us directly to the wharf, which we reached at ten o'clock, having accomplished our fourteen mile ride up the valley in about two and a half hours. As we boarded the little steamer awaiting us and looked over its side into the water below, the immediate shock of surprise cannot be well described. Every pebble at the bottom showed as distinctly as if held in the open hand. We had all seen clear water before, but, as a severe but unscholarly sufferer once said of his rheumatism, {never such as *these.*"

The day being perfect, no breeze stirring, and the Lake without a ripple, the gravelly bottom continued visible when we had steamed out to a point where the water reached a depth of eighty feet. Two gentlemen on board who had made a leisurely trip around the world and were now on their way home to England, remarked that they had seen but one sheet of water (a lake in Japan) of anything like equal transparency. It is presumed that they had not visited Green Lake, Colorado.

Our course lay along the California shore, toward its southern extremity, the steamer stopping at several points for exchange of mail These stopping places are all summer resorts, where the guests, snugly housed at the base of the mountain range, divide the time between lounging or rambling under the shadow of the tall pines and angling for the famous Tahoe trout in the brightness of the open Lake.

All looked inviting, but we were not wholly enchanted until, gliding past many a snowy peak, we suddenly changed course and put into Emerald Bay. This little bay, or rather lake in itself, about three miles in length, is the gem of the Tahoe scenery. Through its narrow entrance, formed by perpendicular cliffs some two thousand feet high, we moved on toward an island of rock and a succession of flashing waterfalls beyond.

• • •

For a time the dazzling mountain crests and glistening gorges absorbed attention. So high, white, silent! We longed to be upon the loftiest one, from the top of which can be seen thirteen charming little mountain lakes, mid-air jewels, varying in feature according to the situation. Two of these lakes, widely dissimilar in character, are but two miles distant from Tallac House, a comfortable resort at the base of the noble peak from which it takes its name.

But not even the crystal summit ridges delighted us as did the changing waters in the path of the steamer. Following immediately upon the transparency preserved to a depth of some eighty feet, a blur passed over the surface. This changed by imperceptible degrees to a light green. The green, again, speedily deepened, shading into a light blue; and finally, in deepest water (where the Lake is all but fathomless), the color becomes so densely blue that we could not believe our eyes. Indigo itself was outdone. Description fails; the blue deep of Tahoe must be seen to be appreciated.

• • •

The ride from Glenwood back to Tahoe City was not so calm. The Lake was considerably agitated; less so, however, than on the following day, when, as we learned afterward, our little steamer lost its rudder. Owing to the gorges in the mountains upon either side, through which winds rush unexpectedly, Tahoe has her dangers.

She is a wild, wayward child, but thoroughly lovable throughout all her frowns as well as smiles, equally captivating in her moments of unconquerable willfulness as in her seasons of perfect submission. Reaching Tahoe City at four o'clock, we found the stage standing in readiness, and, with a last, hasty look at the Lake, we were soon on our way by the banks of the Truckee, back to town.

APPENDIX E

THE RESORTS OF LAKE TAHOE – 1914

IN the body of this book I have given full account of some of the resorts of the Tahoe region, including Deer Park Springs, Tahoe Tavern, Fallen Leaf Lodge, Cathedral Park, Glen Alpine Springs, Al Tahoe, Lakeside, Glenbrook and Carnelian Bay.

But these are by no means all the resorts of the Bay, and each year sees additions and changes. Hence I have deemed it well briefly to describe those resorts that are in operation at the time this volume is issued.

It should be remembered that each resort issues its own descriptive folder, copies of which may be obtained from the ticket offices of the Southern Pacific Railway, the Lake Tahoe Railway and Transportation Company, or the Peck-Judah Information Bureau, as well as from its own office. All the resorts not already described in their respective chapters are reached by steamer on its circuit around the Lake, as follows:

Homewood

The first place for the steamer after leaving the Tavern is Homewood, a comparatively new resort, but already popular and successful, conducted by Mr. and Mrs. A.W. Jost. This is six miles from Tahoe City. The hotel was built inthe summer of 1913 and has hot and cold water piped to all rooms.

In addition there are cottages of two and three rooms, which, together with single and double tents, provide for every taste and purse. The tents are protected by flies, have solid boarded floors, are well carpeted, and afford the fullest opportunity for outdoor sleeping. Homewood possesses a gently sloping and perfectly safe bathing beach for adults and children. It also boasts a unique feature in an open air dancing platform, with old-fashioned music. It owns its power boat for excursions on the Lake, and its fleet of rowboats and fishing boats. A campfire is lighted nightly during the season, and song and story cheer the merry hours along.

McKinney's

Three and a half to four miles beyond Homewood is McKinney's. This is one of the oldest and best-established resorts on the Lake, having been founded and long conducted by that pioneer of Lake Tahoe, J.W. McKinney, as fully related elsewhere. It is now under the management of Murphy Brothers and Morgan, and

The famous Tallac Hotel.

is essentially a place that is popular with the crowd. The resort was built, as are all the older places, to meet ever-increasing needs, the mail hotel being supplemented by numerous cottages and tents. McKinney's has a fine new dancing hall, dark room for amateur photographers, iron and magnesia springs, fleet of fishing and motor boats, free fishing tackle, etc., and during the season its accommodation for 200 guests is more than taxed to the limit.

Moana Villa

The next steamer stopping place, about 200 yards from McKinney's, is Moana Villa, the comfortable, unpretentious and homelike resort conducted by Mr. and Mrs. R. Colwell, who are also the owners of Rubicon Springs, reached by daily stage during the summer season, nine miles from McKinney's.

Owning its own ranch in the mountains where milk, cream, butter, eggs, poultry and game are plentiful, the table at Moana Villa is provided with all the substantials and luxuries, cooked and served in home style.

One great advantage is offered to guests at Moana Villa, viz.: they may divide their time between it and Rubicon Springs, as both are under the same ownership and management.

The new Scenic Automobile Boulevard passes through the 700 acres of delightful surroundings which belong to the place. The best fishing grounds on Lake Tahoe are close by and numerous smaller mountain lakes and streams afford excellent fly fishing. Deer, bear, grouse, quail, ducks, geese and other game abound in the locality.

Hunting, fishing, bathing, boating, dancing, launch trips, beautiful walks and drives and numerous games give ample opportunity for amusement and recreation. The assembly hall and office is of logs. Sleeping accommodations in cottages and tents or out of doors if desired. Water is piped from a clear mountain spring, and an equipment of up-to-date sanitary plumbing, bath and toilet appliances has been lately installed.

Pomin's

A little beyond Moana Villa is Pomin's, the latest acquisition to the resorts of the Lake, having been opened in 1914. The hotel is an attractive, well-equipped, up-to-date structure, located on a knoll 150 feet from the Lake, and is surrounded by pines. Enclosed verandas, open fires in lobby and dining rooms, electric lights, hot and cold water in all the rooms, tents and cottages are some of the conveniences and luxuries.

There is an attractive clubhouse on the Lake shore.

Emerald Bay Camp and Al Tahoe have both been described in their respective chapters.

Tallac

As explained in Chapter XVIII, Tallac House was built by E.J. (Lucky) Baldwin. For many years it was the principal hotel on the Lake, but what was a fine and superior hotel 25 years ago did not satisfy the demands of modern patrons. Hence some years ago Mr. Baldwin planned to erect a new hotel near the site of the old one. Unfortunately the work was not much more than begun when he died and nothing has been done to it since. The hotel is under the management of a San Francisco firm.

Pine Forest Inn

Built, as its name implies, in a pine grove of trees, this is one of the older resorts of the Lake. It is unique in that it keeps open throughout the year. Like the rest of the resorts of its class it has hotel and dining room with cottages and tents. Under its new management a new casino has been built, and every room and cottage, etc., equipped with electric lights. Especial attention is given to camping, fishing, and hunting parties. It is on the state highway between Placerville and Carson City,

Nevada, and therefore makes all provision for automobilists.

Camp Bell

Located between Al Tahoe and Bijou is Camp Bell, conducted by Russell W. Bell. The camp consists of tents and an open-air dining room.

Bijou Inn

This is another well-known Inn and Camp at the southeastern end of the Lake. It is on the Lake Shore Drive near to the state highway and close to Freel's and the other mountain peaks of this group. The beach in front of Bijou is of clean white sand, with a gentle slope, offering excellent facilities for bathing. Nearby Lakeside Park, just over the Nevada state line, is described in Chapter XXV.

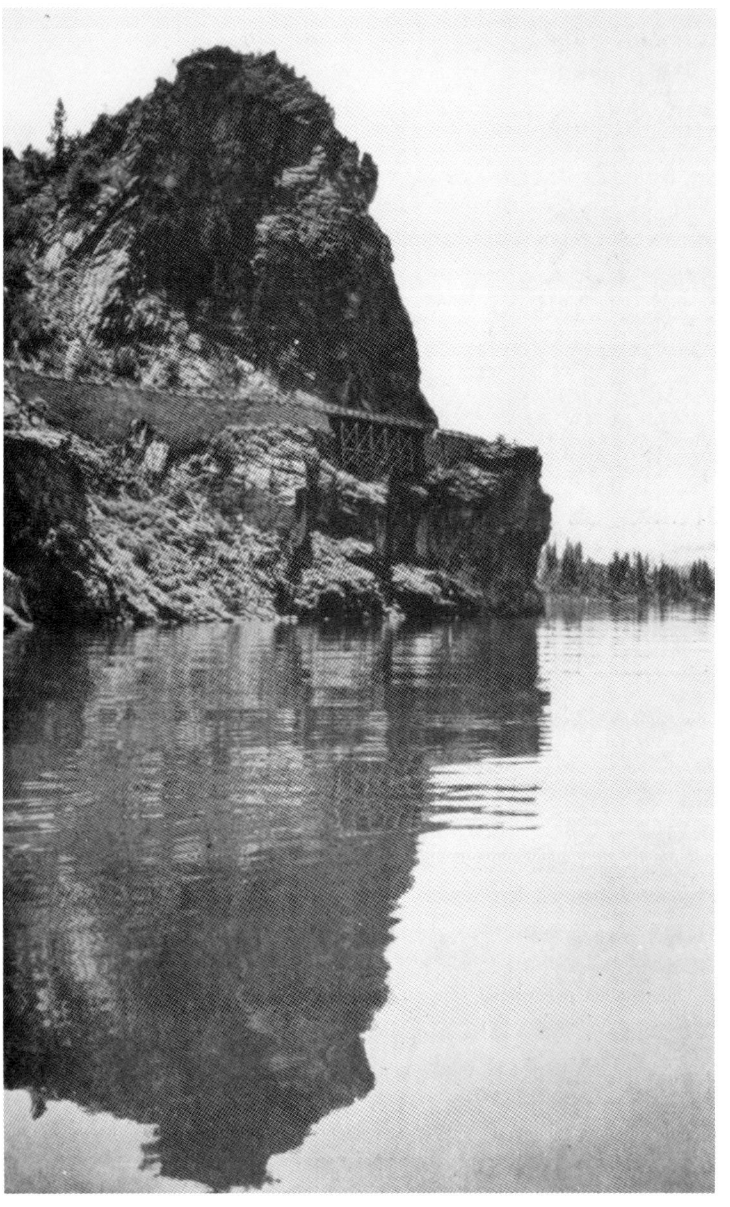

Glenbrook

This inn on the Nevada side was a regular stop for both steamer and stage lines. It is a comfortable unconventional resort where the trout fishing is particularly good. Saddle horses are available for trail riders. See also Chapter XXVI.

Brockway

This old-established and popular hot springs resort is on the north end of the Lake, beautifully situated on State-Line Point between Crystal and Agate Bays. The hot springs and mineral swimming pool here have a

The precipitous automobile road around Cave Rock, on the Nevada side of Lake Tahoe, served the needs of infrequent motorists until increased travel necessitated tunneling through the huge rock just before World War II.

The Brockway Hotel and boat landing on Stateline Point, between Crystal Bay and Agate Bay, could accommodate more than 200 guests. In the days of George Wharton James, it was a handsome new hotel with private baths and a circulating water system from natural hot springs. Cottages rented for $2.50 a day and up, on the American plan.

tested quality which thousands of guests can testify to, and they are annually patronized by a large number. The resort and springs are under the management of the owner.

Tahoe Vista

On the shores of Agate Bay a new resort was started two years ago, known as Tahoe Vista. It has a modern hotel, equipped for convenience and comfort.

Bathing, boating and fishing in Agate Bay at Tahoe Vista is at its best. The white sanded beach is broad and is safe to the smallest child, the bay being shallow for a distance of five hundred feet from its edge and affording a temperature to the water that is more pleasant than to be found at any other part of the Lake.

The fame of Lake Tahoe's trout fishing is world renowned, and in Agate Bay that sport is superior. One of the public fish hatcheries is located near Tahoe Vista, insuring a constant supply of the most favored varieties of game fish. Twenty-five thousand Eastern brook trout were recently placed in Griff Creek, a lively little stream that dances through the glens of Tahoe Vista.

To those who wish to own their own homes on the Lake Tahoe Vista affords excellent opportunities in that lots are for sale at moderate rates. A direct automobile road connects with Truckee, and also with Tahoe Tavern.

Carnelian Bay and its attractions are fully described in Chapter XXVII.

Tahoe City

This is the starting and the ending point of the steamer trip around the Lake. It is a historic place, the first town founded on Lake Tahoe, and destined ultimately to come into large importance. There is a small hotel, together with housekeeping cottages, and free camping facilities.

Brockway's Hot Springs Hotel.

INDEX

Titles of Books are in *Italics*. Book chapters are in SMALL CAPITALS. (q) = quoted.